BY THE SAME AUTHOR

The Polish Connection
A Woman Undefeated
Dreams Can Come True
Ping Pong Poms

To Nina.

With Best wishes
from
Vivienne Dockerty.

INNOCENCE LOST

Vivienne Dockerty

DISCLAIMER.
Although places and events exist in my story, this is a work of fiction.
All the characters, names, incidents and dialogue is from my imagination
or have been used fictitiously.

Matador
5 Weir Road
Kibworth Beauchamp
Leicester LE8 0LQ, UK
Tel: (+44) 116 279 2299
Fax: (+44) 116 279 2277
Email: books@troubador.co.uk
Web: www.troubador.co.uk/matador

ISBN 978 1848767 430

British Library Cataloguing in Publication Data.
A catalogue record for this book is available from the British Library.

Typeset in 11pt Aldine401 BT Roman by Troubador Publishing Ltd, Leicester, UK

Printed and bound in the UK by TJ International, Padstow, Cornwall

FOREWORD

Growing up in the Dockerty household in the austere years after World War Two, with a father who reigned supreme as head of the household and a mother who was duty bound, didn't bode well for a middle child that was defiant and rebellious.

My childhood moulded me into the teenager I became, looking for love in the wrong quarters, facing challenges through situations brought upon me and the choices I made that affected my life in my adult years.

Although most of the places exist in my story, the names of the characters have been changed.

CHAPTER 1

I struggled along the rutted farm track, trying to keep up with my giant of a daddy as he strode along. I stumbled in the black wellington boots that were far too big for me, but kept my balance long enough for my daddy to grab my hand. He gripped my grubby hand tightly, trying to balance the rifle slung over his right shoulder and the rabbit that swung limply through his rifle strap. This day was my first real memory of the events that would effect my life.

Eddie Dockerty was not a big man, though I saw him as so. He was medium in stature, very slim and wore his dark hair cut army style. He had brown eyes and a tanned complexion as he mostly worked outdoors. I remember his rather handsome face was wearing a scowl, as he quickened his pace and spoke impatiently to me, his middle daughter.

'We must hurry, Vivienne. Your Mum will be waiting for this rabbit I've caught for our dinner. God knows why it took so long to catch one today. Looks as if the buggers caught our scent and dug themselves in. This one we got looked as if it was giving up the ghost anyway, it was running so slow across the field. Don't know why I bothered coming back after the bloody war when I've got to go shooting rabbits to feed us. Talk about living in a land fit for heroes, bloody place is just the same.'

I sighed to myself unhappily. Not again. I was only three years old and didn't understand a lot of what my father said, but I did know the word 'War'. I sucked on my dummy nervously and looked ahead to see how much further I had to walk to the big wooden gate. Usually my daddy would swing me into his arms whenever I got tired and carry me the rest of the way home, but I

1

knew he wouldn't today, because he had his rifle and the rabbit to hold. I kept to my dad's other side, feeling sorry for the poor bunny. It would only be staring at me sadly anyway.

Every time I came through the back door at home, I would hear the clump of a rabbit's body swinging from a nail behind the door and would always look up in fascination at a pair of soulful looking eyes.

I waited for my father to push the heavy wooden gate open, just enough for us both to edge our way through. While I waited for him to put the iron chain back into place, I gazed at the masses of dandelions that grew in profusion along the grass verges of the main road. Dad's hobby was winemaking. He had built a lean to behind the wash house where his wooden barrels were installed. Many summer's evenings I would hear the sound of my father's boozy friends, as they sampled his latest brew of parsnip or elderberry wine.

I sighed thankfully as my father gripped my hand tightly again and ignored the lure of picking a few pounds of dandelion heads for his next concoction. My baby sister had kept me awake all night with her crying and I was looking forward to creeping up the stairs and curling up on my bed. Besides, I always felt nervous when my daddy mentioned the word 'War'. It seemed to start a lot of shouting in the house where I lived, so it was best to keep out of the way when Dad started to mention it.

We walked slowly along the country lane that lead to our 'semi'. The houses had been built for the working classes that could afford a higher rent. Most of our neighbours were 'townies' lured to the fresh air of the country to bring up their families in. Factory workers and Artisans lived there side by side.

'Let's hope she's out when we get home, Vivienne,' Dad said, as we walked through our garden gate. 'Her time's up as far as I'm concerned, she can go and stay at the aunt's. Can't get through her thick head that a man wants his house to himself when he comes home from the war. Her days are numbered living with us, you'll see.'

I felt myself stiffen with fear. My dad was working himself up to another row with my granny. My lovely granny who smelt of lavender and bought me and my sisters Rolos out of her pension, who read me stories at bedtime and took me to the farm to buy the milk.

I loved my granny more than anybody. More than my mother because she was always busy with my little sister, more than my daddy because he was always shouting, more than my elder sister, Gina, because she never bothered to play, and certainly more than the baby because she had taken away my mummy's love. If granny left I would only have Paddy. A curly black haired mongrel that was tied up in the yard.

'We're going to have a good crop on that apple tree this year,' Dad said, noticing the abundance of white pink flowers on the thickly covered boughs. 'And my bean pole's growing nicely, look at those fronds already in the air.'

I nodded in respect of his observations, then looked over to the pig pen where a sow and her litter of piglets were making a terrible noise.

'Shurrup yer bleedin' critters! Hasn't anybody fed 'em yet? Irene, these pigs want feedin', we'll have the neighbours shouting next.'

My mother came shuffling out of the wash house. She was a smallish, slender woman with shoulder length greying hair. She was dressed in a white short sleeved blouse which was covered in stains, a navy pleated knee length skirt and on her feet she wore a pair of worn out shoes. Her roundish face scowled in annoyance.

'How many pair of hands do you think I was born with, Eddie? I'm in the middle of the washing! It wouldn't harm you to feed them now and again. Would it?'

'If that mother of yours did a bit more, yer wouldn't be asking that question. Where is the old bat anyway? Gone to bed fer a rest?'

'No, she's taken Audrey out in the pram', up to Mrs. Edwards at the farm. Look at the state of our Vivienne, she's covered in filthy mud.'

'It'll wash off, woman. Here take this rabbit I've caught yer and

3

hang it behind the door. And, where's the ruddy swill then, I'll feed the buggers meself?'

'There is no swill yet until I boil up the cabbage, perhaps you could shift yourself and do that for me. I've used half of one cabbage for our tea tonight and there's still a few potatoes to peel.'

'I don't know. Why have I got a wife when I have to do everything meself? Vivienne, go and take yer boots off in the wash house and perhaps yer could find something to feed the dog.'

I ran off to see Paddy. The little dog barked excitedly, jumping up and down as I approached. I put my arm around his neck and tried to cuddle him, while he licked at my face and neck.

'Vivyen find Paddy bone, good doggie,' I said, before running off to see my mother, who was hanging out our wet clothes on the washing line strewn between the wash house and the lean to.

'Bone for Paddy, Mummy.'

'Oh, not you as well, Vivienne. We don't have any bones until I've been to the butcher's, the dog will have to wait. Go and look in the cupboard in the kitchen, will you? See if there are any biscuits left.'

I did as I was told and triumphantly found half a packet of digestive biscuits on the shelf in our larder. But, digestive biscuits were my favourite, so I wasn't going to share any with Paddy, even if I did love the little dog. I sat on a low kitchen chair and started to nibble one, swinging my legs in pleasure and making sure I didn't drop any crumbs on my shabby green dress. I did not see my daddy watching, as he stirred something in a large saucepan.

'Didn't I tell yer to take your dirty boots off?'

'You did, Daddy.'

'Then why are they still on yer feet instead of in the wash house?'

'You've still got your boots on, Daddy.'

'That's it! I've had enough. Get to yer bedroom at once and take off yer ruddy boots!'

'Now, Daddy?' I struggled to get the wellingtons off under my father's baleful stare. It was difficult with my tears starting to run

4

and my eyes all misty and my fingers trembling, though I still held onto my biscuit while he watched over me angrily.

Suddenly I found myself in the air, being swept up by my exasperated parent, deposited upon the bottom stair and told to get myself off to bed.

'What's going on here?', came the indignant voice of my granny, as she came into the kitchen. 'What's she gone and done this time to put you in a mood?'

'Oh, you're back are yer?' I heard my father say. 'Well it's none of your business. What I say goes in this house and you'd do well to remember that.'

'Oh yes, I remember my place very well, Eddie Dockerty,' Granny replied. 'Tiptoe round the man of the house. Never mind that it's my pension that keeps it going, never mind that I see to yer children, while your poor wife works her fingers to the bone while you're in the alehouse.'

That was enough for me, I ran up the stairs as fast as I could. I knew there was going to be more shouting and it was safer off in bed.

I got under the army greatcoat that served as a blanket and talked to my little brown teddy as I tucked a pillow under my head. Teddy was a great friend of mine. He listened without shouting like the grownups did and once when I was recovering from a bout of measles, I found a piece of chocolate tucked in the hole under his arm. I asked him whether he knew why my daddy didn't like me and why my daddy was always talking about something called the war? There were things called bombs that could blow a man into little pieces, brave soldiers who had died in my daddy's arms, lots of bangs, but my daddy wasn't frightened, you'd only be scared if you were a silly girl. Teddy never replied to my questions, he just smiled sweetly and cuddled into me.

I pushed my dummy into teddy's mouth as I liked him to share the comfort I drew from it, then stuffed it into my own mouth chewing on it furiously. I wanted to go for a wee wee, but it meant going downstairs again to find my potty. I knew that there was a chamber pot under Granny's bed. It was round with pretty flowers on and it was better to use hers anyway, than being smacked for weeing in my pants.

My diminutive granny, Lily Wilson, had been given her marching orders. The row earlier had been the final reckoning and now it was time to pack her bags. She had had it up to here with Eddie Dockerty's bullying ways and as she had just said to her daughter, 'There was plenty of room at Aunt Marie's house if she wanted to leave the bugger behind'. They'd manage somehow.

Irene, my mother, could go back to work and she would look after the youngsters. Better that than be dictated to, hadn't they just won a war to be free? But my mother would have none of it. She had made her vows to Eddie and the girls had to have a father in their life.

'Vows,' Lily had sneered. 'Vows made in a bloomin' Registry Office, not as if they're sacred like ones in a church.'

That had started my father off again. It wasn't his fault that his parents hadn't given them their blessing, wasn't his fault that Irene wasn't Catholic, he wasn't going to become a Proddy, so how could they have got married in a church?

'But it was your fault she got pregnant, wasn't it?' had been Lily's final fling and here she was packing a suitcase, ready to catch a bus into town.

'Oh, the shame of it,' Lily muttered to herself, as she dragged her cardboard suitcase out from under her bed. Her youngest girl had been five months pregnant before Eddie made her his bride. Why couldn't Irene have kept her hand on her halfpenny, then she could have married Alfred whose father owned a hardware shop? Lily couldn't understand the young people of today. Mrs. Edwards at the farm had only just been telling her about one of the Whittle sisters. Fallen for one of them G.I.'s that was stationed at Burtonwood and leaving soon for Texas when he was demobbed. Texas! Where was that for heaven's sake? Thousands of miles away according to Mrs. Edwards and Mrs. Whittle was beside herself with grief. Lost a son at Dunkirk and now according to rumour the daughter was up the duff!

'Granny, what yer doing?' I had been sitting on the chamber pot listening to my granny muttering.

'Oh, Vivienne, I'm sorry I didn't see you. Come here to Granny and give me a hug.'

I got up and after pulling up my knickers went into my granny's warm embrace.

'I'm going to stay at my sister's. She's not been very well and I'm going to try and make her better, but I'll come and see you every day.'

'Why are you taking all your clothes then, if you're coming back tomorrow?' I said astutely.

'I said I'll be coming every day, but I won't be living here any more.'

'Why?'

'Your mummy and daddy think it's better this way.'

'Granny, before you go will you tell me all about your nine sisters?' I said, stalling for time as I didn't want my granny to leave me. 'I wonder if I'll have a lot of sisters, 'cos isn't difficult to remember all their names?'

But my granny had returned to her packing, her bus arrived at ten past three.

I climbed onto my older sister's bed by the window, so that I could see my granny from the bedroom, as she walked with my mother to the garden gate. Granny walked proudly, her back straight in her old blue coat, her blue flowery hat sitting on her white curly hair and her black shiny shoes clicking on the paving stones. It was a very sad moment in my life, as I had lost my friend and ally in that miserable house.

My mother sat on the back step of the house later, crying quietly. Audrey, the baby grizzled in the pram as if in agreement with her. My father had walked down the path in disgust once his mother in law had gone. He had left Mother white faced and tightlipped, a sure sign she was ready to have a go. What was it with women?, he had thought. Never satisfied. Now he'd got rid of one of them, he'd make sure he would get the rest of them under control.

My mother dried her hands on her pinny and drew herself up to her 5feet 2 inches in height. She was feeling better now that the crying had relieved all her tension and there was a lot of that since Eddie had won the war. One minute he would be kind and loving, bringing her wild flowers or a Cadbury's chocolate bar. Then next minute he would be screaming, at herself, her mother or me, for nothing that she could see that we had done at all! She stared at the rabbit that she had flung in the corner of the wash house and wondered if it was worth his wrath if she decided not to skin it. Should she be a good housewife and greet him with a steaming rabbit pie? No, why should she, they would have corn beef instead? He'd just got rid of her lovely mother, the only help she'd ever had. There was the baby first to deal with, my mother could smell the baby's dirty nappy from where she stood and my tears would need mopping and somehow cheered. Then, Gina would be home, and the pigs still needed feeding, she could hear their bellowing from their sties. My mother knew where Dad would be at that moment, around at his mother's eating toast and drinking a nice cup of tea. My mother wiped her tears again, wondering how she was going to cope?

It was all right for Dad being waited on and telling his mother, who we called Nana, how he had just got rid of my grandma, but it was my mother who would bear the brunt of it all, now that her mother had gone. She could picture it very clearly. Dad would be doing the wounded soldier, telling his woeful tale to his mother, then flopping down on the sofa and snoozing for an hour or so. As far as my mother was concerned, Dad could stay forever at my Nana's, she wasn't going traipsing after him like she had so many times before. The last time she had gone round to Nana's to tell him that his tea was ready, she'd been kept like a fool on the doorstep, while Nana laughingly told my father that his nag of a wife was at the door!

The Dockerty's had never liked my mother, she wasn't good enough for the likes of them. She'd met the family once after Dad had decided to marry her and he'd persuaded his mother to invite my mother to Sunday tea.

In the front room they called the parlour, eight pairs of Dockerty eyes scrutinized his intended as she nervously stood in the doorway. Pa Dockerty, Nana, Sheena, Caitlin, Rosaleen, Terry, Michael and Sam had all looked pointedly at my mother's burgeoning bulge that she had desperately tried to conceal.

My mother could still remember the embarrassment as she stood there on show. Not one of the family had stood up politely to offer her a chair or extend a hand in welcome. My aunts on the sofa had tittered behind their hands, egged on by Caitlin, the eldest one.

My mother had muttered to Dad that she wasn't feeling well, made her apologies to the parents and fled. To be fair to Dad, he had been very angry, saw the family gathering as a plot to make their point that his betrothed wasn't welcome. She was a Protestant and they were from an old Irish Catholic family. Her parents were nobodies, while the Dockerty's had been well heeled property owners in their time.

My mother smiled in satisfaction when she thought on the Dockerty's downfall. Pa Dockerty had owned all these houses in Whaley Lane and Brian Avenue. Then during the 30's slump he had lost everything. His big fancy house on Oaklea Road, his building business with the fleet of trucks, his quarry, the dairy and two swanky cars. Now they were left with just a tiny semi, because before the bank called in his loans, he had put the small house in Nana's name. How the mighty had fallen, my mother mused. Nana now shared the house with her younger son, Sam.

Pa Dockerty had died of a heart attack just before the war was declared, the daughters had all got married and moved away and the sons all taken on factory or labouring jobs. Their mother had been lucky, all her sons had come back from the war unscathed, unlike Caitlin's husband who had lost a testicle. 'Shot in the plums' was my father's coarse remark when he heard.

My mother scooped up my squalling smelly sister with resignation and carried her into the living room. She listened for a movement from the upstairs room, where she knew I would be happy to stay until my meal was ready. It wasn't easy for me to be the middle daughter, especially with Eddie for a dad. His affinity seemed to be with Gina, that is, he had doted on Gina before he joined the war in 1943. When he was demobbed in 1946, Gina had forgotten what her father looked like and had hidden behind her granny on his return. That hadn't gone down very well. Eddie just turned about and went off to see his mother, returning the following morning after celebrating with his brothers and his pals. He never seemed to pick on Gina as he did with me and my mother often wondered why that was? If Gina had made a mess of the kitchen floor with her wellingtons, he would have spoken kindly and told her to put them outside the door. He had been devastated when he saw that Gina's legs were bowed because of the rickets, another casualty of living with deprivations through the rotten war.

In a tender moment that sometimes my parents had, Mother had asked him what was it about me that seemed to get under his skin? She was aghast when she heard that I reminded him of Aunt Caitlin.

'She has that defiant look about her when you give her an order, our Caitlin was the same,' he had scowled. 'Yer know with me mother helping with the business and having our lot as well, it was up to our Caitlin to bring me and the younger ones up. She used to get me on the floor and punch the living daylights out of me. Vivienne's got that look about her. She's the spit of Caitlin and I aim to bring her to heel. If I don't, she'll become rebellious and then where will we be?'

My mother had scoffed at him and teased him, trying to lighten his mood. Maybe his down on me was because I wasn't a boy? My father had coloured guiltily, but had told her that it was Audrey their youngest, not me, that he had hoped would be a boy.

Well, he'd had his chips now anyway, thought my mother, as she deftly changed the soiled nappy for a clean one that she had kept warming on the clothes horse by the fire. Her sister Isabel was visiting on Saturday and she was bringing one of those new fangled douches for my mother to try. Father wouldn't hear of using one of the protective rubber sheaths that were available now at the chemists. Although he had been born into a Catholic family, he was a lapsed one, but conveniently used the church's teaching that marriage was for procreation and to use birth control was a sin. The douche appeared to be working for her sister, so she would try it and my father's dreams of a boy to kick a ball around with, would dissolve into thin air!

My mother sighed as she put the baby onto her nipple. Her mother- in- law was a saint according to Eddie. Bearing all those children and helping Pa with the business in between. He couldn't understand why my mother wasn't coping, she only had three blooming daughters to rear!

She was awoken from her musing when she saw a fair haired little head appearing around the living room door. That was me, then I flung the rest of myself across the room.

I began to smack out at my little sister, shouting that she was hurting Mummy and to stop it straight away! Audrey fell off my mother's nipple in surprise and began to wail lustily, while my mother put out her free hand and tried to push me away.

'Vivienne, stop that, you naughty girl!' she said angrily. 'I've told you before that the baby isn't hurting me. This is the way it has to be, she can't eat the same food as us when she's so tiny. Now, sit on the sofa and I'll tell you a story. What about the three bears?'

I glared at my mother and said defiantly. 'No, I want my potty.'

My little face was as red as a beetroot and wet with angry tears. My mother tried to put the screeching baby back on her nipple, thinking that I was such a pain. This always seemed to happen at feeding times, I'd appear from nowhere and cause an upsetting scene.

I brought my potty that I'd found behind the armchair, close to where Mother was sitting on the arm of the sofa. I sat there rubbing my head against my mother's legs and singing a little tune.

'Tiggedy winkly, winkly, winkly, tiggedy winkly woo, I love you,

Tiggedy winkly,winkly, winkly, tiggedy winkly woo, love me too........'

'That's nice, Vivienne,' said Mother. 'Did your Daddy teach you that?'

'No, it was Gina,' I replied, sucking on my dummy whilst staring up at Mother. Then quick as a flash I fell off my potty, smiling as I did so. I watched my mother's face as the warm yellow liquid splashed all over her legs, her shoes and the newly washed linoleum floor. She leapt up in shock! The baby began to roar loudly and I stood there paralyzed with my arm up shielding my face. I'd done it this time, my Mum was bound to smack me and send me back to the bedroom, but it would be worth it because I'd taken her attention from Audrey.

Mother stood there for a moment, poised to do just what I had been thinking, then she must have taken pity on me. She gripped me by my shoulder and told me in a firm tone.

'Take your potty into the wash house and then get a floor cloth. Bring the cloth here and then you can wipe the wee off the floor. Then after you've done that, you can wait by the gate for Gina. Send Paddy to meet her from the bus stop. Understand me? Now go.'

She waited for me to argue, but I pulled my knickers up gleefully, then ran off to do as I was told.

Mother let her breath expel, sat in the chair with a plop and gave the baby her care.

I had been doing this little act, at least twice a week since she had brought the baby home from hospital, a month before. I would sit on the potty looking all sweet and innocent, humming a happy little tune and when mother was lulled into a false sense of contentment whilst feeding Audrey, I would start acting up again. First thing tomorrow, my mother decided, she was going to teach me how to use the toilet and when that was accomplished, the dummy would have to go!

After I had done as I was told, I raced to the yard to let Paddy off his rope.

'Come on, Paddy, you've got to go and fetch Gina,' I said happily, smelling freedom as my mother was busy with my sister.

We ran down the path to the big wooden gates, listening to the pigs as we passed their sty, but only momentarily diverted from our mission. I stopped and pointed to the gap in the hedge further along from the gates. 'Fetch Gina, Paddy, fetch.'

The little black mongrel rushed through the hole and set off at speed down the lane. He did this every weekday, if one or other of the family remembered to let him off his chain. He had been trained since a puppy and always met the bus on time.

I climbed up onto the third slat of the gate, where I could just about see over from my vantage point. I looked across at the high wild hedge that edged the field across the lane. There were dog roses and honeysuckle rambling through it and I could hear the squawking of baby birds fighting in their nests. I looked up the lane to where I knew Mrs. Edward's farm was, the building was too far away for me to see, but I knew Dobbin, the cart horse would be there.

A few minutes later I heard heavy footsteps coming along the pavement, the noise brought a tremor of fear to me as I thought it might be my daddy. I knew I should really be in my bedroom as he hadn't said I could come down. I held my breath in trepidation, faltering on the slat, wondering if I should make a dash for it. Phew! It was only Mr. Braiden on his way to the factory, where he had his work.

'Hello, Mr. Braiden. Are you going to work?'

'Yes, I am, Vivienne. On the night shift again.'

'Can you hear our piggy's shouting for their food, Mr. Braiden? Mummy's feeding Audrey, so the pigs have got to wait.'

'Your daddy wants to be careful that somebody doesn't call the Council in, Vivienne. The neighbours will be complaining about that dreadful noise.'

'Mmmm. Can you lift me down, Mr. Braiden? I can keep you company 'til your 'bus arrives.'

'I don't think your Mummy will be very pleased if I do that, Vivienne,' he said to me cautiously.

'I wouldn't let our Letty walk me to the 'bus stop and she's the same age as you.'

'Pooh, I'm three, nearly four now,' I said feeling important. 'Anyway, Gina will be getting off the 'bus and she can walk me back.'

'Well, if you're sure your mummy won't be cross, I'll lift you down,' he said, glancing rather nervously in the direction of our house. Then putting down his canvas satchel that carried his flask and wrap of sandwiches, he did just that.

'Whoops a daisy, there you are now, we must hurry, the 'bus is due at quarter past four.'

He picked up his satchel and continued walking, with me trotting happily, chattering away sixteen to the dozen at his side.

'What is Letty doing? Is she having a party for her birthday? What did you call your little baby boy? Did the stork bring him to his house or did he come from the hospital with his mum?'

He answered my quick fire questions with amusement, no doubt thinking that I was so much brighter than their Letty, though his opinion of my progress wouldn't be what the wife would want to hear. The sun shone out of Letty Braiden's backside as far as Mrs. Braiden was concerned.

'Hold my hand will you, Mr. Braiden?', I insisted, when we came to the kerb where the road turned left into Oaklea Road.

'Yes, of course. Why's that, there's no traffic coming along?'

'I'm not allowed to cross the road on my own and anyway there's a big monster at the top of Oaklea Road. It lives in the bull rushes just by my Nana's house. That's what my Daddy said anyway.'

'Well, who protects your Nana from the big monster then?', chuckled Mr. Braiden, holding out his hand to me.

'Oh, Uncle Sam, I suppose. But the monster only eats children and Daddy said he really loves to eat naughty ones.'

Smiling at my nervousness, Letty's father walked the next twenty yards with me, then he quickened his step as he had heard the bus come chugging up the hill.

I waited then when we reached the main road, waving to him as he hurried across it. He turned and smiled in my direction, before placing himself to wait for the noisy charabanc to come to a halt.

I could see Paddy sitting patiently on the grass verge opposite, then saw him wag his tail as Gina raced from the 'bus to pat him.

'Good old Paddy,' I could hear my sister say. 'What would we do without you, you little black imp?'

The old blue 'bus chugged on its way to the town of Birkenhead, leaving Gina openmouthed in amazement as she spied me standing alone on the opposite kerb.

'Vivienne,' she shouted, 'stay there, don't you dare cross the road!'

Gina dashed across with Paddy barking beside her in excitement.

'Who let you out of the gate, you little rascal or did you follow the dog through the hole?'

I stared up at my big sister and said to her importantly, 'I'm a big girl now, Gina, I came to meet you on my own.'

For some reason, deep in my childish conscious, I knew I would be getting Mr. Braiden into trouble if I said that he had helped me and I had heard enough shouting at our house that day.

'I wanted to tell you that Granny has gone to stay with the aunties,' I said, with my eyes beginning to fill with tears and my arms out so that she could hug me. 'Oh Gina, I think I want to cry again 'cos Daddy shouted at me, then Granny took all her clothes and then Mummy was cross 'cos I upset my potty on her shoes. Will you carry me home, Gina?'

'No, Vivienne, you're getting too big for me to carry and I'm carrying my satchel,' my sister said, wondering for a moment if I was making it all up, as I was apt to tell tall stories. 'Look, let me sit you on that wall and you can tell me what happened.'

Gina sat with me on a low wall that ran around the garden of the first large house in Oaklea Road. I poured my heart out, ending my tale with what had happened with the pigs.

'And Curly, Wurly and Oink Oink haven't been fed at all.'

My sister groaned, lifted her satchel onto her shoulder and holding my hand walked slowly up the lane. She knew what would be facing her when she got back home. When Granny was living with them she had been allocated certain jobs, but now there would

15

be even more of the blasted chores to do. She was seething, more against her father than her mother. He had got his wish now hadn't he, got rid of their little granny, like he had always wanted to do?

Gran' had been a rock for us all to lean on, even before Gina came to be born. Irene and Eddie had lived with Lily at Pear Tree Cottage in Wallasey. The house had been rented, it was old and had neither gas, electricity or piped water, but it had a huge garden and Lily made a meagre living from selling seasonal fruit and vegetables outside the door.

When Eddie had been refused his parent's blessing on his marriage and the ceremony was delayed, Lily had offered him a home. It wasn't the done thing for an unmarried couple to live together under the same roof, but Lily had decided she would be their chaperone. That is until they met her with the news that a baby was on the way.

Gina knew all this, because Lily had to have an ally whilst she lived in Eddie's household and so wasn't adverse to blackening her son- in- law's character to get Gina on her side. War broke out when Gina was four months old and the family were all in grave danger, as the house was close to the docks. There was just the four of them, as Aunt Isabel, Lily's other daughter, had got married and had moved over to Southport.

Eddie had been working on demolition in Liverpool, but decided for their safety they should move out into the countryside. He had found a house to rent near a village, the place where he had grown up and not far from Nana's home.

Lily had been angry and had told him that he wasn't getting her to shift out of Wallasey, to live in the country where she'd be bored and feel marooned. Then one night the bombers came and made short work of the flour mills, the warehouses and the ships moored at the docks just down the road. Eddie bundled all the possessions on a borrowed handcart. Even then there'd been tears and recriminations from Lily, especially as she was to leave her precious rosebushes behind.

He had locked the door and promised he would come back to get the bushes and anything else she damn well wanted from the garden, but one week later Pear Tree Cottage had been blown to smithereens!

Gran' had been homeless then and so it was her turn wasn't it, to be invited to stay in their new home?

Gina sighed as she and Vivienne walked into their garden. She could hear what her first job was going to be. Her mother must have forgotten to feed them, but surely even she could hear the pigs squealing? Everyone in the neighbourhood must be hearing them and some would be intent on writing to the Council to complain.

My sister suddenly began to feel resentful. Granny had told her that Mum had been courted by a man who had prospects in the department store where she used to work, but she had thrown him over for Eddie, who could dance and always had a mischievous twinkle in his eyes. According to Gran', they could be living in a big house in West Kirby and Mum would have a daily woman to help her with the chores. Mum wouldn't be tired like she was all the time and she would wear pretty clothes, maybe even have a car of her own.

Now that Gina was eleven, she had begun to notice how other families lived and where her parents were in the scale of things. She compared the clothes she was given to wear, the house she lived in and the non possession of a family car. At the school she attended there were girls who lived in big houses close to the sea. Their clothes were bought from department stores, such as Hendersons' and George Henry Lee's in Liverpool, nothing like the homemade ones that Gina wore and one girl had even been to Italy!

That was Milly Tilden, whose father owned a chain of grocery stores. Gina was surprised that Milly attended a school such as St. Bridget's, but as Milly had explained her father had said, 'What use is an expensive education when you'll be married off as soon as you're old enough and a decent fellow can be found.'

Gina hated school. She would rather be out horse riding instead of stuck inside a boring school. Her friend, Alison Grey, let her ride her pony Simba at the weekends. Gina repaid her by mucking out the stable and grooming the handsome little horse.

Audrey was settled back in her 'pram in the back garden, when Gina and I arrived. Our mother was busy at the kitchen sink peeling potatoes and adding the peel to a concoction of cabbage leaves that were bubbling on the stove. Her eyes lit up when she saw my elder sister, as Gina was her reason for putting up with the rotten life she led. My sister had turned out to be a well rounded little character, despite the deprivations she had suffered in the War. A bit of a tomboy maybe, but could turn her hand to dressmaking and some knitting if required.

Gina wore her mahogany coloured hair in a short bob and it bounced in curls around her head. Her eyes were brown and framed with very long lashes, her face was on the round side and her mouth usually curved in a smile.

Today though my sister was looking worried, her mouth was downcast and she spoke rather abruptly to our mother as she pushed me, not unkindly through the door.

'Look who I found on the corner? She was standing there as bold as brass, waiting for me to come off the 'bus. Honestly, Mum, it's all right Dad sending Gran off to Aunt Marie's so that he can be king of the castle, but who's going to keep an eye on our Vivienne? You've enough on your hands with Audrey. No wonder I can't concentrate on school with all that's happening here.'

'Oh, Gina, that's not fair. It's the best thing anyway to separate your Dad from your Gran. It had to happen sooner or later and Aunt Marie has been complaining of feeling ill. Anyway I'll make us all a cup of tea while you change out of your uniform and Vivienne, you naughty girl, you know you shouldn't go out of the gate!'

I followed my sister up to our bedroom, while Mother put the kettle onto the stove. Gina changed into a blue polo neck jumper and a pair of cream jodhpurs, putting her navy uniform on a hanger at the back of the door. She peered into a wardrobe checking that her granny's clothes had gone.

'Never mind, Gina. Granny said she would come and see us

every day and she'll bring some Rolos,' I said, watching my big sister in admiration and wishing that I could wear trousers like she did. Frocks were for babies and got in the way when I attempted to climb into our apple tree.

'That's all very well, Vivienne, but remember I'll be at school all day and when I get home she'll be gone, as she won't want to be here when Dad comes home, will she? Still, perhaps Mum will let me have some money for the bus fare and I can go and see Granny at Aunt Marie's home.'

'I've never been on a 'bus Gina. Will I go on one when I go to school?'

'Not a chance, little one,' she answered. 'Hail, rain or snow you'll be walking there. The school you'll be going to is only ten minutes away. It's not built yet, but by the time you're five you'll be spared the two buses and one hour travel that I have to do.'

By the time I was five, Gina's prophecy had come true. September 1952 saw me sitting on the apron of the high 'pram with Audrey within, being trundled along the main road to the newly built primary school.

I wore a white open necked shirt, a grey gym slip and a blue hand knitted cardigan. My golden curls had now been cut off into a short cropped style that father had insisted upon. His skills as a barber in the army ensured that our family never looked shaggy haired, besides there could be a child with nits at the school and short hair was easier to inspect!

I still sucked my dummy, Mother having failed in her endeavours to take it away from me, but at least I was now toilet trained, which resulted in one less aggravation for my mother to have to bear.

Gina was also at a school closer to home, as the government had expanded its education programme and a nearer secondary school had now been built. Only one 'bus to travel on now for my sister, as she had failed the 11+ exam', so wouldn't be going to the grammar school. She didn't care really, though Mother was disappointed, but better to be a big fish in a little pond so she settled in her new school very well.

My mother sighed to herself as she pushed the big 'pram along. It had only seemed a short while ago that she had been pushing Gina up to a private school in the village. It had been run by a Methodist man, who because he cared for the community had decided to establish a place for the education of the local children. Unfortunately, as he hadn't been trained as a teacher, the parents soon lost confidence in his abilities and Gina and many others transferred to another school a few miles away. Mother blamed my father for Gina's poor education. If they had had a bit more money Gina could have gone to the local convent school. They took day pupils as well as boarders, but Dad never seemed to earn enough to run to things like that. There was barely enough to keep them some weeks if the weather had stopped him working. My mother was grateful that Granny still gave her a little bit from her pension.

At St. Bridget's, the school that Gina eventually attended, she had never made up those vital years which were the foundation of her learning skills. Father had said he didn't know why Mother was worrying. The girl could read and write, which was more than he could do when he was Gina's age. He had attended the Dame school down by the estuary, though more often he played truant by the River Dee or Thurstaston Hill.

I was sitting humming a little tune to myself as we bounced along.

'The sun has got his hat on, hip hip hurray, the sun has got his hat on and it's coming out today.'

I wasn't worried about my first day at school, because I was a big girl now, like Gina, and soon I would be able to read all those books that my sister kept in a book case in our bedroom.

I had no real idea of what school was like, except I knew from Gina that you had to sit at a little table and be good. No talking, unless the teacher asked you a question and you had a playtime, a dinnertime, another playtime, then you went home. I was looking forward to the playtimes, because I could play with Letty Braiden and Caroline Thomas and Gina said I would make lots of other friends. My mother had told me that she would miss me, but I knew she didn't really mean it, because now she had more time to see to Audrey.

Audrey was a little dumpling now, with hazel eyes and straight brown hair. She never gave our parents any trouble, played happily on her own in the garden and never tried to follow Paddy through the hole in the hedge. I also knew that Audrey had some secret friends who she talked to behind the hen houses. One was called Paula, another Brenda and someone called Johnny, though they seemed to vanish quickly when ever I came along. I wondered if my mother knew anything about them, but then a small group of boys came dashing up behind us, so I dismissed the thought of Audrey's friends from my mind.

My mother groaned. It was Jackie Lee and his two younger brothers, Simon and Mason. The family had recently moved into one of the houses further up the lane and they already had a reputation for being little horrors. They plundered old Mr. Reilly's apple orchard, tied tin cans to pussy cat's tails, squabbled like little heathens and whooped like marauding savages around the pond on the other side of the lane.

My mother held onto her temper as they knocked against the pram, then Jackie stopped at the side of us and cheekily sang a little song.

'Baby, baby in the pram', sucks a dummy like Vivienne.'

Oh no, my mother thought. The dummy. As much as she had implored me to leave it behind at home, I had been resolutely against it. The Lee brothers ran off laughing and Mother waited for my reaction. I didn't cry, I had learnt that crying didn't get me very far in my world.

I handed the dummy to Mother. 'I've decided I'm a big girl now, so I won't be needing my dummy,' I said. 'When you get home will you put it in the bin?'

My mother nodded, stifling her amusement. I had been so serious and it must have been a hard thing for me to do.

Audrey was watching all this intently, she had never had a dummy. In fact, she spat it out when Granny had introduced her to one. My granny had been the culprit who had kept me supplied with new ones, but she knew that out of all her grandchildren I was the one who needed its comfort to get me through each day.

I put my arms out and asked my mother to get me down when we neared the start of Glenwood Drive, which was where the new primary school had just been built. There were other mothers waiting with their children to cross the road and a bus disgorged its young passengers on the other side. I told my mother that she could leave me if she wanted to, I had my dinner money and a clean hanky in my knicker pocket and I didn't need her company as I was a big girl now.

But Mother shook her head and replied that as it was my first day, it was essential that she took me to school.

We joined a steady stream of children, some first years like me, some who were older and had transferred from other schools, all chattered excitedly, wondering what this state run school was going to be like.

Suddenly there was a commotion ahead, all heads were turned to look at a child that was screaming. As we rounded the corner it was to see a small boy red in the face and clinging with his two hands to the garden gate. He was kicking out at his mother and screaming at her.

'No, I won't go to school, you can't make me, I want to stay at home!' Then he fell to the floor and began to sob. 'Don't make me go, Mummy, I want to stay with you and Johnny.'

My mother stopped the 'pram and asked the harassed woman could she help in anyway?

The woman was heavily pregnant, she looked worn out and about to cry herself. There was a little brother standing in the porch way watching, his thumb was in his mouth as he wondered what was going on?

'Perhaps your boy would like to walk with us to school?', said my mother, though she said it doubtfully. She hadn't much to do with little boys and hoped that he would come with them willingly, or otherwise his mother would have to drag him there.

'I'm not going to school with any cissy girls!', the boy bellowed, having heard my mother's offer.

'I'll walk there myself on my own and if I don't like the place I'm coming home.'

'All right then, Raymond,' his mother had said soothingly, 'if that's what you want to do dear, you run along. Come here first and let me wipe your face and look what you've done to your nice new shoes.'

She gave Mother a relieved smile and whispered an embarrassed 'goodbye'.

Raymond trailed behind us then by ten paces. His tantrum being over, he was now feeling rather nervous, but he wouldn't have felt very comfortable walking with a girl.

'Well, here we are, Vivienne,' announced my mother as we came to the gate at the back of the school.

'You can go in this way, you'll be just in time. I'll be waiting here for you at a quarter to four. Be a good girl and do as your teacher says.'

She gave me a kiss on the cheek and a friendly little push in the playground's direction.

I went off without a backward glance leaving my mother watching me bleakly, hoping that I would start to behave myself now. My willfulness was still in evidence, though not as much if my father was around.

Mother pushed the 'pram down to the bottom of Glenwood Drive thinking of the day that stretched before her. The pigs had been sold a few weeks before which made her life a bit easier, but now she had taken on a new responsibility. Her aging aunts. Aunt Maggie was ninety and Aunt Jenny eighty one. They lived in a small bungalow in a crescent not far from my school, so naturally Mother had promised to call in on them every day. She would help with the heavy work that the aunts couldn't manage. She felt she owed it to them. They had been good to her in her teenage years when Isabel, her sister, was creating mayhem in her mother's home.

Granny had sent her to holiday with the aunts when Mother was sixteen years old, on the pretext that Aunt Maggie needed someone to cheer her up after Uncle Walter had passed away. The real reason was that she didn't want Mother mixed up in the family scandal. Isabel had left her husband, brought her children home and was after a divorce.

Thank heavens, my Granddad Eric hadn't lived to witness the scandal, it would have killed him, had he still been living, though a heart attack had caused him to pass away.

Her dad had been such a gentleman, thought Mother sadly, her mother hadn't deserved him really. She had never heard him raise his voice in anger and he had a lot to put up with. Granny had nagged him day and night, to do this for her and do that. Mother thought his death had been a release from his torment when he went and had a heart attack. He'd been a clever man, liked fixing things and had worked as an electrician on the submarines during the First World War.

I stood in line with the other children of my age, outside the school in the playground.

This Raymond boy had tagged along with me and he was scowling there behind me in the queue. Letty had her nose in the air in front of me, but I could see that her eyes were red as if she'd been crying. I suppose she had found it hard to leave her doting mother and the comfortable home she lived in.

A whistle was blown and six lines of children were led along a corridor into a large school hall. We were ordered to sit cross legged in rows on the wooden parquet floor.

I felt very nervous all of a sudden. Gina hadn't told me that there would be so many children, I had never seen so many in one place in my life. The class that I had been allocated to, sat on the front row in front of the stage where serious looking teachers looked down upon us. I wondered which one would be my teacher, would it be the bald man, the man with glasses or one of the women, especially the pretty one with the golden hair? I hoped it wouldn't be the bald man, because he held a cane in his hand. Gina had told me about the cane, you got it if you were naughty, on the back of your legs or across the palm of your hands!

Suddenly the whole school bristled to attention as the sound of

24

slow footsteps and the tap of a walking stick could be heard. Mr. Lawson, the headmaster, was on his way and me and the occupants of the school hall held our breath!

My mother pushed the' pram through the side gate that led to the back of her aunts' bungalow. She stopped for a moment on the concrete patio and gazed with appreciation at the scene before her. A whole garden full of fruit trees met her eyes. Apples, plum and pear trees, their boughs laden with a bountiful crop. Her aunts were going to be busy with their bottling, preserving and wrapping. No doubt they would give some to my mother, they were always generous at this time of the year.

She smiled as she remembered back to when she lived there. At sixteen she'd been horrified when her mother had insisted that she lodge at the aunts' house. Irby was miles away from anywhere! Seven miles from Birkenhead, whole tracts of farmland all around, no street lighting, no picture houses. Just a scruffy village hall, a row of small shops, a post office and a drinking club for men, where she would not have been allowed in anyway! Lily was insistent, Irene could go back when Isabel had come to her senses and gone back to the family home. Lily was a great believer in making your bed and lying on it, but had taken her daughter in to give the marriage a breathing space.

The elderly aunts had made Mother very welcome, they seemed to understand that a young girl might feel awkward with two old ladies, so they went out of their way to make her feel at home. Aunt Maggie had never had children with Uncle Walter and Aunt Jenny was a spinster, though she hinted that there had been someone she'd been sweet on in the first World War. Someone she had met whilst working as a taxi driver, a job she had volunteered to do.

Mother had stayed. She had travelled each day to work by charabanc, to her job as an assistant in a Birkenhead department store. In the evenings she read to the aunts or played a few games of bridge or canasta and sometimes she would play the piano while they would sing.

They cooked her nourishing meals and helped her make new skirts and dresses and they giggled together over Aunt Jenny's exploits from the war.

Then one weekend, when Mother had just turned eighteen, she read a card in the newsagent's window that said there was to be a dance the following Saturday at the local village hall. She had hurried down the lane to the bungalow, to ask the aunts if they would help her make an evening dress. She had a pattern, all she needed was the material and she would get that on the market during her lunch hour.

The aunts had always trusted her and they didn't object to their niece going to the village dance, in fact they urged her to go out more. At her age she should have had a beau!

Little did they know, reflected my mother sadly. There had been a boy when she had lived at Pear Tree Cottage. He had asked her to go with him to the Argylle Music Hall, but Lily had refused her permission saying that the age of sixteen, Irene was too young to go. Her daughter was always malleable, like her father had been, and regretfully she had told her admirer that her mother wouldn't let her go. Next thing she heard he was courting Doris Tickle, but as Isabel had told her, 'there was plenty more fish in the sea.' Then there was Albert Harrington. He was the under manager at Saltbury's, the department store where Irene worked. He was always very nice to her, helping her to carry the heavy boxes from the stockroom, opening the doors, smiling at her in the staff canteen when she was eating her lunch. He made her heart beat madly, but she knew her crush on him would never come to much. One day he would be a Manager, marry a girl from a better background, not a lowly shop girl like my mother was.

Then at the dance that Saturday she had met Eddie. She had gone to the dance with a girl named Mabel, the daughter of a neighbour a few doors away. They weren't great friends, they didn't have a lot in common, but neither girl wanted to go to the dance alone.

Eddie was leaning against the bar talking to one of his brothers. He was bored already, having wanted to be with his mates in Chester, but his father had refused him the loan of the car.

Eddie had looked around and saw Irene. She was new to the village, he thought. He liked her swinging chestnut curls and the blue satin dress that she wore, it shimmered in the light as she waltzed with her girl partner. So if she hadn't come with a male friend then he'd seize his chance to dance with her when he could.

The next dance was a tango, he asked her to dance and their footsteps together were a work of art. Other couples began to watch as they danced the tango so beautifully.

That was the beginning of a very long courtship, my mother reminisced, a relationship based on dancing for two protracted years. My father never asked her for a date, never walked her home or even tried to get to know her, just assumed she'd be there each Saturday to be his partner on the dance floor.

To be honest, she hadn't been looking for a long term partner, she was still in love with Albert, though there was never encouragement on his part. She hadn't really liked my father, he was a show off, he would get snappy with her if she stumbled on a step. If they entered a competition he would insist on her turning up early so they could rehearse, then usually blamed her if they didn't win! On some nights he would ignore her until he felt like a turn on the dance floor, but if she was asked to dance by someone else, his eyes would follow her around the room.

He wasn't mature enough for my mother she had realized and still wasn't if the truth was known. The reason why she married him still haunted her. It had been because of Albert when he had announced his engagement to Felicity Trent. Her heart had broken on the spot and she had taken to her bed with a mysterious illness, couldn't be coaxed out of it though her aunts did their best.

Then one morning, as the sun streamed through her bedroom window, she came to a decision. She would change her job away from her love and try to forget he ever existed.

The following Saturday she decided to make a play for Leonard Stanton. On the occasions that Father ignored her, this young man always asked her would she like to dance? He was tall, not as good looking as Eddie, but had a friendly open face and an attractive smile. They were pleasantly engaged in a quick-step when a voice bellowed across the dance floor.

'You can let her go now, Stanton, I'm here to dance with my girl.'

The couples around Leonard and Irene stopped and looked in horror or amusement at the scene. It was Eddie Dockerty, wasn't it, drunk as a mop and swaying by the door?

My mother excused herself to poor Leonard and hurried over; she grabbed Father by his shoulder and hustled him out of the village hall.

'How dare you embarrass me in front of all those people? I'm not your property, you don't own me or tell me what to do.'

He'd had the grace to look ashamed, but said with drunken authority.

'But you are my girl and I was worried what might have happened to you. I missed you last week when you didn't turn up to meet me. You know if you ever consider marrying someone, will you give me first refusal?'

Had Father wondered when he'd sobered up what he had drunkenly committed himself to, my mother had begun to think wryly? Though after his strange proposal his manner seemed to change. She became the centre of his world right up until they married, he was attentive, loyal, caring and supportive. Even stood up to his family when they closed ranks against her.

He'd been over the moon when she told him she was to have a baby and that certainly wouldn't have happened if there'd been contraception in her day!

How the war had changed him. Changed everybody, but it was a chastened moody man she had now as a husband, not the chirpy confident Eddie she had known before the war had taken him away.

28

My mother startled back into reality as a tapping sound on the window caused her to jump guiltily. It was her Aunt Jenny beckoning her niece to come in.

Later that morning, I was sitting on a bench in the school dining room contemplating a bowl of tapioca pudding. It looked grey and glutinous and I wondered what would happen if I pushed my bowl away? My dinner had been acceptable, mince, mashed potatoes, cabbage, the kind of meal I was used to at home.

Suddenly I heard a man shouting in the doorway. 'Can I have your attention all of you? Be silent, I've something to say.'

One hundred pairs of eyes, plus teachers and the dinner ladies, turned towards the speaker and a hush fell in the room.

It was Mr. Tenby, the man with the bald head that I had hoped I wouldn't have as a classroom teacher. My teacher was called Miss Moffatt, a strict no nonsense kind of woman with salt and pepper hair.

Under Mr. Tenby's arm squirmed a small boy screaming to be let down. His bottom was bare for all to see, his short grey trousers half way round his knees.

'Now this young man is being made an example of,' the teacher shouted above the poor boy's cries, 'he has been found doing something he shouldn't have done and I just won't tolerate it.'

I noticed some of the women teachers shaking their heads in dismay at what Mr. Tenby was doing. The other children near me looked frightened and like me were quaking in their shoes. We watched in horror as the man brought his free hand down and smacked the little bottom three times, then he threw the terrified boy to the floor and calmly walked away.

There was a stunned silence for a moment as everyone looked on in disbelief, then the youngest member of the women teachers ran towards the blonde haired child. She picked the boy up in her arms and cuddled him gently.

I felt sick when I realized who the little boy was, it was Timmy Parry, the youngest member of a family from up our lane and he was only four years old.

At playtime that afternoon, as I played hopscotch with my new friend Christy, a boy a year or two older than me, came up and began to twist my arm. I cried out in pain and began to kick out at him with my heavy black school shoes.

'I'll tell my teacher of you,' I shouted angrily. 'You're a bully and Mr. Tenby will give you the cane.'

A crafty look came into the horrid boy's eyes and he released my arm with a sneer.

'You're just a stupid girl,' he said, 'you don't even know that on your first day at school you're allowed to go home at last playtime. Why don't yer take this other dumb girl with you? Your teacher will have gone home by now, so you've no one to clat to anyway.'

I didn't even think to question what the boy had told me, as I couldn't wait to get back home.

The incident at dinner time had disturbed me greatly and all I wanted to do was curl up on my own little bed. Christy looked at me with doubt in her eyes. She had recently moved into Whaley Lane and was a year older, but if the boy said it was time to go home she might as well go too.

We set off at a pace and soon crossed the main road at the top of Glenwood Drive. Neither of us wondered where the rest of the children were, as Christy was telling me of how her little brother was a pain.

Suddenly I saw Mother walking slowly ahead, pushing the 'pram in a desultory fashion. She wasn't in any hurry, as it was an hour or so before it was time to collect me from school.

'Look, Christy, there's my Mummy,' I cried gleefully. 'If we hurry we'll catch up with her.

Shush, don't say anything, we'll creep up behind her and give her a surprise.'

Mother was away in a world of her own and certainly did get a surprise when I shouted, 'Boo'.

She turned to see me looking very flushed, out of breath and grinning from ear to ear.

'Vivienne! What are you doing here at this time? Is there something the matter and who's your little friend?'

'This is Christy, Mummy,' I said proudly. 'We came home together. Didn't you know that on your first day at school you get to come home at last playtime? You didn't tell me that, but a boy at school told me. See, aren't I a big girl coming home all on my own? Well, at least I came home on my own with Christy.'

I looked up at Mother, expecting to be told I was a very clever girl, but she was staring back down the road with a bewildered look on her face.

'But if that's the case, Vivienne, where are all the other children? If it was the first day for everyone, because all the children came from different schools.............? Oh gosh, what have you done? I'll have to take you back again and explain it was a mixup, they'll be worried for you both by now. Christy, where do you live, I'll have to see your mother and see what can be done?'

Christy began shuffling her feet and looking rather red faced at the floor.

'I live at number eighty nine Whaley Lane, Mrs. Dockerty. When Vivienne said she was coming home I thought it best if I came with her. It was her fault we came out early, so I don't think I should get the blame.'

Mother sighed and told us to follow her, though I kept my distance from Christy as she had been telling lies. Christy's mother just raised her eyes to heaven, when she had listened to the story and declared she wasn't taking her daughter back to school again.

'You go, Mrs. Dockerty and tell them of my daughter's part in it. I've a husband coming home for his tea soon and there'll be hell to pay if it's not ready.'

'Haven't we all got husbands,' my mother replied resignedly and turned the 'pram around to walk down Whaley Lane again.

All this time my suspicions were beginning to turn into horror, my mother was going to take me back to school again. I couldn't see why she needed to, as surely an explanation for my absence could be given the following day? I suddenly had a flash of what had happened to Timmy Parry at dinnertime, that would be me at assembly next morning, showing my bare bottom to the rest of the school.

'No, Mummy,' I shouted, 'don't take me back to school. The man will get me and he'll take my knickers down!'

I began to sob and ran ahead, darting through our front gate before Mother could restrain me.

She ran after me, jogging the 'pram in her desperation, causing Audrey who had been sleeping inside to wail.

'What man, Vivienne? What man is going to take your knickers down, Vivienne? Come here this minute and explain yourself!'

The tone of my mother's voice made me slink back down the path again. I had intended to hide behind the black currant bushes, a favourite place of mine as I'd grown older, to escape from the wrath of a parent, but now I thought better of it. I was tired and hoped that my mother would relent and let me go upstairs to lie on my bed.

'Now tell me what this is all about, Vivienne,' she said worriedly. 'What man? Come here and let me wipe your eyes and then you can sit up on the 'pram.'

She held out her arms and scooped me up, then slowly pushed the 'pram along listening to me as I told her the tale of what had happened to Timmy Parry. Audrey, who now was two years old, sat up and took note of it all, patting me on the back and making sympathetic noises.

My mother was outraged when I had finished telling her. She knew the family. A big drunken lout of a father, a weary worn out wraith of a wife, an older boy who had terminal cancer and Timmy with the looks of an angel already feeling the cruelties of the world. She had heard that Betty Parry went begging around the neighbours, when her old man had spent all his wages in the local 'pub. She felt despair, what chance had a child like that got, when already he was being picked on by a teacher? If she was his mother she'd make a complaint to the school.

Strangely enough, my tale of this cruelty didn't dissuade my mother from taking me back to face the music. She was a naive soul, who thought that if she explained that I was new and didn't know the rules yet, then all would be forgiven. But I knew different. I had already had a board rubber whistling passed my ear that morning, as the teacher targeted a whispering boy behind me and watched as another boy had his knuckles rapped with a ruler, for holding his pencil in his left hand. I told my mother that I never wanted to go back to school again, as I was sure I'd be made a show of for my misdemeanor. She wouldn't listen, kept up a brisk pace resolutely until I leaned over the pram and was sick on her shoes. Even then she just wiped the sick off with a handful of grass and began to whistle an annoying tune.

When we got to the school entrance she tidied me up, wiping my blotched face with her hanky and ran her fingers through my short cropped hair.

'Now, Vivienne,' she said kindly, 'we'll leave Audrey here in her pram while you and I go in to see your teacher and explain what happened. What was her name again?'

'Miss Moffat,' I replied fearfully, my heart doing somersaults and all sorts of butterflies flitting around inside me as I followed her into the school. The final bell had just been rung and many curious eyes stared at me, as my peers pushed and jostled past us in an effort to get home. I blushed a furious red and waited until my classmates had gone.

Miss Moffat didn't look unduly worried about a pupil disappearing, she continued to wipe the blackboard and while doing so regarded us at the door.

'So the wanderer returns, Mrs. Dockerty,' she said, looking coolly at me. 'Don't worry about an explanation, Rory Phillipson has confessed his part in it and he has been dealt with. Now, Vivienne, what about your punishment? We can't have you running home just when you feel like it, can we?'

My mother began to protest that I didn't need punishment. I had made the mistake of believing this older boy and she had only brought me back in case the school was anxious of my whereabouts.

Miss Moffatt took no notice. I was instructed to stand against a desk with my feet apart. Six lashes of the ruler on the backs of my legs was my punishment. My mother watched me proudly, as worn out from my earlier weeping, I never shed a tear.

CHAPTER 2

My father walked along the road with a spring in his step. It was Friday afternoon and he had just received his cards and finishing pay from the foreman. He had been working for two long years on the council estate near to where we lived and today had slipped the last tile into place on the kitchen floor of 58 Blueberry Street. The 'Berry' estate was finished, the gang would be moving on next Monday, but this time without their 'finisher' because Father had decided he had other things to do. The regular money that he had been earning, had given us many things that we had never had before. He had moved the downstairs toilet to the recess in the upstairs double bedroom and put up a partition wall, so that Gina had a room of her own. Mother had bought a carpet for the living room and a wireless too and on Saturday, Father was going to see about buying a second hand car.

He turned into Whinberry Street, admiring the archways over the semi- detached red brick homes. It gave him great satisfaction to think that he had contributed to such a pleasing effect over so many doors. He frowned though when he passed a small number of prefabricated homes, they were like miniature dolls houses with no beauty to them at all. Temporary shelters to house the poor had been the government's thinking of the day, but he knew of at least one family who wasn't poor, that had taken up residence in one of them.

My aunt and her husband had moved into one and my uncle's family were not without money. Father disliked the swarmy bastard that Rosaleen had married, with his double barreled accent and eyes that never returned your gaze. He was a show off, an officer in the Royal Air Force during the war and never tired of telling you that when you were in his company.

Father thought back to his own years in war torn Britain. He had been lucky in that he was in a reserved occupation when war was declared. His brothers, more fool them, had been full of patriotism and had enlisted virtually straight way. Father had been working in demolition though and that had been reason enough not to have taken the 'King's shilling'. There would be conscription anyway if the war dragged on. His job in Liverpool was just as dangerous he had thought, with being on call after a bombing raid to make a dwelling safe with a temporary repair or knock down an unstable property, or help if a gas main or water pipe was blown. Sometimes he assisted the wardens in digging if someone was buried under the rubble of their home.

But then Father's own world was blown to pieces. For a few weeks he had been increasingly suspicious that two labourers he worked with were doing a spot of looting. He didn't care to do that himself, as it was robbing from the vulnerable and the poor. He told the foreman, Big Irish Murphy, who said that he would look into the problem right away. Then one night as he was packing up his tool bag in preparation for going home, his way was barred by the Muldoon brothers, Callum and Stanley.

'So, yer thought to be puttin' a word in about us to Mr. Murphy,' Stanley had said menacingly, 'and what's it got to do with yer anyway?'

Father had felt frightened, but he squared up to the two men resolutely. He hadn't been brought up with three brothers without a scrap now and again and he could sense that this was what the pair were after.

Well, he'd show them, Eddie Dockerty was as good as anyone in a punch up. The first blow was struck by Stanley, with Callum waiting to do the kicking when Father was on the ground. The blow hit him on the temple and for a moment he saw flashing stars. Then he charged at Stanley, head down into his combatant's stomach, while Callum jumped across his back and the three men sprawled on the floor.

Just then the men heard Big Murphy shouting.

'Come out of it the three of you, Dockerty get up. Now what's this all about?'

'It's these two, they jumped me,' Father replied, gasping for breath as he stood before the foreman.

'Could it be that you told them that I was onto their little game?'

He could see from Murphy's guilty face that it was as he had suspected, the man was also looting and the three men were sharing the spoils. He waited for a denial, none came, but sitting in the foreman's hands were Father's cards and three days wages.

He saw red and snatched the cards and bank notes, pocketed them quickly, took one step back and crashed his left fist into Irish Murphy's face. Then not waiting for any reaction, he picked up his tool bag and jacket and ran for his life!

Retribution came almost immediate. Three weeks later in the year of '43, Father kissed my tearful Mother goodbye at Lime Street and caught the train up to Scotland. He was to do his six weeks Army training at Hawick, where he had been assigned to the regiment of the Royal Ulster Rifles. Though he had protested strongly to the recruiting sergeant that he was third generation Irish and his ancestors came from Galway in Southern Ireland anyway, the man was unrepentant, declaring that the name Dockerty was undoubtedly Irish, so he would have to join an Irish regiment. Anyway, what did a surname matter he had added, Dockerty was to be gun fodder at the end of the day!

With that remark still ringing in his ears, my father had got on the cramped and crowded troop train on its way up to Edinburgh. This was the first time he had been anywhere other than Liverpool or the local towns and villages. His morale was low, his nerves all shot and the men aboard were mouthy and brash.

He found a space in a corner of the corridor and shut his eyes and ears to the deafening sounds. The journey was long, tiring and extremely uncomfortable, with no stop for refreshment or exercise.

He was thankful when at last they arrived at their destination. A fleet of trucks were waiting to carry them in convoy the rest of the way.

He made himself known to his fellow conscripts and was surprised to find that he was the oldest squaddie there. At twenty eight, he was ten years older than some of the lads and was pleased to receive the respect he thought was due.

Father smiled to himself as he remembered those first few weeks of training. Sergeant Mannion was the chap in charge, taken out of retirement when the war began. He was very strict certainly, but compassionate towards his men, saw the lads had comforts at the end of a rainy square bashing day on the borders of blustery Scotland.

He tried to get to know his raw recruits individually and it soon became apparent that Private Dockerty couldn't read. Thanks to the old timer, Father could now read and write a fair hand, was trained to be a barber, so he was always in demand.

Then the awful day came when the platoon received its 'marching orders'. Before long Father and his mates were in the thick of it, fighting for their lives in the muddy fields of Arnhem, the place where little Billy Watson took a bullet in his back. Joey Flanagan took the brunt of a grenade that landed in their dug out and many more went down like ninepins as the 'stuccas' flew overhead. Father's nerves were shot to pieces as he waited for his turn to die.

The men then moved on to fight at Nijmegan, not so many as started out, but 'jerry' had seemed to have quieted down. At this point Father was ordered to go ahead and do a bit of foraging, the rations were low and the corporal announced he quite fancied a nice fried egg for his tea.

Being a country boy, Father had not been adverse to a bit of poaching, so in the dusk that was fast approaching he squirmed on his belly, snake like, until he came to the edge of a wood. He was used to the kind of noises he heard, the crackling of twigs, the moan of the wind in the trees, the squeaking of little furry animals and the twitching of birds in their nests. He used all his senses to guide him to a hen house that was at the back of some farm buildings ahead.

He crept as lightly as he could in his army boots, until he drew level with a small wooden shed. The hens began to clutter in alarm, as he swiftly put his hand inside to feel around for his prize. With two precious eggs clutched ready to put in his knapsack, his heart nearly exploded when a hand grabbed his shoulder from behind. He whirled in panic to see his attacker, a soldier dressed in German uniform and grinning from ear to ear! Father nearly wet himself, then began to tremble, but his enemy just put out his hand. He gestured to Father to give him the eggs, then turned on his heel and ran!

Still in shock, Father managed with shaking fingers to find another egg, then just as swiftly as the German soldier, he ran the opposite way!

God, that had been a close one, remembered Father as he ambled along the road, and they hadn't believed him when he went back to his unit and told them all the tale.

My father sat on a stone wall and looked across the farmer's field towards the village. In the distance he could see a copse, that brought back memories of his next brush with fate.

The corporal had decided in their trench outside Emmerich, that he rather fancied something different to brighten up his day. Perhaps Private Dockerty would like to use his skills to seek out an orchard or perhaps a vegetable field? A cabbage or some apples, he didn't really mind which.

So Father silently crept into an orchard where red apples sat succulently on drooping boughs. With racing heart he plucked a few and placed them in his knapsack carefully. He could hear the murmuring of voices in the distance and a dog began to bark. He decided he had better get a move on, it could be friendly folk or a quisling, but he didn't want to take that chance.

He sped as quietly as he could around a copse, through a hedge and slunk along the perimeter of a field, then suddenly he tripped over something lying prostrate on the ground! He picked himself up, his whole body shaking with terror as he saw that it was a German soldier he'd fallen over! The man had been having forty winks, his body stretched out in the grass. Too late, the soldier stood up and pointed his rifle in Father's direction, his face contorted in a menacing scowl.

'Gott in Himmel', the man exclaimed. 'Rasch, rasch!'

Father's mind went then. He stared blankly down at the soldier's fixed bayonet. This was it! It was all over, Eddie's Dockerty's time on earth was up!

He looked into the enemy's eyes, the seconds ticking into eternity, then the German gestured with his rifle and repeated the words again.

'Rasch, rasch, schnell, schnell!'

The he began to count out numbers.

'Eins, zwei, drei, vier, funf.'

When he had got to five it clicked with Father. The man was giving him a head start as if he was a fox or a rabbit. It was like a sport to the German. Rather than killing his foe in cold blood, Father was now his prey!

He turned on his heel and fled as fast as his great coat and army boots allowed him to. As he told anyone who would listen in years to came, he ran a mile in a minute that day!

Father felt morose as he recaptured all those emotions. It was the dreams at night that got to him. Sometimes he never escaped that menacing soldier and as the bullet pierced through his back to puncture his lung, he would awake clutching his heart, sweating and screaming with pain. Sometimes he was immersed in a swamp of mud and would wake to find his blanket wrapped around his face. The worst times were when he acted out his guard duty and challenged Mother or us girls in the middle of the night!

He knew he wasn't the only one, both Terry and Michael his brothers had suffered, but life was bearable if you could down a pint or two and drink those devilish demons away.

That's where he was heading now, Father thought whistling happily. A bath, his dinner and a bevy at the Club. Half his pay to my mother, a round of drinks for his pals and tomorrow he'd get that good looking shooting brake. No more walking for Eddie Dockerty, from now on he'd be arriving in style!

A week or so later, Father was polishing his new car on our drive way. He hadn't bothered finding himself any work since leaving the Council estate, because he still had money. Why shouldn't he have a holiday, he had told my mother? He'd never had a holiday in his bloomin' life.

Father had spent his time driving his car around the place, showing off to his neighbours and taking Nana or Mother shopping. It was a great feeling to be the only one in his lane to have a motor car and when he thought about it, he'd got it at a very good price. Sixty pounds wasn't a lot, when you thought of the freedom the car would bring to him. He was even considering driving down to Woodchurch, where the gangers he had worked with had started on another housing estate.

But not just yet eh? He had to take me up to the doctor's surgery, because I was due an injection for chicken pox.

According to Father I had been a right pain in the arse recently. I had kept everyone awake with my coughing after being pushed into a local stream by one of the Lee brothers and catching a heavy cold because of it; ripping the dress that my mother had made me for Caroline Thomas's birthday party, after she had pushed me into her garden rockery out of spite and fighting with Audrey over a doll that my father had bought her. My father despaired of my unlady like behaviour, telling me I was rebellious, undisciplined and needed bringing into line.

I was a great one for eavesdropping outside my parent's bedroom by the time I was seven, I could use the upstairs toilet and hear every word. It had got around that the Australian government wanted youngsters from Britain to help the country repopulate and one of my father's pals was seriously thinking of sending his troublesome eldest girl there. Had Father been joking when he told the tale to Mother and was it my name that was mentioned, as I hastily pulled the chain?

I had been brave in the doctor's. I had missed an earlier appointment through being ill and the nurse had offered me a lollypop for not causing any fuss. My father had refused it on my behalf. It was nearly tea time and it would spoil my appetite.

I was very angry as I walked to the car with my spoilsport of a father. I whined and whined at him until he promised me a thick ear.

'But you know I'll eat my dinner up and look I've got some money,' I said, showing him the pennies I had in my pocket. 'Let me go to that shop over there, I'll buy myself a lollypop.'

'Get in the car, Vivienne,' my father said sternly, not wanting to smack me in front of passing people or causing an upsetting scene.

I climbed aboard my Dad's shooting brake and slammed the passenger door, he forgot in his annoyance to check that the bolt was in place. In my usual way to attract my father's attention, albeit good or bad, I snivelled and moaned as he drove down the hill from the village. I really wanted that lollypop, treats were hard to come by and I had saved those pennies to buy some sweets of my own. I don't know what made me do it, the rebellious streak that I was told I had, must have suddenly taken over and I opened the car door in defiance and landed on the road.

Father never remembered what happened then, though he swerved the car to avoid the back wheel from going over me, then whack, the car wrapped itself around the nearest lamp post, leaving my stricken father with his head on the horn!

A man jumped out of his car that had been following just behind us, shouting to a passerby to go to the nearby telephone. His wife ran over to me where I was lying unconscious, while the man took a look at my father, who was slowly coming to.

It served me right though. I was lucky to have got away with a broken ankle and a gashed leg for my defiance, spending the next three weeks under the grim regime of the local children's hospital!

My father seemed a chastened man for a while after, possibly feeling that he had been rather harsh with me that day. The shooting brake was scrapped and a shiny green car replaced it.

It was the day of the Coronation, Princess Elizabeth was going to be crowned Queen.

The school had given the children a day off to celebrate and there was to be a pageant and parade.

My sister Audrey and I were not taking part, as we were both recovering from another bout of measles, but Mother had said that we were well enough to watch the parade and attend the local street party. All the mothers were chipping in with sandwiches and special cakes.

My granny had made me a long pink satin dress before I had become ill and I was allowed to wear it for the occasion, along with a pink oval shaped hat and a pair of pink ballet slippers and not to leave little Audrey out, she wore a long flowery dress and old straw hat.

Granny was back in our lives again after Father had called a truce, Mother had got enough on her plate dashing down to the auntie's house. So Granny came back much to everyone's delight and soon took up her helper's role again. Washing and cooking and generally being around for us, though my father wouldn't let her live with us again.

He had bought my mother a second hand bicycle, so that she could peddle off down to Seaview Lane where our aunt's lived, after Granny got down from the eleven o'clock 'bus.

We stared gloomily through our bedroom window on the morning of the Coronation. There were black clouds ominously threatening rain, not a bit of blue to brighten up the sky.

'If it rains, Audrey,' I said, 'we'll not be able to go and see the Parade and the street party will be stopped, 'cos we'd all get wet when we sit down for our tea.'

'P'raps Mummy will make us some jam butties and we can have the party here instead,' said Audrey hopefully.

'Pooh,' I replied. 'You're such a baby Audrey, we can have jam butties anytime we like. This is a hist...orical occasion that we shall remember for the rest of our lives. We have to have a Parade and a street party and go to Aunty Sheena's to watch the Coronation on her television.'

'I don't want to go to Aunty Sheena's to watch her television. I don't like Tiddles, he smells and he scratches. Can't I just stay here and play with my friends?'

'No, Audrey. You can't. You have to come with me and help me show off my Queen Elizabeth costume, 'cos you are my attendant. Granny said that this dress she made is an exact replic' of the old queen's, the first one that is, though I haven't got a ruff.'

The rain held off just long enough so that the villagers and school children could watch the Parade. Trumpets blared, drums banged, cymbals crashed as the Salvation Army band lead the way. Then came the members of the Royal British Legion, followed by a carnival float pulled by a tractor. On board was a girl dressed as a queen and a boy dressed as her consort. The Parade wound its way round the village, down the hill and cut through the side roads, eventually disassembling outside the Anchor Inn. After that, it was one mad scramble as everyone hurried off to find a T.V, so that they could watch the Coronation.

It was a long way back from Aunty's Sheena's and I still hobbled a little, even though I'd had my plaster cast off weeks ago. The accident was never mentioned again and Father had changed his car, so we were delighted to find our father waiting outside the house after the Coronation had finished. We didn't find it strange that he didn't come inside our aunty's home to collect us, as our minds were on the yummy feast that would be awaiting us. We were not encouraged to visit our relatives' homes normally, unless by special invitation.

As it happened the street party was a washout, as rain came down like stair rods, but a kindly mother from a house up the road, let sixteen excited children have their party in her home.

My sister tossed her curly head away from the leering ferry- man. He always seemed to be there when she walked down the landing stage at the Pier Head in Liverpool. It was embarrassing, she thought as she waited for the 'Mountwood' ferry that would take the passengers over the River Mersey to Birkenhead. The man must be nearly thirty and here he was trying to catch the eye of a girl who was only fifteen. She supposed she should be flattered, because she was looking smart in her black and white check coat with her black handbag and matching high heel shoes, but he probably had a wife at home and a couple of little kids.

Gina was feeling tired after her day at the secretarial school. She had been going there for six months now and she felt she knew it all. She could type and take shorthand at a fairly impressive speed, but now they had begun the boring bits, role play with the other students on the course.

Answering the telephone, taking dictation, honing up their social skills and being the perfect employee. All she wanted to do was get out into the real world and start to earn some money. She owed such a lot to my mother, as she had scrimped and saved for this training and the family had gone without.

Gina thought about the weekend ahead of her as she waited in the queue. She had joined the tennis club at Heswall and had met a young man named David. His father was a doctor and most of the young people she had met there were from professional backgrounds. David seemed to have taken a shine to her and he, Dicky Rogers and Tina Jones made a foursome up with her.

They were going to the pictures together tomorrow, a Western was the boy's choice but the girls didn't mind as they liked the hero, John Wayne.

David was definitely someone that Gina wanted to hold on to, she could already see her future in her mind's eye. The big detached house overlooking the River Dee, joining the Ladies Circle, attending the Equestrian Club at Thurstaston and learning to drive David's shiny new Rover car. It would be easy to fall in love with David. He was so handsome, tall, well built, blonde and athletic, she was so pleased that he seemed attracted to her.

Gina knew that she had grown into an attractive young lady. Her Uncle Spencer had confirmed that when he had asked her to pose for him in Aunt Rosaleen's evening dress. He had said that he had bought the latest model of a professional photographer's camera and she was just the person he could practice on. He aimed to make a living with it, at weddings, family portraits, christenings. Since he had moved up North, he had never really taken to the jobs that had been on offer. He wasn't a labourer, he was a white collar worker and he was choosy, seeing he had an independent income now that his folks had gone. He liked to keep his options open, so photography would be just the ticket in his mind.

Gina hadn't really taken to being his model. She felt her breasts and shoulders were too much on show, her uncle kept touching her in places she rather he didn't, but his excuse was he had to 'arrange her' to bring her true potential to the fore.

If it hadn't have been for her cousins, Francis and Billy, sitting in the next room watching television and her aunt chatting across the road at her neighbours, Gina would have felt defenceless and a little afraid. Especially after the eldest boy, Francis, showed her a picture of another cousin Maureen, tastefully decorated in a mink coat, with her knickers and brassiere on show. That had been enough for Gina when she saw it and never went near Uncle Spencer's house again.

'Vivienne,' my Uncle Spencer called, 'would you come here a moment and help me with something in the bedroom?'

I sighed when I heard his request as I had only been watching 'Muffin the Mule' for a couple of minutes with my two boy cousins and Audrey and here was my uncle disturbing my viewing time. It was a pity we couldn't afford a television at home, then me and my sister wouldn't have to pike it round to this place in all weathers. I knew though, that my Mum like a bit of peace on a Saturday morning. She said it was to do the housework, but the house didn't look much different when we came back home.

I was scared of Uncle Spencer. I had seen him hitting my elder cousin Francis with a plimsoll and I was always careful not to draw attention to myself, in case he decided to do it to me.

So I dragged myself unwillingly to do his bidding, walking carefully on tiptoe in case I stood unwittingly on the paw of Bruno, the 'ferocious dog.'

'There you are, Vivienne,' said my uncle, as he walked out of the bathroom with nothing but a towel around his naked body.

'I want you to help me with something in the bedroom. Your Aunty Rosaleen has had to go into hospital and left me with the boys. So I can't do this for myself, can I? You're such a good little girl that I said to myself, Vivienne will help. So you come with me and stand by the side of my bed.

See, I want you to rub this cream all over my body.'

Reluctantly I put my small fingers into the pot of creamy white solution, as Uncle Spencer settled himself on the edge of his bed. I began to daub it half way up his back. I could just about reach if I stood on tiptoe, as at the age of seven I was not very tall.

'Good, good. That's right, now come down a bit further, Vivienne,' he said in a drawl of a voice, 'but a little bit stronger with your rubbing. Very good. Now I'll turn round to face you and you can do the front of me. See like this.' And he took my hand.

I stared between his legs, mesmerized at the thing that looked like a large pink sausage with lots of gingery hair at the base of it. It just looked like one of the bangers that my mother bought from the butcher's in the village, but this one was quivering as my uncle guided my hand.

'Now I want you to move your hand up and down until I tell you to stop, then I'll find some sweeties for you and your sister. Ready?'

I did as I was told, taking a quick peek at my uncle's face to see if he was pleased with me. He seemed to be, he didn't look angry anyway.

Suddenly something happened that made me jump back in fright! The sausage burst just like it did sometimes in my mother's frying pan. When that happened my mother would jump back in fright like I had just done, but my uncle wasn't running to put his hand under the tap like my mother would have, he was lying now on the bed, moaning gently.

I suddenly felt my eyes filling up with tears. My hand was aching because my uncle had gripped it so tightly. I felt scared, hearing him making noises as if he had a pain somewhere. I wanted to go home then. Forget 'Muffin the Mule' on the tele', forget about the sweeties that my uncle had said I could have. All I wanted was my mummy's arms about me, or if she was busy, a cuddle of my teddy bear.

I ran wildly from the bedroom, shouting to Audrey that we were leaving and we were never coming back again. The 'ferocious dog' snapped as I trod on his paw, the cousins yelled their indignation and I sped through the kitchen door as if the devil was after me!

Mother was pegging out her washing when she heard my voice shouting from the corner of the lane. She must have groaned to herself, thinking of the book she had promised herself to read when she'd got the next lot of clothes through the mangle. Usually we didn't get back until after twelve, time for her to have made the beds, finished the washing and sat herself down with a book she had borrowed from the Library. She hurriedly carried her basket through to the wash house, then turned in alarm as I threw my trembling body against hers.

My sister stood a little way off, her eyes enormous with unshed tears. She had been enjoying watching 'Muffin the Mule', until I had dragged her out of there.

'What is it, Vivienne?', Mother cried. She was taken aback, because hugs from me were few and far between.

'I want to tell you something,' I said in a muffled voice, still with my arms around her middle, 'but not in front of Audrey though, tell her to go inside.'

'Oh, you're not going to tell tales again, are you?'

She pushed me gently away from her and looked into my eyes sternly.

'Whatever she's done, you have to remember that Audrey is only five years old. Have you been getting her into trouble again?'

'No, Mummy,' I said, shaking my head adamantly. 'I want to tell you something and I don't want Audrey to know.'

'O.K., Audrey, you go up to your bedroom and play with your

dolly's. I'm sure your sister is being silly, but I'll call you soon when I've got some soup ready. That's all we have for lunch, but it's your favourite tomato. Now, go along there's a good girl.'

Audrey looked bewildered, but she was used to strange things happening when she was with me, her older sister. Look what happened the other day when we'd gone to a children's party at daddy's club. I had been sick all over my party dress, when I'd been asked to sing a song for the members.

I took my mother's hand and drew her into the living room. I sat on the sofa pulling her down to sit beside me. My stomach was jumping up and down with nerves, I was desperate for a wee and my heart felt as if it would leap out of my chest. I felt confused, I didn't know whether my mother was going to be happy or angry. Had something happened at Uncle Spencer's that was good or bad?

'Mummy,' I began, 'you know how men have dangly bits between their legs?' I knew about dangly bits, because once when my father wanted to swim at the seaside and hadn't any trunks with him, he had borrowed my mother's nylon knickers and I could see his dangly bits through them.

My mother looked shaken, but before she answered my question she said, 'Vivienne, have you been peering around toilet doors again, I told you what would happen if I caught you doing that? You really embarrassed your daddy's friend last time he came for tea. Don't tell me your Uncle Spencer caught you doing the same.'

'No, Mummy, I wasn't watching him in his toilet,' I replied seriously.

I faltered for a moment, because I saw that my mother's face had taken on a look of disbelief.

'I was watching television with Billy, Francis and Audrey, then Uncle Spencer shouted that he wanted me to go to his bedroom. You know how you're always telling me that I have to be a good girl, Mummy? So I did as he said. Then he asked me to rub some cream on his back.'

I ventured another look at my Mother's face, as I had been

telling my tale resting my hands on my chin. Mother was now looking at me in near panic!

'Go on, Vivienne,' she urged, whispering grimly.

'Then. Then, he turned round to me and his towel fell off and suddenly I could see his dangly bit but it looked like a big sausage. He grabbed my hand, it's still hurting Mummy and he made me jerk his sausage up and down. Then suddenly he fell over and some stuff came out and I ran!'

My mother began to look horrified as if she couldn't believe what she was hearing. I could see that she was torn between believing my tale, or putting it down to Vivienne making a drama out of something, as I was wont to do. I could see her taking deep breaths to stop herself from fainting, then suddenly she ran into the kitchen and threw up in the sink!

I followed her and said in a scared little voice, 'Mummy, did I do something wrong? Why have you just been sick in the sink?'

My mother stood trembling, wiping her face with the tea towel and looking at me in a funny sort of way. I could see that she thought I must be lying. Uncle Spencer was from an exemplary background, he had been privately educated and came out of the War with distinction.

'Are you making this story up, Vivienne?' she asked, as she made herself a cup of tea with a shaking hand, from the kettle that permanently simmered on the stove. 'Was it your cousin Francis who put you up to this? I know he dislikes his father, so perhaps he told you a dirty story to even up the score.'

I looked up at her innocently. 'It isn't a dirty story, Mummy, I promise.'

She seemed to have made her mind up that I might be telling the truth after I had said that, whipping her pinny off, tidying her hair in the bathroom mirror and changing her slippers for her outside shoes.

'Vivienne,' she said quickly, 'I'm going round to your uncle's house and I'll ask him if what you're saying is true and if I find out you're lying to me, you'll be in a lot of trouble. I want you to look after Audrey and if your daddy comes home, you're to tell him I've gone to the shops.'

'I'm not lying to you, honest, Mummy,' I said, beginning to cry through shock I suppose, or the fact that my mother was going to beard the lion in his den, as it were. 'Uncle Spencer said I was a good girl, so why should I tell you otherwise?'

My mother left me then. She felt so mixed up, with her mind in a whirl as she walked up the road to my uncle's home. She wondered nervously what she was going to say to Spencer? If she told him the story that I had given her, she knew she would die of embarrassment and shame.

Spencer was leaning against the door jamb at the front of his house, when Mother arrived breathlessly. His arms were folded across his chest, as he gazed across the grass to where my mother was hesitating at the top of the path.

'I wondered how long it would take before you came around.'

'I'm sorry?' Mother replied diffidently, walking towards him. 'What do you mean?'

'That daughter of yours, Vivienne. She was out of here like a bat out of Hell not so long ago. I got angry with her, when I saw she'd trodden a load of dog dirt into the carpet. I tell my kids to take their shoes off before they come in. Obviously you haven't trained your girls properly, so I shouted at her. Tough little nut isn't she? Stared at me defiantly then just ran away!'

'Oh, I'm sorry Spencer, she didn't tell me that,' my mother said, feeling all her tension draining out of her. 'She came home with this big exaggerated story. I won't go into detail because it's probably something she heard from one of her cousins. Just say I'll give her a stern talking to when I get back.'

'Would you like to come in and have a cup of coffee with me, Irene?' he said in a conciliatory voice. 'As you know Rosaleen's back in hospital, woman's trouble again.'

Mother gave Spencer an embarrassed shake of her head and turned to walk down the path.

Oh, where are my manners? she thought suddenly. 'Give my

regards to Rosaleen, won't you? Hope she'll be better soon.'

Mother felt relieved as she made her way back home. Thank God it was only about trailing in dog dirt, she should have asked could she clean it up for him? Poor man, having to cope without Rosaleen. Now, what was she going to do with me, I must have been telling fibs to her?

Later, when the three of us had finished lunch and the soup bowls had been cleared away, she tackled me. 'Was that a made up story, Vivienne? I won't shout if you tell me the truth.'

'About Uncle Spencer's dangly bits?' I whispered, as I didn't want Audrey to hear.

'Yes, he told me you had trodden in some dog dirt, so he shouted at you and you ran away.'

'Uncle Spencer's a liar then and I shall tell Daddy when he gets back.'

'No, no,' my Mother whispered back hastily, 'come out into the wash house with me for a moment. Audrey have that last biscuit, your sister's helping me get in some coal.'

She pushed her me through the kitchen door and gripped me tightly by the shoulders when we got outside.

'What happened today was our secret,' she said in a very firm voice 'and you must never tell your Daddy or anyone. If your Daddy knew about what Uncle Spencer did, he would get his gun from the loft and go round and shoot him! You don't want Daddy to be put into Walton Jail, do you?'

I thought for a moment. I would get some peace from all his shouting if he was put in prison, but then we were going on holiday to a neighbour's caravan in the summer and if Daddy went to prison we'd have no one to drive us there. I didn't want to miss a holiday because of my uncle's dangly bits, did I?

'It'll be our secret, Mummy,' I said seriously, 'but I'll never go to Uncle Spencer's house again.'

That night, as my mother tucked me into bed, I asked for reassurance, because I hadn't been sure whether she had really believed my tale, preferring to believe the dog dirt story.

'I am a good girl, aren't I, Mummy? I wasn't telling you a story today, what I told you was true.'

'Shush now, Vivienne,' she said, a sweat beginning to appear on her brow as she said it, 'yes, you are a good girl, but we must never talk about it ever again.'

Gina had become quite a remote figure in my life by the time she was seventeen and enjoying her first job at the Cunard shipping company. I only saw her briefly, mostly at weekends when she dashed around getting ready to go out with friends, or off to town to spend some of her wages. I heard her tell my mother that the work was demanding but varied and she had made a best friend called Vanessa or 'Nessie' as she was known, and that the two of them had a lot of fun together. They window shopped in their lunch hour, treated themselves to a sandwich and coffee in the Kardomah, eyed up the boys that passed them by in the city streets and chatted over the clothes they would wear on their nights out together.

Gina was allowed quite a lot of freedom now that she was a wage earner. Providing she was home on the last bus from Birkenhead, my parents were not too concerned about her. She had always been sensible and at seventeen she had never given them anything to worry about.

Until one evening when she came home straight from work, which was unusual for her.

Mother had just finished mashing the carrots and there was a good smell of braising steak coming from the new gas oven. Father had been chopping logs in the lean to, he had been busy sawing down the branches that overhung from the garden next door. He was washing his hands in the downstairs bathroom, when he heard Gina talking to my mother in the kitchen.

'So you don't mind if I invite him for tea on Sunday? Just a few sandwiches and a shop bought cake, but I'd really like you to meet him. You'll love him, Mother. He's tall and fair- haired and so handsome in his uniform........! Oh, hiya, Dad,' she said. 'I was

53

asking Mum if I could bring Lester for his tea on Sunday. He's such a long way from his home and family and he said he'd love to meet the kids and you two and get to know you all. Dad, is that O.K. with you?'

My sister could see that Father was scowling and she quickly turned to Mother for her support. Mother shrugged helplessly and continued serving our meals onto plates warm from the oven.

'We'll talk about it later, when the youngsters have gone to bed.'

Mother could see that there was going to be confrontation, she could read the signs. Scowls from Father didn't bode well. I was all ears, I could see a storm brewing in the way that the grownups were avoiding each other's eyes. I reluctantly went to bed, but I hovered on the top stair in my nightie.

Father hit the roof when he heard that Gina had been spending her evenings with an American, he had been under the impression that she was 'courting' David from the tennis club.

He ranted on and on about how the Yanks had only got involved in the War at the back end of it and how they should all go home and take their foreign ways with them! No daughter of his was going to be made a fool of, made pregnant, left with a baby or becoming one of them 'GI' brides.

'No decent Englishman will touch you if they find out you've been hanging around with one of them Yanks, now get to your room and out of my sight and not another word about it again! Irene,'

Father turned on Mother.

'This is all your fault, you've been too lax with her. I want you in this house every night by 6 o'clock in future, Gina, until I think you can be trusted again.'

My sister decided not to argue, it was no use even trying when her father was on his high horse. She walked glumly up to her bedroom, where she could hear Audrey and I chattering excitedly through the dividing wall.

I crept into Gina's room and sat on the edge of the bed.

'Is it true, Gina, you've got a G.I. boyfriend? I sat on the top of the stairs before and listened to Daddy shouting at you. Will you marry him do you think and go to live in America?'

My sister shook her head unhappily.

'Fat chance, Vivienne, if Dad has his way!'

Gina lay on her bed and thought back to her and Lester's first meeting. Nessie, her friend from the office, had met two American guys on the train as she travelled back home after work. They got talking as the train steamed slowly along the track to Southport, introducing themselves to her as Lester and Jim. Eventually they got round to asking if Nessie had a girlfriend, so that maybe they could make up a foursome and go out on the town?

She smiled to herself as she remembered that first meeting. It was on a Saturday night six weeks ago. She'd spent ages in the bathroom, splashing on her Eau de Paris perfume, after putting on her pink mohair sweater and her grey pencil skirt. Her naturally curly, brown shoulder length hair shone with a hundred brush strokes and she had dusted a little powder on her cheeks and nose.

At five o'- clock, wearing her new black swagger coat that she had splashed out on in Blacklers, she promised my parents that she would be back on the eleven o'clock bus. With her black stiletto heels clicking and her heart beating wildly, Gina waited for the bus to take her down to Birkenhead. By six she was sitting on the underground train as it went under the River Mersey to Liverpool.

In the same carriage, two American airmen dressed in their smart blue uniforms gazed over appreciatively at the girl who had caught their eye. One was gorgeously handsome with short fair hair and cornflower blue eyes, his long legs sprawled out in front of him and he drawled laconically to his friend, a shorter stocky fellow with light brown crew cut hair.

Gina caught them looking and turned away in embarrassment, but not until the taller one had brazenly winked at her.

She wondered briefly why she was going on this blind date with a stranger? David was her boyfriend, wasn't he, but that was all he was to her, a friend? She craved a little excitement, a bit of romance and tender loving, someone who would treat her like a princess and bring her pretty flowers. Maybe this American that Nessie had arranged for her to meet? She had heard that they were generous with their gifts and compliments.

Gina looked at her wristwatch. There was just time to walk up to Lime Street to get there for six thirty, Nessie had said she'd be waiting under the station clock. Her heart did a somersault as she got up quickly to alight from the train, as the airmen had got up too and were smiling over at her.

Oh, blast it, they were following her. Up the ramp and into the city the grinning airmen were never far away. She quickened her pace, they quickened theirs and as she turned into Lime Street they were right behind! Gina stopped in her tracks and turned to face them in annoyance, nothing was going to spoil this evening for her.

'Could you please tell me what you think you are doing, by following me all the way from the train station? Who do you think you are? Have you nothing better to do?'

She drew herself up to her full five feet five inches and glared in their direction.

'I can call a policeman you know, in fact I think there is one over there.'

The two men burst out laughing, as they had seen Nessie hurrying to join them, but Gina had her back turned and couldn't see.

'May I introduce ourselves, Ma'am?,' asked the tall good looking one. 'I am Lester McKay and this is Jimmy Bannerman, both pleased to be your escorts for this evening.'

After that gloriously wonderful evening, when not a penny had been spared in the lap of luxury restaurant, then jiving and jitterbugging until their legs ached, Gina and Lester walked to the Pier Head hand in hand. Jimmy had accompanied Nessie back on the train to Southport and it looked as if the couple would meet again.

It had been so romantic as Gina and Lester stood together on the top deck of the ferry, watching the lights of Birkenhead come even closer as the boat headed towards the landing stage. He told her a little of his family back home, but mostly he just held her close with his arms wrapped around her. Then he had put her on the last bus to Heswall, promising he would keep in touch via her office telephone. He had told her he was stationed at Sealand Aerodrome, which as the crow flies was nearer on the Wirral to where Gina lived. She decided though to keep her new love secret. It was early days yet, Lester might decide he didn't want to know. Let her parents think that she was still seeing David, she had an uneasy feeling that it was better that way.

And she had been right, she thought to herself that evening as she had an enforced early night, but six weeks on it was now imperative that her parents meet her young man. According to rumour on the camp, his unit would soon be moving out. Not yet, but definitely by Christmas, then what were Lester and Gina going to do?

Our Mother became an unexpected ally, while Father huffed and puffed. Mother got on with her knitting while Father talked to himself. This usually happened when he felt he was being backed into a corner, he would never discuss or calmly listen, just dug himself a hole that there was no getting out of. Next would come the silent treatment, he could go for days before announcing to us that everything had been Mother's fault.

Mother waited until his ranting became a little calmer, then suggested meekly that it might be wiser if they met the young airman. Surely they should make an effort, rather than turning the girl against them? Gina was sensible and wouldn't have fallen for just anyone.

Father grudgingly agreed, it was his way of saving face, but said he wasn't giving up his Sunday afternoon at the Club for anyone. Mother was to give the Yank fish paste sandwiches, that would put him off and there would be trouble if she went to any expense.

Gina was over the moon when her mother gave permission, at least her romance would be on a proper footing if Lester could come to her home.

The following Sunday afternoon, Lester still in his uniform, knocked tentatively on our front door. He was carrying flowers in his hand for Mother, though he noticed ruefully that the garden was full of them. One of his pockets held a bottle of rye for Father and in the other a small dolly each for Audrey and myself.

The door opened to reveal two little girls dressed in our best clothes, both gazing wide eyed up at him and Gina smiling happily. My mother stood in the hall way trying to put a welcoming smile on her face.

Lester felt the tension and made a resolve that he would win over my mother by the time we'd finished tea. Of Father there was no sign, but Gina had warned him that this would be the case.

Mother dominated the conversation the whole afternoon, she was fascinated by this stranger from a foreign shore. We girls sat quietly on the sofa equally enthralled, as he told us all about the wooden house his family lived in, the acres of farmland that his father possessed, his brothers and sisters who still lived at home and the horses and cattle at the ranch in Tennessee. He was lavish with his praise over the sandwiches, Victoria sponge cake and tea in a china cup and complimented Mother on her youthful looks. He called us kids 'honey', ruffled up our hair and we were both delighted by this wonderful person and the beautiful dolls he had given us.

At six o'- clock, Lester thought it was time to make his excuses and lifted Audrey and I up into his strong arms to give us both a hug. Then he solemnly shook Mother's hand and thanked her for her kindness in inviting him for tea. Then Gina walked him down the lane to catch the bus.

'Gina, honey, you're going to have to tell them,' he said urgently, once they were wrapped in an embrace inside the bus shelter. 'If we've any future together you've got to be strong . If you want to come back home with me to America, we'll have to marry. They won't let you in the country otherwise and we need permission from my Commander too.'

Gina sighed heavily at his words. They had been through all this before, the rumour had finally become reality and Lester's unit was being transferred. She felt as if she was being pulled in two directions. To pull up her roots and make a new life far away was scary, it meant leaving the familiar and all her friends behind. It meant asking her father to give his permission to marry as she was only seventeen. The prospect of that was making Gina quake inside her shoes.

She approached Father later that evening, as my sister and I were getting ready for bed, having been encouraged after hearing Mother giving Lester a good report.

'Well, your Mother seems to think a lot of this young fellow,' Dad said in a conciliatory voice, 'but let's not get too hasty for now, shall we? I've decided that I'll meet him next time he visits, especially if he brings me another bottle of the American rye. I'll give you my verdict then on whether you'll be allowed to continue seeing him. And I'm pleased to hear he's based at Sealand and not Burtonwood, as I've not heard any bad reports regarding the airmen that are stationed there. And from Tennessee, eh, a country boy just like your old man?'

Father was determined to be light hearted, because deep down Gina was his favourite girl. He had spent all day mulling things over in his mind and at one time had nearly left the Club so that he could be at home. Then someone called for another round and Father felt he couldn't leave because the next round of drinks were on him. But now he was feeling calm and mellow, his little family seemed to have done him proud.

He soon came to his senses when he heard Gina's request for permission to marry. Everyone cowered at his outburst and we youngsters as usual fled up the stairs! Mother sat with her head in her hands as he worked himself up into another frenzy and Gina ran to pack her suitcase. We could hear her sobbing in the next bedroom as she opened and shut her chest of drawers.

'Please don't go,' Mother pleaded, as Audrey and I watched her trying to take the suitcase out of Gina's hand in the hallway. 'Where will you go at this time? Stay and let me calm him down. Your father's right though, you're far too young to tie yourself down and

America is so far away. Gina, if you go with him, we'll probably never see each other again!'

Mother ended her pleading with a cry of anguish, but Father shouted from the kitchen that she should let Gina go.

'No doubt she'll come to her senses, leaving her comfortable home. If she wants to turn her back on her family after all we've done, then let her do it. Go to your bloody Yank, Gina, but you'll not get permission to marry from me!'

My sister snatched her suitcase back from Mother, then giving a tearful glance at Audrey and I, who were watching openmouthed at the scene going on at the bottom of the stairs, she hugged my mother, saying, 'Don't worry Mum, I can go and stay at Nessie's home.'

It was like someone had died in the days and weeks that followed, with Mother walking around with a grief stricken face, Dad not speaking to any of us and Audrey and I tiptoeing around in case we upset anyone.

CHAPTER 3

It was the week before the school's summer holidays and I wasn't looking forward to what was to come. My class was to be divided according to ability and on Monday there was going to be an exam'. If I passed it, my reward would be that I went up to Mrs Worthington's class, the golden haired teacher who smiled a lot and didn't shout. If I failed then I would be taught by Mr. Tenby, who could still cause terror in my soul!

Since Gina had left home around three months ago, the light had seemed to have gone from my parents' world. Father still walked around morosely and Mother seemed to cry a lot. Granny only visited once in the week now that she was getting old and had a lot of trouble with her legs, so I was looking forward to running wild throughout the holidays without a guiding hand. School would be over for a whole six weeks and I couldn't wait for all that freedom to come.

Out of our class of twenty eight children, I was number fourteen. It had always been like that since I was taught by a teacher named Miss Hardy, who gave out tests for us to do on Friday mornings and gave out our marks on Monday. I wasn't bright, just a gentle plodder, not like Letty Braiden who was always number one. That Monday I was terrified I'd sink to the bottom half of the classroom and nearly choked myself on my vomit before I got to school! The whole thing was nerve wracking, on every question I dithered, but I did manage to answer every one.

I sat in the classroom that morning like Marie Antoinette waiting for the chop, Miss Hardy read out our places working backward from number twenty eight. There were groans from those who realized they were destined for Mr. Tenby, but thankfully

I wasn't number fourteen, my usual place. So, I was to be with Mrs. Worthington, my heart felt cheered and I listened intently as the teacher hurried through the rest of the list. I took my place at the top of the class, number one, numero uno. I looked for Letty Braiden to show off my glee. But Letty wasn't there that Monday, she'd been rushed off in an ambulance on her way to school.

My favourite place was Thurstaston, the hill or shore it didn't matter, as long as I had got my freedom to do what I wanted to do. Sitting on top of the hill filled me with pleasure as I gazed across the estuary to the Welsh hills far away. Down on the shore there was peace and quiet, except for the gulls who lived on the cliffs. On the beach was a white washed cottage owned by a lady named Sally McCrae and I often wondered at her isolation, thinking how lucky the lady was.

On the following Saturday after we had broken up from school, I ate my breakfast whilst planning my escape. Father sat for ages eating his bacon and egg, Mother was jittery, pouncing on anything she could find to rattle about in the washing up bowl. Audrey was quietly playing with a dolly at the side of her plate.

The sun outside was beckoning and I fiddled with the buttons on my cardigan, waiting while my father mopped up his fried egg with some bread. I had heard him say that he was finishing off a customer's crazy paving, so hopefully he wouldn't notice if I stayed away all day. Granny had given me half a crown, which meant I could ride on a bus to West Kirby, instead of walking all the way via Limbo Lane. The island of Hilbre tempted me and I wanted to ask the Marine Manager the time of the tides.

I decided to help myself to an apple and a piece of cheese from the larder, as I planned to be away at least until tea time.

'What do you think you're up to, Vivienne?' my Mother said quietly, as she appeared in the doorway behind. 'You're not going anywhere today.' She looked pointedly at the food I was clutching in my hand and shook a finger.

'You've only just had your porridge and that should do you

until lunch time. Wherever it was you were going to, will have to wait for another day.'

I slunk out of the larder without a word, listening for the revving sound of the car engine in the yard to tell me if Father was still around. I swung my legs listlessly against the legs of the kitchen table making ugly faces at my sister, who protested loudly for me to stop.

'That's it you two, I've had enough!' my Mother shouted. 'I wasn't going to tell you yet, but today I'd planned a little treat. We're going out in a couple of minutes, so we'll wait until your daddy's out of the gate.'

'But I wanted........', I began.

'I want doesn't get, go and get your coats on. It'll be cold down there at Glenwood Drive.'

Both Audrey and I looked at our mother mystified. Glenwood Drive, that was where the school was and it was closed for the holidays?

'Why are we going to Glenwood Drive?' I asked curiously.

'You'll see why when we get there,' was all my mother would say.

We hurriedly went to put our coats on while Mother took off her pinny, tidied her hair in the mirror, threw her jacket around her shoulders, then stood by the door as we tied the laces on our shoes. She took off at a pace down the drive while we ran quickly behind her. We arrived about ten minutes later by the stone bridge at the top of Glenwood Drive. All three of us sat on the wooden bench at the bus stop, waiting for ages, or so it seemed to us girls, for a bus to arrive.

'Why are we waiting here, Mummy?,' asked Audrey 'We could have caught a bus at the bottom of our lane?'

Mother gathered us to her, then looked around as if a thousand spies were waiting in the nearby woods. 'I'll tell you a little secret, but not a word to your daddy, promise me?'

We nodded our heads solemnly. Neither of us wanted to get our mother into trouble, nor wanted to be the cause of Daddy exploding into a rage!

'You know that Gina left home a few months ago to live at her friend's house, because Daddy was cross with her? And you know that occasionally Miss Radkin next door asks me round to have a cup of tea with her?'

Both of us nodded in agreement, as Mummy seemed to have suddenly taken a liking to Miss Radkin, our next door neighbour.

'Well, the reason I go to Miss Radkin's house is because Gina telephones me there. She rang me yesterday to ask if I would meet her here this morning, as she has something to tell me that she couldn't say on the 'phone. So we're waiting here for the bus to arrive, instead of at the bottom of our lane, because if someone were to see us and tells your daddy, he'll be asking what we've all been up to, won't he?'

'So we'll be seeing Gina then today, will we?', both of us shouted excitedly and did a little dance together to show our mother how pleased we were.

'Now sit down nicely, we don't want to bring attention to ourselves. Someone who knows us could pass us by in their car and tell your daddy you were showing me up by dancing around. I know, we're a bit early, so what about a game of 'I Spy.'

Eventually, after much fidgeting as boredom set in from running out of things to spy, the chugging of the bus engine could be heard coming along the road. A couple of minutes to wait we hoped and Gina would be back in our lives again.

A different looking Gina alighted from the platform of the blue Daimler bus. After hugs and kisses had been given and warmly received and the bus had pottered off into the distance, Mother took an appraising look at her eldest daughter.

'Well now, Gina, you're looking very smart,' I heard her say. 'That's a beautiful suit you've got on and I like your new hair cut. So what was so important that you couldn't tell me on the telephone? Oh God, no.....'

My mother moaned softly and sat down quickly on the bench behind her. Gina followed and tried to put her arm round our mother's shoulders. We stood there goggle eyed as we watched poor Mother shrug our sister off.

'Please, tell me I'm wrong and that stomach you're showing is through over-eating. Gina, what have you gone and done? Your father will kill you!'

Audrey and I huddled closely together when we heard Mother's words. Why would Daddy want to kill our sister? It was too awful for words! Audrey began to cry softly beside me and I could feel my eyes filling with tears. Mother pulled herself together and spoke to us brightly.

'Right, I know what we'll do. Let's go for a nice long walk with Gina through Harrock's Wood. You girls can look out for some flowers to pick, but don't go near that stream because you'll get all muddy. I've enough to put up with as you know, so do be careful and don't fall in!'

We scampered off filled with delight, tears were wiped with the back of our hands and our fear forgotten. It was good to dash and dart through the small dark forest, to come out in the sunlight by the farmer's field.

Mother and Gina wandered slowly behind us, stopping now and again, voices raised occasionally but mostly in hushed tones.

Strangely enough Father didn't react to the situation as he was expected to. He took the news of Gina's pregnancy quite calmly considering his temperament. It was as if he knew that something like this was bound to happen, remembering when he and Mother were in a similar predicament too.

'So, is the Yank going to marry her then?', I heard him ask Mother in a perfectly reasonable voice, though I could detect a hint of menace if her answer was a 'No.'

'Well, he has to get permission from his Commanding Officer as he's over here with the Forces and he's got to get permission off his father as he's under twenty one.'

'Meantime my daughter has to wait for all these sodding formalities, growing bigger and bigger for all the neighbours to see.'

'Gina won't be living with us, Eddie, they've got a flat now in Birkenhead.'

'You can tell our Gina she's to come back home. I'll not have people saying that I didn't stand by her, like my folks never did.'

Then Father put his head in his hands and started to weep. I felt concern, but I wasn't moving from my listening place on the stairs.

'Let's face it, Irene, we may never see her for a very long time and I know she's done this to punish me.'

'Why would she do this to punish you?', my mother replied sharply.

'She's done it to force your hand into giving her permission to marry, just like you got me pregnant all those years ago. She had no choice but to leave home with you not accepting Lester. If you had welcomed him and been a bit friendly, Gina would have lost all interest given time. But no, you have to play the role of the heavy handed father and now see what's happened. She's three months pregnant, the threat of not getting permission hanging over their lives and our daughter and grandchild going to live a million miles away.'

I heard my mother begin to cry bitterly.

Father shifted in his seat uneasily, then wiped his eyes with his shirt cuff and began to pat her gently.

I moved my bottom into a more comfortable position, which alerted my father to the fact I was listening. He crept to the bottom of the stairs to see me sitting there.

'You, Vivienne, get down here,' he shouting angrily, making me leap into the air with fright.

'Haven't I told you before that eaves droppers never hear any good of themselves? Well get down here and I'll tell you the plans I've got for you.'

I scuttled into the kitchen and faced my father squarely, quaking in my shoes maybe, but standing to attention like I was used to doing.

'Right now, let me tell you what is going to happen in the future so that this doesn't happen again and listen to me too, Irene, because you're too lax with these kids. Vivienne here and Audrey too are going to attend the Gospel Church I've just been working on. A Mr. and Miss Hetherington are going to run it and I hear they're full of damnation and Hellfire. Then with that fine education you got at that private school in Wallasey, you'll get the girl's through the 11+. Then we'll be the first ones in the street to have kids who go to a Grammar School and maybe on to University!'

Fat chance of going to a university, I thought, as I sat pondering over a question in the 11+ exam', nearly two years later. My father's instructions to do my best for the family pride had been ringing in my ears that morning, as he dropped me off at the designated school where all the clever students had been directed to. I had to get to Grammar school first and although Mother had been cramming my head with facts and making me look over past papers, my mind was totally empty and the questions were rather grim.

I scanned down the list of topics looking to see if there were any there that I could answer straight away, chewing on one of the mints my mother had given me to aid concentration. I looked around the room at the other students bowing their heads and busily writing away.

Ah, there was a history question, I was good at history, so I answered that Henry V111 had six wives and wrote down the names of all of them. Geography, I hated the subject, where was Argentina for heaven's sake? English, what was a noun, what was an adverb?

The room was hot and stuffy and my head began to ache. I hoped I'd fail, I hated school, hated the restrictions on my freedom, although Mrs. Worthington was pleasant and full of good advice. She had told me that she was sure that I would do well, when Mother had insisted I take the eleven plus.

This past week had been an eye opener for me, or rather a shocking week that I would remember all my days. I had awoken early one morning with a stomach ache and had tiptoed to the toilet to see if I needed to do a poo. Between my legs felt warm and sticky

67

and I wondered if I had wet myself? To my horror I saw a trickle of blood and became beside myself with fear! Had the predictions of the woman at Sunday school come true, that I was to be punished for my terrible sins? I began to cry quietly, then ran quickly down the stairs to the kitchen to make myself a cup of tea. That was what my mother did if she felt nervy or sometimes frightened and I thought it may help me to think what to do. Mother found me at four o'- clock in the morning, shivering in my nightie, holding a hanky between my legs and waiting for the kettle to boil.

'Vivienne, what are you doing?,' she had said, sounding alarmed. 'I heard a noise and thought it might be Paddy off his lead, scratching at the door to try and get in. Whatever is the matter, why have you been crying?'

She pulled me into her arms and gave me a quick hug.

'I'm bleeding,' I said shakily, 'between my legs and I know it will be a punishment because I'm not a good girl, you know?'

'Oh, don't be silly, let me have a look.'

But even Mother seemed worried as she took a quick peek at my hanky, though suddenly the penny dropped and she clutched me to her again.

'My God,' she said in a muffled voice, 'it's your period already when you're only ten and still at the primary school! I never thought to warn you, your sister didn't get hers until she was fifteen!'

'Got what Mummy and what's a period?' I said looking at her in bewilderment. 'Will it go away now that you've seen it, or will I be bleeding every day?'

'No, unfortunately you'll have this every month until you're fifty. Now be a good girl while I find some cotton wool, then keep it there until I make you a little pad.'

She hurried off to find her sewing basket, leaving me scared witless. Bleeding until I was fifty, I didn't like the sound of that!

The letter had come from the Council, the Education department to be precise, Vivienne Dockerty had passed the 11+.

My father and mother were over the moon, but sadly I wasn't. I wouldn't be going to the West Kirby school, my parent's first choice, as my pass grade had been borderline.

'Still, at least you're the first Dockerty in the family to be given a place,' said Father cheerfully. 'We'll get you down to town next week and have your uniform fitted.'

I felt really depressed. At least if I was going to the West Kirby school I could have sat on the shore in the lunch time, or even run across the sands to Hilbre Island if the estuary tide had been out. Now I would have to travel on four buses a day, two in the morning and two at night if I went to the County grammar school. It wasn't going to give me much time to play and there was so many things I wanted to do. The evenings were lighter and the countryside beckoned; there was Arrowe Park and the new Pensby 'rec' and I'd be saying goodbye to some of my friends who had all passed for the West Kirby school.

I ventured a question to my mother, knowing the answer before I asked.

'Couldn't I go to Gina's old school and maybe become a secretary?'

My mother was horrified!

'I should think not, Vivienne! Do you know that your poor sister has to work all the hours God sends in America? She has to leave her baby with her mother-in-law and go out to work each day.

That's what happens to people who don't get a good education, they have to work hard for their living and we don't want that for you.'

If my mother was honest, the thought of her second daughter falling for someone as Gina had done, appalled her. The letters she received from Tennessee were from an unhappy girl who regretted what she had done. The couple were sharing a home with his family of brothers and sisters and already Gina had asked her parents could they send her the money for her ticket home!

'I can see you as an Almoner at the hospital or a Librarian maybe,' Mother said to me.

'In fact they're looking for someone at the local library to put the books back on the shelves, so I'm going to tell them how well you've done.'

'But I don't want to work in a Library, Mother,' I wailed. 'If I'm going to be on four buses a day, I want to be out playing on a Saturday!'

'But just think of the money they'll give you, Vivienne. It's a ten shilling note for just one day!'

That September saw me dressed in a navy blue gym slip, long sleeved blouse and matching navy blazer waiting at the bus stop. In one hand was the velour bowler hat, as it wouldn't fit over my much prized pony tail and in the other was my brand new satchel that carried a pencil case, lunch money and a spare pair of navy knick's. My period had come again and I was feeling tense and nervous, as I looked over enviously at the children who were waiting to catch the West Kirby bus. Maybe if I had worked that bit harder I'd have been starting school along with them. I waved over bravely to Letty Braiden and Caroline Thomas, who wore a similar uniform without the stupid hat, but they turned away and began to giggle to each other. My spirits sank even lower, they were probably laughing at me.

Forty minutes later I joined the huge throng of children as they walked through the gates to the County grammar school. I'd been lucky to catch the connecting bus, though I'd had to run quickly. The new girls were directed to the Main hall where we were to be welcomed by the Headmistress, the boys were sent around the corner to the buildings just for them.

'Five bloody years we've got to do here, yer know,' came a voice at my elbow. 'More if you're clever and you want to go to university.'

I turned to see a dark haired girl looking balefully in my direction and nodded at her understandingly.

'Wished I'd gone to the same school as my sister did,' she continued, 'there's none of this farting around in a stupid school uniform. You can wear what yer want there and you don't have to wear a bloody stupid hat!'

I nodded again, totally in agreement except for the girl's swearing. Swearing wasn't allowed at my house and I didn't think it was ladylike.

'What's your name then, my name's Hazel? I live down the road in Rock Ferry, saw you coming off the bus.'

'Oh, my granny used to live in Rock Ferry, near the old landing stage,' I said happily. 'You won't have known her, it was ages ago. Oh, I'm sorry, my name's Vivienne, pleased to meet you I'm sure.'

'Pleased to meet you I'm sure,' mimicked Hazel. 'If yer want to be my mate, Viv', yer can drop the mimsy accent. The best way for me and you to get through these next five sodding years is to find a mate and stick it out. Now yer can be my friend or be my enemy. It's up to you, I don't care.'

I looked at the girl uneasily. I wasn't sure that I was going to even like her, she seemed so hard and menacing.

I was saved from making a decision, as the teacher on the stage before us clapped her hands and announced that the Headmistress was on the way.

It was all so very different, I thought, as I caught the bus that would take me home that afternoon. All those rules and petty regulations! Walk in the corridor, silence in class, never take your hat off until you get back home. Never to do anything that that would bring shame on the damn school and a satchel full of homework that brought an ache to my back! Already the girls had been split into groups, the clever ones, the mediocre and the not as bright! It was up to each one of us to climb the rungs on the ladder, so people like Hazel and I would achieve our ultimate goal!

The atmosphere in the Dockerty household was one of misery. The joy that I had generated by going to grammar school had been replaced with a sense of doom. A letter had come from Gina to say that she and husband were thinking of divorcing, but as their child was born American she was having difficulty bringing her home.

Granny had come to live with us now that her legs were not working and had her bed in the living room, which were causing tempers to fray. There were still the aunts to look after, so Mother was rushing everywhere.

We two sisters, were left to our own devices, though Audrey was content to read in our bedroom, I could have been anywhere!

I had met a girl called Sally, a girl the same age who lived at the top of Oaklea Road and she had a brother that I admired greatly. He was handsome and a few years older, but he played tennis in the street with us and he also had a guitar.

The field across the road had now been given up to the building of brand new bungalows.

One of these had a caravan situated in the grounds under shady oaks and elm trees. It was a perfect place for adventure. The caravan was really a gaily painted gypsy cart, just the thing to set off my imagination. We could dress up as Romany gypsies and charge people to come and see!

Sally and Ciaran, her brother, thought it was an excellent idea, a way of making some pocket money and entertaining as well, so I asked old Mrs. Smith could we use it and got her permission to do so. We had great fun delivering invitations, written by hand on pages from an exercise book, deciding to charge people sixpence to sit on our twenty borrowed chairs. Sally and I dressed up in white puffed sleeve blouses and red flowery skirts, while Ciaran wore cowboy boots, a frilly shirt and a red bandana round his head. He played fast and lively music and we girls clapped and sang, then the people in the audience got up and started dancing around. It was so exciting and colourful and everyone had a wonderful time, then Mrs. Smith went and spoilt our fun as the crowd had made a mess of her lawn!

I realized that day that if you wanted to make a little money you had to come up with a profitable on going scheme, so I borrowed my father's garage and we did a children's show this time. People came from far and wide that day and I gleefully counted my money at the end.

I went off on my bike to my auntie's garden and enlisted my sister to help pick all the apples and pears, then off we went around to neighbours' doors and sold the produce at sixpence a pound. There was no end to my enterprises, a lending library, jumble sales and a Christmas bazaar, all held in the garage again and all the time my savings account was growing a little each time.

My homework suffered, my school work was poor but what did it matter, I was an entrepreneur!

They say that all good things must come to an end and one day when I got home from school, my mother was waiting for me with a letter in her hand. It had been sent from the headmistress, requesting that she made an appointment to see her, as her daughter wasn't behaving as a good pupil should.

'So what is she going to tell me when I get there, Vivienne?' Mother asked worriedly. 'You know your father will go mad if he finds out you're in trouble. Out with it now, what have you been up to? Have you not been handing in your homework again?'

I hung my head thinking of what I'd been up to. Some of it was my fault, but really it was Hazel who made me do bad things. It seemed better to give in to Hazel, than make a fuss and end up with a Chinese burn, but the thought of my father's reaction was even worse and I hoped my mother would keep the contents of the letter to herself.

I wondered what I had been caught out doing? Was it smoking in the toilets, or the story I had told the teachers to get out of games? Was it all the giggling in the classroom when Hazel had told a smutty joke, or the fun we made of Mrs. Danson because she had chalk dust in her hair? Maybe it was a complaint about my homework, done in a hurry on the bus to school? Or that my test marks were fair to middling, because I couldn't be bothered to swot for them?

I couldn't tell any of this to my mother, especially as one of the aunt's had just died and Granny was sick in hospital. I mumbled that I was sorry and would try my best to behave.

It was difficult to be a model student as I found out in my very first year. I wasn't up to it, the other girls were brighter or came from better backgrounds where their parents were more supportive than mine. Mother had much on her mind to worry her, especially as the problem with Gina had still not been resolved and she mourned the loss of her aunty, who had been Mother's friend in her younger years. Then there was Granny, who was visited each day at the hospital, even though now she was beginning to lose her mind. Father was tired from his work each day and had no time for Audrey and I, so we were left to our own devices again. Not that I minded.

My saving grace had been my ability to make a success of my ventures, but all that was taken from me after that appointment with the Head.

After a sleepless night for both Mother and I, we were shown into Miss Preston's study, a comfortable room lined with shelves of books and bright coloured rugs on the floor. The headmistress was a kindly woman who had devoted her life to education, but had never come across a girl like me with my imaginative mind, but lack of worth.

'Do sit down, Mrs. Dockerty,' she said kindly. 'Vivienne, please stand over there. I'm sorry we have to meet under these circumstances, but I think you need to understand that we are not getting the best academically from your daughter. I would like to begin by saying that Vivienne writes the most marvellous compositions and her English teacher is extremely pleased with her, but she doesn't seem to be interested in anything else. When it came to the streaming of our pupils this year we had great difficulty in deciding which subjects were suitable for Vivienne. She doesn't want to do Chemistry, Geography, French, Biology, Games or Maths. So we have decided that she must take Domestic science, Arithmetic, Religious studies, English and History. Subjects that she could have taken in any secondary school. So what are we to do with Vivienne, a girl whose naughtiness has brought a lot of complaints from my staff? For instance, did you know, Mrs. Dockerty, that your daughter can have a period every Monday when it's games or swimming? She tells Miss Butler one week, Miss Whitely the second and Miss Fairclough the same old story when it's their turn to take her class! We've only just found out at a recent meeting that your daughter has had a period for three weeks on the trot!'

Mother hung her head at this because she wanted to laugh. Trust me to come up with that story. I hated hockey, swimming and lacrosse, especially outdoors on cold winter days and there was icy water in the swimming baths.

'Then there's been a complaint from Miss Powell from the biology class,' Miss Preston boomed on. 'Vivienne refused to dissect a jar of worms and told the teacher to do it herself!'

Again Mother nearly choked on her laughter, she would have done the same!

'Then there's the smoking. Did you know that she has taken that up? What I would like to know is where she gets the money from?'

Now that was serious, my mother thought, chucking my hard earned money away on cigarettes and I was only twelve!

'So what have you got to say for yourself, Vivienne? These are serious accusations from your teachers and won't be tolerated as far as I'm concerned?'

I felt my face flush at the headmistress's scrutiny. Should I tell her of the embarrassment I felt in the shower room after games, when the teachers on duty would stand at the door and watch as the pupils appeared naked before them, staring at our private bits as we passed by? Could I tell on the teacher who lovingly caressed my little breasts, while pretending to be checking my work over my shoulder? I could do, but would it be worth all the hassle? Last time I had complained to my mother about a grownup's strange behaviour, I had been thought to be lying. So why would Miss Preston believe me if my mother had never done?

I hung my head and said nothing, arguing with authority never got you anywhere.

'So the cat has got your tongue, eh, Vivienne?' she continued. 'Well, I think you should be given some responsibility, you've got in with a rough sort of girl who I think has been leading you astray.

Don't think we haven't noticed, but you two always seem to be at the bottom of things.'

'I didn't know that Vivienne had one friend in particular here, Miss Preston.'

'She doesn't have any friends other than this Hazel. They're known as the 'terrible twins' by the rest of the class and they tend to have little dealing with both of them.'

'So what do you suggest, Miss Preston?' asked Mother, desperately hoping that I would be given a second chance. What if I was excluded from the school? Oh yes, please!

'I have decided that in her third year she will be given the role of Form Captain.'

Both women turned their heads as I let out a gasp.

'Please Miss, perhaps you could expel me instead, the other girls won't be liking that.'

'Don't be silly, Vivienne, that's exactly why I want you to be the Form Captain, an important role that will earn their respect. No more dallying about with Hazel Cummings, because you will be too busy organizing the class.'

That's all I needed, I thought, as I said goodbye to my mother and went to the toilets to light a cigarette. Form Captain! Still it might cause a split between me and Hazel, who wouldn't want to be friends with the third form clat!

One afternoon when I was in my third year at school, I caught the bus at the junction that would take me straight to my home.

It had been a satisfying day for me, in that I had last thrown off the shackles of my friendship with Hazel. The girl wasn't going to be friends with the bloody teacher's pet.

That had suited me down to the ground as I was enjoying my new position in the school. I liaised with my form teacher, reporting any problems and suddenly the other girls all wanted to be my friend.

I chatted to the young man who sat beside me, a man I knew slightly as he was often on the route I took for home. He was an off duty bus conductor and very friendly that afternoon as he listened to all my hopes and fears.

'You know, Vivienne?' he said, as the bus began its ascent up the Arrowe Park Road. 'It's too nice to be going home to be stuck indoors in this weather. So why don't we get off at the next bus stop and we can take a walk in the park? I've always liked you, you're growing into a pretty young woman. Perhaps me and you could be more than friends and we could meet each other now and again?'

'Do you mean like boyfriend and girlfriend?' I asked eagerly. 'Could we go to the pictures or out for a meal like my sister used to do?'

'Well, maybe, Vivienne, I don't know yet. Let's wait and see how we get on this after' and then I'll let you know.'

'I mustn't be long though, Alec, because my mother likes me to be back for tea or I'll be in a lot of trouble.'

'Sounds to me as if you have it tough at your house,' Alec said sympathetically, as we walked through the park gates and along the leafy sun dappled path. 'Never had any problem with the parents meself with coming from a large family.'

'It's been hell since my sister left to live in America,' I sighed. 'All they seem to do is worry about Gina and baby Mandy. Saving up so they can get a trip out there, sending her letters and ringing her up from our new telephone. It's as if me and my younger sister don't exist anymore, or should I say we exist all right, but have to make them proud of us instead.'

'And I bet you don't get much in the way of loving, do yer, sweetheart?' Alec said, leading me into a wooden shelter that was positioned just inside a secluded copse.

'Well, come to think of it, no,' I said, pleased with his sympathy. 'My parents aren't the kissy types, maybe the odd one to say goodbye or hello.'

'Come here,' he said, 'let me show yer how.'

He took me in his arms and began to kiss my lips gently. It was a strange sensation for me as I had never been kissed like this before. I wasn't sure I liked it, but if this was what it took to have a boyfriend, well I would just have to get used to it. When Alec began to put his tongue in my mouth though I began to feel a little sick. It was horrible, like being force fed a wet and smelly slippery eel and I felt like retching all over the place. I pulled away from him and took my hanky out from up my sleeve, pretending to have a coughing fit.

He laughed and began to pat my back, drawing my body to him so he could kiss me again. This time though his hands began to wander, under my school shirt, above my knees, all the time holding me tight so that I could hardly breathe.

Suddenly I began to feel panicky. This wasn't anything like I thought having a boyfriend would be like. Weren't boys supposed to hold your hand, take you dancing, buy bunches of flowers and profess their love for you? Alec hadn't spoken of love or held my hand and his face was hot and sweaty. There was an enormous bulge in his trousers that hadn't been there before.

I tried to pull away from him as he clamped his hand on my breast, then he pushed me roughly into a corner of the shed. I stumbled and felt really annoyed, as he righted me by hitching up my skirt and pushing me against the wall. I shouted for him to stop, but my breath was taken from me as he fastened his lips to mine and began to pull at my underwear.

My heart was thudding, as the fear of what he was about to do began to filter into my brain. It was something to do with Uncle Spencer. My mind raced back to when I was seven, a scene that had lain dormant until then. I could see it all clearly, that bewildering day in his bedroom.

By this time the man was trying to enter me, not Alec anymore, but a man who was trying to hurt me. And it did hurt. I felt the tears springing into my eyes, as he huffed and puffed with his exertion and difficulty.

'Fuck me, Vivienne, you've never done this before, have yer?' he grunted into my ear. 'Trust me to get a virgin. Here, forget all this for a game of cricket, you can finish it off for me instead.'

So released from his grasp I did what my uncle had shown me, though the tears were raining down my face and the man didn't seem to care.

We sat for a few moments in silence while the man adjusted himself and I wiped my tears with my hand. I was trembling and between my legs felt wet, but the man stared ahead with a dazed look on his face.

'I'll have to go home now,' I said in a shaky little voice, wondering whether I dared pick up my satchel and hat that was on the dusty floor beside us. 'My Mum will be wondering where I am and I've got a lot of homework to do.'

'O.K. then I'll see yer around,' he said, as if nothing had happened and we'd just been discussing the weather. 'I'll nip over the fields to catch the bus home, there's another one at a quarter past.'

I nodded, then walked stiffly from the shelter, bending briefly to tie my shoe lace that had come undone. My chest was aching with the flood of tears that was threatening to overtake me. My satchel slung over one shoulder and my hat all squashed and dusty in my hand.

The daylight was fading fast as I walked along the main road home. I let my tears flow until there was nothing left to cry with. I felt hurt now and indignant at my gullibility in believing that Alec had even liked me. What had happened in the park couldn't have been what couples did to prove their love for each other. It was disgusting and degrading, nothing like the romance I had read about in Granny's Peoples' Friend. I began to run, as the thought of my mother's anger at me being late interrupted my self pity. The books in my satchel jostled and my knee high socks worked their way down to my ankles.

My heart sank even further as I saw my father getting out of his car at the top of our drive, as I ran breathlessly through the wide open gates. I had hoped he would have got in much later so that he wouldn't find out that I had been late home from school.

He frowned when he saw me, taking in my bedraggled appearance, ready to give me a telling off for not taking care of my uniform.

'Look at the state of you,' he began, walking to meet me as I staggered up the drive. 'We paid good money for that outfit and here's you looking like Tilly from the wreck and what's happened to your face, for heaven's sake?'

'Oh, Dad, don't start,' I said in a weary voice. 'I missed the bus home and I've had to walk the last two miles and I'm tired and I'm hungry.'

'Well, get yourself in to your mother and let her get you sorted. I don't know, there's our Audrey so neat and tidy and you looking like you've been pulled through a hedge!'

He wandered off to his barrels in the lean to, to sample his latest batch of elderflower wine. It was coming on nicely. He'd bottle it in a week or so, then he'd pick the elderberries from the trees down by Nana's, so he would also have a few barrels of red.

Mother was stirring the saucepan of stew on top of the stove, when I crept sheepishly through the kitchen door.

'So where've you been until this time, Vivienne?' she said snappily. 'Audrey's been home for at least an hour and is upstairs reading in her room.'

'She doesn't have all the travelling, does she, with her going to West Kirby, or have a teacher that makes you stay behind?' I fired back, stung at her unfair criticism. 'Then I missed the bus at Singleton Avenue and had to catch the Moreton bus.'

'And that took you two hours?'

'Mum, I need to talk to you.' I decided to tell her what happened. Perhaps she'd send my father down to the bus depot to sort this Alec out. 'Come into the bathroom, will you, where no one else can hear?'

'Oh, Vivienne, what have you been up to now? Look, I'm busy putting the dinner out, can't it wait?'

'Well, can I have a bath then?' feeling that the moment was over and she wouldn't believe me anyway. 'I fell over when I was coming past the cemetery and I think I've come on my period again.'

'I thought you looked a bit of a mess when you first walked in.

I noticed you've got some mud on the back of your good school skirt when you turned around before. You're in luck anyway. I put the boiler on earlier so I'd have some washing up water. Be quick then and I'll leave your dinner on top of the pan. Would you like me to ask Audrey to bring down a change of clothing? Your jumper's still clean and your blue pleated skirt and there's some knickers airing in the living room.'

I nodded thankfully and dumped my satchel and dratted hat under the kitchen table. Soon I sat in a half bath of water gratefully, washing the nastiness away.

Was it my fault?, I asked myself, as I lay in my bed that evening listening to the gentle breathing of my sister. I knew I'd been stupid going off with Alec, thinking that he was going to be a kind and caring boyfriend. He wasn't even handsome, not like Ciaran, Sally's brother, who had made my heart beat madly. Alec was old, at least in his twenties, whereas Ciaran had only been fifteen when we had performed at the gypsy caravan two summers ago. It was a pity that the family had moved over to Liverpool, now I would probably never see him again.

I ran my hands over my body, touching my breasts that still felt tender, then patted the pad that I was wearing between my legs. The soreness had gone, replaced with the dull ache that I always felt when a period was due. At least I was clean and smelt nice, after feeling so dirty a few hours ago.

I think that was when deep down I developed a dislike for men, not boys, because there were some friendly ones on the bus I caught each morning, but Uncle Spencer, Father, now Alec, all had made me feel intimidated somehow, if they didn't get their own way. Perhaps though there was something about me, something sinful that they could see?

Perhaps I would be wiser praying a bit harder in Assembly, instead of staring out of the window at the boys playing sports outside.

That was it!, I thought, suddenly brightening. There was a trip soon, organized by the Sunday school my father sent me to, a Rally being held in Liverpool. I had pooh hoohed the idea when Mr.

Hetherington had announced it, thinking it was for religious nuts and not for the likes of me, but maybe I would learn something from it, instead of shutting my ears to religion like I did in my Sunday school class. I felt better, my spirits were uplifted and I fell asleep at last.

I found myself amongst a crowd of people as they swarmed through the doors of the Guild Hall, a few streets up from the Pier Head. There was only me and the Hetherington family, as the trip had not been popular with the rest of the children from the Sunday school class, but I was on a mission to find out how I could save myself from these terrible sins that I must be committing.

I was handed over to a woman named Florrie, a serious looking woman in her forties who had her grey hair tied back in a bun. Florrie was to be my chaperone and 'bring me to Christ' if she thought that was necessary. I didn't have a clue though of what was expected of me.

The place was full of happy excited people and I leant over our balcony position at the sea of expectant faces below. The band struck up and the choir began to sing, then a man appeared on the podium and everyone applauded him. I was swept along with all the exhilaration, yes I was a sinner, yes, I wanted to be saved. I wouldn't have to burn upon the fires of Hell if I repented all my sins! When the man asked his audience if there was anyone who wanted to repent, I was the first one on my feet!

I was lead to the front by an emotional Florrie and soon doused with water to cleanse me from my evil ways. Then I was solemnly guided back to my seat where I basked in the light of other Christian's praise.

But long term I didn't feel any better, though I spoke to God more often than I had before.

I tried to be kinder, thoughtful, helpful, but I still felt a sinner inside my soul.

I took to reading my Bible to see if its words could help me too, but the copy was all in 'thee's and thou's', so I gave up my mission to look for clues.

The following year brought me the chance of going on a school trip to France. Although I had given up French as a subject at the beginning of my third year, I asked Mademoiselle Gueron if I was still allowed to go? The teacher was having a little difficulty filling the coach to its capacity and remembering that I hadn't done so badly in my French tests, agreed that I could.

My sister, Audrey, was studying French at the West Kirby grammar school, a place she had gained easily at eleven and had settled in very well. I knew that if my sister could be included, my parents would give their permission readily. A whole three weeks rolled out before me, freedom from my parents' strict regime.

Mum and Dad were delighted when I told them the news, their daughters going to France for the summer would give them some time to themselves. They had a little money now because Granny had left them a policy. It had covered the cost of her funeral and the rest had been put by for a rainy day.

Poor Granny. She had been stuck in a geriatric ward for months when dementia had taken over. She couldn't even remember who we were when we went to visit. It was a merciful release according to the rest of the family, but I mourned my little granny with her sweet smell of lavender and her gentle caring ways.

We got the Atlas out one evening and Father showed us his route in France that he had taken with the Army. Audrey and I sat and listened politely, as he took us on his manoeuvres in his mind.

'But we aren't going anywhere near those places,' I had argued. 'We're sailing into St Malo and driving down to Brittany.'

'Oh, so now you're the expert are you?' Father said angrily. 'Doesn't matter that I spent time in France from Dunkirk up to the Belgium border. Know it like the back of me hand and our lads died for people like you to go on holiday there.'

'Give it a rest, Eddie,' Mother sighed. 'The children are looking forward to their trip. Does it matter where in France, as long as they get something out of it? I'm more concerned about where we are going to put the French when they come on a return visit. We don't know what kind of place they'll be living in, it could be far superior to ours.'

'It's not a problem, Irene, kids can sleep on washing lines. I'll borrow a couple of beds from somewhere and they can bunk up with ours in the front bedroom.'

So at the beginning of July 1962, Audrey and I boarded the coach in the early hours at Central Station and travelled with our peers to the docks at Southampton. We were all dressed in our summer school uniform of a pink or blue striped shirt dress, navy blue cardigan and round cream boater hats.

Audrey was dressed in a similar fashion, as her grammar school had the same uniform as ours. She was still a quiet gentle girl, who never had a lot to say for herself. She seemed to live in my shadow as I had taken on the role of speaking on her behalf. Audrey had inherited the plumpness of mother's side of the family, she was still only five feet in height, but Mother said she still had a lot of growing to do. She wore her brown hair in a short pageboy style and her serious hazel eyes often stared fearfully at the world around her.

In contrast I had inherited the greyhound features of the Dockerty family. I was slender and gamine, full of restless energy, still wearing my brown chestnut hair in a pony tail, refusing to be barbered by my dad.

For the last three months we had sent and received letters from two French girls, called Renate and Mireille Saimur. They were from a place called Nantes, where they lived above a supermarket with their mother, who was a widow by all accounts. That is to say a father was never mentioned, which brought certain relief to me. Renate was the same age as me, though her birthday was in the December, whereas I would be fifteen at the beginning of August. Mireille was a little older than Audrey, who had just turned twelve.

We all got off the coach at the side of the largest ship anyone amongst us had ever seen, that is with the exception of our two French speaking teachers, who had journeyed across La Manche many times before. We were split into two groups of fifteen and escorted to the gangplank, where instructions were given before we boarded, as to the venue we should meet in when we had freshened up. Our suitcases were loaded onto a four wheeled trolley and taken off by a porter to some place we knew not where.

We all shot off excitedly to the toilets and formed an orderly queue. We tried a little French as we stood there. 'Bonjour, comment allez vous?' we said to each other, trying to perfect our accents before we got to France.

It was all so different, this standing on the deck looking out at the vast expanse of water we must cross before we touched dry land again; watching boats and yachts as they sailed past the harbour mouth; looking with interest at the tankers and the supply ships anchored at their berths, while the stevedores worked to unload them, then dashing down the metal stairwell that lead us to the passengers' salon.

Mademoiselles Laval and Gueron had made themselves comfortable on two of the easy chairs that were lined up in rows at the front of the salon. They waved to us all to do the same and soon the ship lifted anchor and started to sail.

It was all too much for Audrey, as the ship began to shift and roll gently. She began to look a little pale and grabbed on to my arm in panic, as her stomach began to churn. The sandwiches she had eaten only an hour before, started to return up into her throat and her head felt hot and sticky as she realized she was going to be sick. She dashed from her seat to the sign that directed her to the toilets and soon had her head in the bowl. I followed and stood outside the cubicle feeling unsympathetic. How could anyone who had sea faring blood in their veins be coming over seasick? All our Mother's family had been Mariners, from the middle of the eighteenth century through to the First World War and the ship was only just out of the harbour. How was Audrey going to cope when we got into open seas?

She didn't. She spent the whole of the journey running from the salon, to the toilet and back again. While me and the other girls ate packets of crisps, drank gallons of pop and ran up and down exploring the ship, poor Audrey had her head down the bowl.

Five hours later we docked at the port of St. Malo, with Audrey having to be helped by the two harassed teachers on to the waiting coach. The two women must have sighed with relief at the thought of three long weeks in a Pensione that they had picked out for themselves. Oh, they'd be there on call if the host families had any problems and they'd planned a few coach trips to take their young charges to historical sites, but there'd be evenings spent sampling gourmet dishes in the restaurants and the bars in Nantes served excellent wine.

The French countryside basked in glorious sunshine, as the coach headed for its destination with the now tired children aboard. We gazed out onto the fields that were faded from the strong sunlight, the little white washed cottages that appeared at the side of the road and the impressive avenues of cypress trees that lead to someone's house or farm.

Audrey was feeling much better now and eagerly tucked into one of the cheese baguettes that the teachers had bought at the quayside, though she moaned quietly to me that she wasn't looking forward to our journey home.

'Pooh, you'll feel a whole lot better once we've had three weeks in the sunshine,' I said stoutly, 'and didn't Mireille say in her letter that we'll be going to stay in their holiday home?'

'I wish I hadn't said I'd come now,' Audrey moaned. 'I don't know any French, I've only learnt verbs at my school. What if people only speak in French to us, we'll never know what to do?'

'Renate and Mireille speak English, don't they? We understood their letters very well.'

'Yes, but only because Mum helped us with the dictionary, they wrote a lot of French to us as well.'

'We'll get by,' I said confidently. 'I'm looking forward to having three weeks of not being told what to do by our parents, being able to run about on the beach all day and of course learning a bit of French as well.'

A few hours later the two of us sat at the kitchen table in

Madame Saimur's small apartment.

We had been met by Renate and Mireille, two dark haired plain looking girls and walked the short distance to a type of village square.

All around the square where shops of different varieties, butchers, bakers and hardware shops and a supermarket that looked like our local Co-op shop at home. At the side was an entrance that had stairs leading up to the accommodation. The place was light and airy, with a fan whirring slowly in the ceiling above.

'Bonjour, Madame,' I said to our hostess, who was a small plump woman with olive skin and short dark brown hair.

'Bonjour, Vivienne et Audrey. Comment'allez vous?'she replied.

'Say tres bien merci,' I said nudging Audrey, who was standing as if she was ready to run from the room. Tears had welled up into her eyes, she hated the smell of this awful place. She shook her head and clutched for dear life to the suitcase that we had brought along between us. Her gaze went to a bowl of fruit on the table, where she could see little flies hovering.

The woman spoke quickly to her daughters and everyone walked off to the bedrooms. I was to share a bed in Renate's room and Audrey to share with Mireille.

When Audrey realized that she was to share a bed with a virtual stranger, she panicked and began to shout that she hated the place and wanted to sleep on her own. There was silence for a moment as everyone looked at her in astonishment, then Renate explained to her mother what the problem was. A torrent of French poured from our hostess's lips, nothing that I could understand, except for the anger and soon it was explained by Renate that Audrey and I would be sharing a bed.

We were left alone to unpack our summer clothing, two homemade cotton dresses, three sets of underwear and a bathing costume each.

'We'd better put our slippers on,' I said. 'Those tiled floors look freezing cold and we can't keep jumping from mat to mat. Come on Audrey, cheer up. This is an adventure for both of us and the time will go very quickly, you'll see. Look, I'll tell you what we'll do. See the drawing pad we brought with us, why don't we make a chart of the days we'll be staying and each evening you can tick the day off and we can count how many more are left? Would you like that?'

Audrey nodded resignedly. Anything to put off going back into that room. There had been a horrible looking sausage sitting on a plate and some cheese that had big holes in it. If that was going to be their dinner, she'd be sick all over the place, she just knew she would.

Madame Saimur glowered at us, as we tentatively tiptoed back in to the kitchen. The French girls sat with their arms folded at the table and didn't smile to welcome us.

'Voulez vous soupe?' asked their mother.

'She wants to know if we want any soup,' I translated to Audrey.

'What is it?' asked Audrey suspiciously. 'I'm not having any frog soup, I'll just have an apple.'

'Qu'est que ce?', I asked politely.

'Soupe de champignon,' came the huffy reply.

'It's mushroom, Audrey.'

'I'll have some of that then. As long as it hasn't got frogs in it, I don't mind.'

And so it went on at every mealtime, Audrey challenged everything that the woman put in front of her, until the mother got so angry that at breakfast time one morning, Madame Saimur nearly hit my sister with the frying pan! Everyone felt tense and very nervous, especially as we four girls had difficulty with understanding each other's language.

One morning, a few days later, we learnt that we were going to a wedding. We were taken to a coiffeuse across the road from the Co-op and treated to a smart and fashionable hairstyle each. As we hadn't known of our invitation, we had to make do with with one of our summer dresses, while Renate and Mireille wore long pink matching gowns and had a ring of pretty flowers in their hair.

We were all picked up in a coach that took us miles away to a small church in the countryside, the ceremony of course was in

French or maybe even Latin, but we got the gist of what was happening anyway.

On the way to the Reception two things happened that put me off the people of France for many years, so much so it wasn't until I was thirty five that I deigned to even go back again.

The coach was full with relatives from both sides of the couple's families. Audrey and I sat together near the back of the bus. Suddenly a woman who was sitting opposite, nudged her husband and said, 'Les Anglais puh" and spat at us in an alarming manner. We cringed together for safety, as even Audrey had understood the message in the words. Then, when we got to the reception that was being held in the hall of a manor house, the woman gave us such a look of venom that we were left quaking in our shoes! Then we needed to go to the toilet and I asked someone to direct us there. We were in for another shock. It was outside, where there were men standing with their willies on show, weeing up a wall! Slinking past them, we went behind a partition that had 'Femme' scrawled in crayon upon it and found to our dismay that there was a hole dug in the floor!

The day after the wedding, the family packed up and took us to a holiday home that was rented in a place named St. Nazaire. It was five minutes walk to the nearest plage and here there was a better atmosphere. Instead of being escorted everywhere like we had in Nantes by Madame Saimur, we were allowed to roam at will while she sunbathed in the tiny back garden. The Saimur sisters had lots of friends in the surrounding community and Audrey and I joined in with many of their games. We played volleyball, made sandcastles, sailed on rafts that the boys had brought and went to the afternoon parties that were held in different chalets. We were beginning to feel accepted, until one afternoon near the end of the holiday when we were barred from going into one of the them. A boy stood in the doorway, held his hand up and said 'Non'.

'Pourquoi?', I asked, taken aback, because this boy was quite handsome and had always been so courteous up to now.

'Allez,' replied the boy with an indignant toss of his head.

So Audrey and I walked back to the beach feeling angry, not helped by the fact that the group of French teenagers who had been allowed in, had been sniggering and grinning as they all trooped past us. We sat for around half an hour looking back at the drawn curtains at the chalet windows and wondering what was going on? All the time we had been in St. Nazaire, those people couldn't have been more friendlier, trying out their English on us, including us in their plans and being very pleasant all round.

'I'm going back,' I suddenly decided, my anger not having cooled as Audrey's had. 'I'm not going to sit here waiting. I shall tell that Renate what I think about her, it's ignorant to keep her guests hanging about.'

'Do you think you should?', Audrey asked anxiously. 'If they had wanted us there they would have invited us in.'

'Well, you could have gone with Mireille to see those sea lions,' I said, 'but you said you'd rather come with me. It's even worse making the two of us sit out here waiting. I'm going, you can come with me or stay here Audrey, it's up to you.'

How I wished later that I had just sat on the beach and minded my own business. I marched up to the chalet and flung the front door open wide. The room was dim, with a sweet smelling odour pervading my senses, along with the sound of jangly music coming from a wind up record player on the table nearby. I had looked about me wildly, scanning the spaced out grins from the faces of 'les amis', as they watched a pair of naked bodies gyrating on the floor.

CHAPTER 4

Back home in England after we, the intrepid adventurers had told our tales, Audrey took to her bed and I wandered about feeling bored. Mother was down at her aunty's again, because the poor old woman had lost the use of her legs. Father was working on the roof of a farmhouse, as a recent gale had blown off a lot of the slates.

I sat on the swing in the garden, moodily scuffing my shoes on the concrete floor trying to decide what to do. It was too dull to walk up to the village, besides it looked as if rain was on the way.

Suddenly from beyond the hedge there came a sound of children crying. At least two were, a baby and a toddler, as I found out as I rushed through the gate.

A dark skinned young woman was pushing a pram up the lane, looking harassed and near to tears herself. By her side walked a boy around seven, another one of school age, one who was just a toddler and twins sitting opposite each other in the pram.

I stopped and exclaimed over the pretty little babies, so that the woman smiled at me proudly and told me their names.

'Oh, Honeysuckle and Lily,' I said delightedly. 'Lily was my Granny's name. Oh, they're so cute and adorable, I love their fluffy little coats.'

'I made the coats myself,' the woman said. 'They're matinee jackets according to my husband, but my kids are not so cute and adorable when they want feeding in the night.'

'Haven't you got anyone to help you? When we were small we had our Granny and she came to help my Mother out.'

'Unfortunately my family are back in Barbados, so there's just me and my husband. He does his best but he has to work to bring the money in.'

'Perhaps I could help you?' I said eagerly. 'I'm doing nothing for the rest of my holidays and I'm fifteen now, so I'm nearly grown up.'

'Of course you are,' smiled the woman. 'I had my first child when I was sixteen. This is him, meet Samuel.' The eldest child smiled shyly and then the woman introduced Terry and Jimsy. They all looked at me seriously, while the toddler wiped his tears away with his jersey cuff.

'My name's Laurel by the way,' the woman said pleasantly. 'Do you want to come for a walk with us then? We are going to walk up to the farm to see the horse and buy some eggs from the lady, then we'll go back to our house and I'll make some lunch before the little ones have their nap. You could stay and play with them while I'm busy, if that's O.K.?'

'Oh yes, I'd love that and I'm Vivienne. Would you let me push the pram?'

For the rest of the summer, I went to help Laurel out with the children. I found to my delight that I was thought of as Laurel's 'au pair' girl and was given fifteen shillings at the end of every week. It seemed that her husband had a good job with the Council and was only too pleased to pay for someone to help his harassed wife.

That September I entered my fourth year at the County Grammar school. It was the beginning of another academic year that brought despair to my spirits, as I thought of the slog that the next few months were going to bring. We were working towards the O' levels and every subject had to be thoroughly gone over and tests completed, to see where each pupil stood in the scheme of things. It meant masses of homework, no free time and rows with Father because he wouldn't let me study in the warmth of the living room. We had just bought a television and suddenly the 'missing link' began to intrude into our life style, so that dinner was eaten on our laps or off a hastily flung cloth over the small dining table.

Father's dictatorial stance, on completing my homework in my freezing cold bedroom brought the worst out in me, so that I finished my work in record time, then depending on where I had decided to go, I was off like a rocket into the evening air. Sometimes I went to visit Laurel and gave a hand with getting the kids ready for bed, but most times I went to the Youth Club that had recently opened down Sparks Lane.

This club was different from the one run by the Hetherington's at the Gospel church, you could only play ping pong or silly games there. Sparks Lane was run by some parents in the Community Hall and they played records on a Dansette and you could dance as well.

I used some of my money to buy a pair of cream shoes with a tiny heel and made myself a column dress in stripes of grey and blue, from material I had found in the Birkenhead market. I wore my hair up, Cleopatra style and drew lines on my eyelids with a black HB pencil, though I waited for Dad to be engrossed in his favourite programme before I rushed to look in the bathroom mirror to do so. Then I would creep along the hedgerow in front of the living room window, hoping he wouldn't see the girl who now looked twenty three!

The Youth Club was full of laughing dancing teenagers, all dressed up in their 'courting' clothes and out for a bit of fun. I was the youngest there as most of the crowd had jobs, but I kept myself a little apart so that no one would ask my age. For the first few times I stood on the sidelines watching, noticing the outfits that the girls were wearing and making a mental note. The skirts were plain and circular, worn over layer upon layer of netted underskirts and their blouses had Peter Pan collars, but open at the neck. Most girls wore winkle picker shoes with stiletto heels, that made them taller than they were and they walked in a strange unnatural way like a man in a circus on stilts.

One evening, as I hesitantly tried to follow the steps of a girl who was jiving, a young man asked me to dance. I blinked a little, feeling startled, as I hadn't forgotten that scary time with Alec; that memory was still examined many many times.

'I'm only asking for a dance, you know,' the young man said.

'I'm not asking you to marry me or anything, but I've watched you the last few weeks trying out a few of the jive steps and I can teach you if you want, I'm quite a nifty guy.'

And he looked it. He was tall and slender, with his light brown hair brushed into a quiff at the front. He wore a dark blue suit with shiny black lapels and on his feet were a pair of black suede shoes.

'I'm Benny,' he said as he pushed me this way, pulled me the other way, tapping his feet to the music as he stood on the spot and I did all the work.

'Vivienne, pleased to meet you', I gasped, as he pulled me to him then made me do a spin again.

'Do you like Del Shannon's music?' Benny shouted.

'Yes,' I cried. 'Especially 'My Little Runaway', it's an easy song to learn.'

'Shall I get you a drink?' he asked, as the music finished and I had collapsed on a bench near by. 'Orange or lemon is all they have, but I'll be going for a proper drink at the end.'

Well I won't be going with you, I thought wryly, looking at my wristwatch that my parents had bought me for passing the 11+. Another twenty minutes then I'll be off. Dad will have finished watching the box and be getting ready to go to his Club.

'Here you are then, Vivienne,' Benny said, as he brought me a glass of orange squash. 'So where do you work then? Birkenhead or local, in a shop or an office maybe?'

'I'm still at school, studying for my O'levels,' I replied, thinking to myself it was a bit of a fib, but it was the mock O'levels even so.

'Oh, a scholar then? I left school at fifteen but now I'm waiting to join the Army. I go to the T.A to keep my hand in, but meantime I work on the buses. Have done for the past few weeks or so.'

I cringed inwardly. A bus conductor. I looked at my wristwatch purposely.

'It's time I was heading for home,' I said.

'So early? Aren't you going to stay 'til the finish? Listen, that's a Cliff Richard song that's playing, what about dancing to Living Doll?'

'No,' I said firmly, 'I've still got a lot of studying to do.'

'Let me walk you home then. Do you live close to here, 'cos I can come back after I've walked you home?'

'I don't need seeing home, thank you, it's only down the road.'

But Benny was up on his feet before I could stop him and with a sigh I let him take my hand.

We walked along the unlit street, until we reached the wall that surrounded the farmhouse.

This was where we got our milk and so it wasn't far from where I lived.

'Come and sit with me for a moment,' Benny said, pointing to the sandstone wall by the farmyard gates. 'It's not often I get to walk a scholar home.'

I did as I was told, but sat trembling a little beside him. If he made a move to touch me I'd be off, I wasn't going through all that stuff again.

'What's the matter, Vivienne? You cold or something? Why didn't you put a jacket on, you'll be suffering next with an Autumn chill?'

I had to laugh, he sounded just like my Granny used to. Have you got your Liberty bodice on? Or never cast a clout until May is out!

Benny put his jacket around my shoulders and I soon relaxed, snuggling up against him as he told me a little about his life. How he was going to make a career in the Army, rise to Sergeant Major if he was good enough, he didn't want to stay in the lowly ranks.

Before I knew it he was kissing me, but this time it was like being stroked with a feather. No urgency, no pressure, just tender velvety caresses like chocolate on my mouth. Then all too soon he let me go and I walked down the hill with wings on my feet.

And so we started our 'courtship', if that was what it could be called, as Benny only saw me once a week at the Community hall. I became quite proficient at jiving, dancing to records by Buddy Holly, whose greatest hit was 'Peggy Sue'. I loved that time with Benny. He was the gentlest soul I had ever met and hoped that he would never leave me, to go and join up as he planned to do.

One night, in late November, he arrived in his Army uniform, he didn't come into the Community Hall but sent someone in to fetch me. My heart began to thud with alarm when I saw him, all smartly dressed in his uniform and looking so different than the young man I thought I was in love with.

'So, you're going then?,' I whispered, looking into his serious brown eyes that usually twinkled with mischief. He nodded.

'When?'

'As soon as I've walked you back home, Vivienne. My train leaves at eight in the morning, so I'm going to stay in Liverpool with a mate.'

I put my coat on that had been hanging on a peg in the nearby cloakroom, my lovely maroon winter mohair that I'd bought with the last of my savings.

'I'll give you my address when we get to our special wall, Vivienne,' he said kindly. 'You will write, won't you, then you can let me have your address?'

'I will, I promise and you'll let me know when your first leave is, then maybe I can meet you off the ferryboat.'

'We'll see. Let's have a cuddle for a bit before I walk you down the hill. I'll miss our little cuddles, won't you?'

I was just about to agree with him, when out of the gloom ahead of us I heard my father's voice.

'Oi!, whoever you are, take your hands off my daughter or I'll ram your bloody fingers down the back of your throat!'

'Oh no, it's my father, Benny. You'd better go, he gets mad when he's in a temper.'

I was ready for flight myself, though I wasn't sure which way to run.

'Didn't yer hear me, back off my daughter? I'll give yer ten seconds start, then I'll be after you matey. No good for nothing soldier comes after my girl.'

I groaned, my Dad must have been watching too many Westerns. I turned to tell Benny so, then noticed that he had left. His Army boots threw sparks up off the pavement, as he dashed along the road to catch a bus that he'd seen in the distance. He passed us by on the platform of the bus with two fingers up.

I walked back home in embarrassed silence, while my father ranted on at me about common tarts and I should know better, that I was grounded until my exams' were over and I'd get a thick ear if I was caught with a boy again. I wasn't really listening, as my heart was broken and I vowed I would never trust another man again.

A few days later, Mother, in her endeavour to cheer me up told me that there was a Christmas job going at our local Woolworth store.

'It's Friday evening and all day Saturday, so it shouldn't interfere with Vivienne's studying, Eddie,' she said to Father eagerly.

'As long as she's straight home on the bus after her shift's finished I don't mind, Irene, but I'm watching our Vivienne carefully now, so there'd better be no slip ups.'

So I started work as a temporary shop assistant. I rushed home from school, got changed into my black skirt and white short sleeved blouse and was behind my counter in Woolworths by quarter past five. It was easy on Cosmetics, though I had to watch out for shoplifters and there was a few of them around.

One Friday evening, I came across a girl who I had seen slip a lipstick into her coat pocket, her back was turned to me so I couldn't see who it was. To my surprise I came face to face with a girl that I had gone to primary school with. The girl just nodded in an embarrassed way, then guiltily placed the lipstick into my hand.

I worked at the store for the five week period up to Christmas and earned the grand total of seven pounds and ten shillings. Six pounds of this was gleefully put in the bank and what was left was spent on dress lengths and presents. Part of this money could buy a lot of material, as my evenings were now spent at Mother's sewing machine. I made skirts, blouses and drainpipe trousers, a skill I had learnt in Domestic Science and did very well.

I was off romance since my betrayal by Benny and though many young men would ask me out at Woolworths, I was inclined to turn up my nose at them.

Then one Saturday afternoon just before Christmas, while I was waiting at the bus stop for the five o'-clock bus, a large white van stopped at the roadside beside me and the driver asked me did I want a lift home? I thought I knew the driver from when I had gone to the youth club at Sparks Lane, he used to dance with a pretty green eyed girl called Helen and I remembered fleetingly that he had a funny name. Dezza, that was it I suddenly thought and now Dezza would save me the bus fare if he gave me a lift home.

I clambered aboard, which I managed with some difficulty as I had on my pencil slim skirt.

I gave him a dazzling smile in gratitude and asked him did he know where I lived?

Dezza nodded that he did and set off up the road to the traffic lights, but soon my face turned to panic when he turned left instead of right and began to drive down the hill to the shore.

'What are you doing, Dezza?' I shouted in alarm above the noisy engine. 'You know I live in Whaley Lane and this way is down to the shore!'

He smiled at me in an unpleasant fashion and told me to hold tight we were going for a ride.

My heart began thudding against my chest, this was a rerun of that time with Alec. What was it about me that caused this to happen, I thought with despair, or had Benny been putting it about that I was an easy lay?

After ten heart stopping minutes, the van roared into a dark and lonely car park, fringed with a dense coppice of trees before opening on to the wild open shore.

'Now , Vivienne,' Dezza leered, as he put the gears into neutral then switched off the engine,

'I've heard that you're a good kisser, so that'll do for a start.'

He leant over and tried to grab me to him, but I pushed myself against the door and tried to open it.

'I don't know who told you that,' I cried frantically, 'but what I do know is if you hurt me in any way my father will hear about it and I know where your girlfriend lives, so she'll be told as well!'

'Oh, hark at Miss Goody Two Shoes,' said Dezza, laughing unpleasantly. 'Come here, you can't get out you know, 'cos I've locked the passenger door? So you may as well just lie there and let me do what I like to you, then if I feel in a good mood after I'll drive you home as well.'

So what could I do but be compliant, though I gritted my teeth the whole time he kissed me and went limp when he took me in his arms. He nuzzled my neck trying to evoke some response from me, but I made my body droop as if I was a rag doll.

Suddenly Dezza gave up and pushed me none too gently against the passenger door, then started the engine so violently that the van began to rattle and complain. He whooshed up the sandy lane to the main road, his face set and very angry, then screamed through a red light recklessly, nearly causing an accident there.

I sat in the seat feeling helpless, too scared to move, even to wipe the tears of relief that were now gushing down from my eyes. I hated men, all they did was try to use me and one day, I vowed, I'd make one of them suffer. One of them would get their comeuppance, if it was the last thing I ever did.

Dezza pushed me out of the van abruptly when we got to the top of Whaley Lane, shouting to me to keep my mouth shut or he would come around looking for me.

Thanks heavens the family were still out Christmas shopping, so there was no one at home to hear me as I sobbed uncontrollably upon my bed. Then I cried some more later, as I noticed the love bite on my neck!

As the New Year dawned and we as a family had experienced perhaps our most fraught Christmas ever, I made three resolutions. First I was going to join the youth group at St Oswald's church, in the hope that I would find some other religious minded teenagers to be friends with, the second was to attend dancing classes that my cousin ran, so that I could move in a higher social circle, then thirdly I was going to concentrate on my studies so that I could go to University.

All this had come to me in a wave of inspiration, as I listened to my sister Gina on Christmas Day, who cried in her bitterness that she was forced to live away from home. I had watched the anguish and seen the tears from my parents, as they tried to bridge the gap on the telephone with a daughter who was living a thousand miles away. They were desperate and spent most of the festivities saying so, then another blow befell them when Aunty Jenny was rushed into hospital.

Mother was devastated and spent most of her time at her aunt's bedside, then fell ill herself with influenza, as the result of having too much to do.

The Youth club was held on a Sunday evening after Evensong and I spent most of the church service trying to work out what was going wrong in my life. I was trying to be good, trying to follow the Bible's teachings, but just when I thought I was succeeding, something would go wrong again.

Had it been my fault that I had walked around most of the week before Christmas with a head scarf tied around my neck, hiding that bloody love bite? Was it my fault that my father didn't like me and treated me to the length of his tongue, if he thought me defiant or disobedient? What was it about me that made men treat me in such a shabby way? Why couldn't I have a boyfriend who loved me just for myself?

I made my way into the large church hall, where a handful of young people who were around my age, waited quietly for the vicar to arrive. They looked nice, they smiled back when I smiled at them and soon we all sat around a large table while the vicar introduced himself. We were going to have discussions about things that bothered us and after we would play a few team games like pass the ball, Chinese whispers or maybe play charades. It sounded good, though not the opening up to each other, so after a few minutes of sheepish silence we played charades instead.

'Maybe some board games next week,' said Reverend Hallet, seeing that his counselling sessions had turned out to be a none starter, 'or maybe a little Bible study? Whatever you think, it's your youth club.'

'Perhaps we could just have discussions about records and pop stars, things that interest us?', suggested a small thin boy with glasses.

'Or maybe we could find a record player and we could all bring a favourite record with us to play?'

That came from me as I had been bought a Ferguson record player for Christmas, but didn't think I'd be allowed to bring it there.

'I think my Mum would allow me to bring mine,' said a handsome looking dark skinned youth with lovely white pearly teeth. 'I only live a few streets away so it's not too far to carry it here.'

'Then that's what we'll do,' said the Vicar, pleased that he had got his youth club off the ground with teenagers who seemed a pleasant group.

'Now, let's all have a nice cup of tea, I put the boiler on when I got here.'

I put my coat on and wound my scarf around my neck before setting off to stand at the bus stop. I passed the boy who had offered to bring his record player and smiled at him a little tentatively. Before I knew it he was opening the outer door for me, then walking at my side along the unlit church yard path.

'Do you live around here, Vivienne? It is Vivienne, isn't it, my name is Colin by the way?'

He spoke so nicely, not in the sloppy Merseyside fashion. He pronounced each word carefully like a person off the 'box'.

I giggled and nodded and he was heartened by my gaiety, as he hadn't made friends very easily on that tough housing estate.

'I have to catch the bus to where I live, Colin,' I explained. 'I could walk it, but my father said he'll be waiting at our bus stop at nine o' clock and he won't let me come again if I happen to be late.'

'I'll walk you to the bus stop then,' Colin said eagerly. 'I know if you were my sister I wouldn't want you waiting on your own. Will you be coming to the youth club again next Sunday? I thought the vicar was very nice, didn't you?'

I nodded again to both his questions, thinking that he was also very nice.

For the next few weeks Colin walked me every Sunday evening to the bus stop. We mixed with the others and played some records and had discussions with our new found friends, but I was the one that Colin wanted to get close to. He thought me a vibrant girl and funny with it and he'd already told his mother that he had a girlfriend.

'Are you sure, dear, that this girl would accept your background, Colin?', his mother had asked worriedly. 'You know what the people have been like around here. A different coloured skin brings suspicion and intolerance. Does she know that you are from a mixed race marriage, especially does she know that your parents are separated as well?'

'You know, Mother, I don't think that Vivienne has even noticed that I have different coloured skin. She certainly has never mentioned it and anyway we don't have any deep and meaningful conversations, we have a laugh together. I've only mentioned her to you because I would like to invite her for tea one Sunday, then we could go to Church from here and Youth club after. I'm not asking her to marry me, I'm just asking her to come to tea.'

'Well, of course she'll be welcome, I just don't want you getting hurt and have you told her that you'll be leaving soon, finishing your course at college and entering the British Army?'

'No, I haven't told her, Mother. There seemed no point in telling her anything until I've asked her if she would like to come around for tea. If she agrees, I'll tell her of all my hopes and dreams then.'

I accepted his invitation. I was delighted to, as I thought that Colin was so courteous and that made a change from other men.

Not that he was a man really, he was seventeen soon to be eighteen, but I never felt threatened by him and he had only ever kissed me on the cheek.

He seemed nervous though on that Sunday afternoon, as he met me from the bus and walked with me down the road. He kept clearing his throat about to tell me something, then he seemed to change his mind.

'Out with it, Colin,' I said sharply, because his manner was making me jittery, 'your mother did ask me to come today, didn't she or is this an excuse to get me alone in your house?'

'Vivienne!'

Colin was shocked. 'I wanted you to meet my family of course, but I haven't told you everything about myself. I'm leaving to join the Army in a couple of weeks.'

'Oh, is that all,' I replied, feeling very relieved. 'So we can write to each other if you want.'

'I thought you might think that I've been dishonest, leading you up the garden path as it were.'

'How so? It's not as if we're going steady and we've professed our undying love to each other. I thought we were friends, muckers, you're just like the big brother I've never had.'

'Oh.'

At least now he knew where he stood, but maybe absence would make my heart grow fonder and I'd begin to miss him after he'd gone.

I was led into a neat and tidy living room, where a woman in her late forties stood waiting to welcome me. She was a slightly built lady, with a streak of white at the front of her very dark shoulder length hair; she had oval shaped brown eyes and a nervous smile hovered on her generous proportioned mouth. She was wearing a burgundy coloured sari over a green satin top and on her feet she wore a pair of gold slippers. She held out her arms in a friendly fashion and kissed me on each of my cheeks.

I went pink with embarrassment, but the tension was broken when a girl of around ten years old came bounding in to meet me. She was a pretty little thing with elfin features and wore a knee length gingham dress with a white knitted cardigan.

'I'm Sarah Jamieson, Colin's sister. I'm ten years old and I go to Arrowe Park primary school. Can we have our tea now that you've come, 'cos I'm starving? We've got chocolate eclairs for afters and Mum has made samosas to go with our salad.'

'Naughty girl, where are your manners?', Mrs. Jamieson chided. 'Come into the kitchen, Vivienne, I've set the table in there.'

Colin's mother seemed to have gone to a lot of trouble, I thought, as we sat in the small kitchen eating delicious little spicy pasties and chewing on homemade bread. The Jamieson's seemed such a close knit loving family and I felt a pang of envy as I sat with them. Later Colin played snakes and ladders with his sister in the living room, while I helped his mother wash the dishes in the sink.

'Has Colin told you that he plans to join the British Army, Vivienne? It seem such a shame that he's only just met you and now he'll be joining up in a few weeks time,' she said, as she handed me the last plate for drying.

'Yes, he told me today, Mrs. Jamieson, but we can write to each other, can't we? I'm sure he'd like a letter now and again and I can tell him all what's going on at the youth club.'

'He seems to think a lot about you, Vivienne. I worry about his future, especially if he was to marry someone like you.'

'How do you mean, Mrs. Jamieson, I don't quite follow what you're talking about? What has his marriage got to do with me?'

My hostess laughed nervously and said.

'Oh, I'm probably being silly, but Colin is from a mixed race family and I worry that if he fell in love with someone like you, then that person would have a lot of thinking to do.'

I looked at her blankly and busied myself wiping down the kitchen table. His mother seemed to be working up to something, but she didn't seem to be explaining herself very well.

'Well, what I'm trying to say is that I'm from India and Colin's father is from Africa, so any children from his marriage could go either way as it were.'

I was mystified, I couldn't understand why I was being told all this, Colin was only my friend!

'Oh, I wouldn't lose any sleep over it, Mrs. Jamieson,' I replied airily. 'Is that us finished then? Why don't we go and play a game of snakes and ladders, it's bound to be a lot of fun?'

Father had a lot to say after I took Colin to our house for his tea on the following Sunday, as Mother had said it was only polite to invite the boy in return. We had the usual ham salad and boiled potatoes, with thin sliced bread and butter and peaches out of a tin. Mother had arranged it nicely on the table in the living room and Father had switched the T.V off, which was unusual to say the least for him. Colin's manners were impeccable and he thanked Mother politely, then Father told him of his war exploits, thinking he was pleasing his guest. The afternoon soon flew by and it was time to get ready for the evening service. One more week for Colin and then he was off down South.

'You will write to me, won't you, Vivienne?' he asked anxiously, as we waited at the bus stop. 'It was so nice to meet your family and they seemed to like me.'

'I told you I would write didn't I, but Colin, don't you think things are getting a bit serious? I don't want a boyfriend at the moment, I've got lots of other stuff I want to do.'

'Like what? What are you going to be doing when I go away?'

'Well, I thought I'd join a dancing class and learn to waltz or do the tango. I thought it would be fun and I could hone up on my social skills.'

'You mean you'll be dancing with men, don't you?' Colin said, sounding hurt. 'I suppose once I've gone you'll be seeing other boys.'

'Oh, lighten up,' I said, trying to be gentle. 'I've told you I don't want a boyfriend, I just want a bit of fun and make a few more friends.'

He drew me into his arms and kissed the top of my head.

'You know I love you, Vivienne, please don't go out with anybody else.'

I was saved from answering as the bus came chugging up the hill, so I squeezed his hand reassuringly and hoped he wouldn't say it again.

When I got home that evening, Father had a lot to say on the subject. Did I know that the boy had a touch of the tar brush about him, what was his intentions towards me and did I want to live in married quarters on a foreign base somewhere?

I answered him defiantly, with some of the old insolent Vivienne coming rushing to the fore.

'Yes, don't know, haven't decided yet,' I answered cheekily. 'That's what I've got to say in answer to your questions, Dad, and if I want to I'll see him again.'

CHAPTER 5

Mother and Father sat in the living room one evening, a few days after Colin's visit. We girls had gone to bed and Mother was busy finishing off a little cardigan she had been knitting for Gina's daughter.

'You know, Irene?,' said Father, as he twirled the contents of his latest brew around his wine glass,

'I think we've got problems with that daughter of yours.'

'Which daughter, Eddie?' asked Mother innocently, knowing that it would be me that he was talking about.

'Vivienne. She's too busy chasing lads instead of concentrating on her studies. First there was that soldier fellow I caught her with, then there's this other bloke we've just had around for tea. He's off to be a soldier, isn't he? If she's not careful she'll end up married to one and then where will we be? One daughter in America, another living God knows where and I didn't tell you this, but I caught a bus driver chatting to her yesterday. I was rounding the corner to come into the lane and she'd just got off the bus from school, and there she was bold as brass talking to this fellow and the passengers were sitting there waiting for the bus to move off. When I was in the Army we had a name for someone like Vivienne, it was jail bait. We'll have to keep a better eye on her.'

'Surely you're exaggerating, Eddie?' Mother replied, taken aback by what she'd just heard.

'Vivienne's just a friendly girl. Don't you remember when she was little, people were always saying how she told them such a tale, while she sat outside the Co-op in her pram?'

'Well that was when she was little, now being friendly with people can get her into trouble. I've been thinking, I'm going to see if your sister's daughter will take her for the school holidays. You know you were saying that your niece had opened up a guest-house in Tenby and was looking for staff to help her run it? It'll do Vivienne good to see how people have to work hard for a living and it will get her away from here at Easter time.'

'It's a bit far though, Eddie, she'll have to get a couple of trains and she's a bit young to be travelling on her own. Anyway, she's starting dancing lessons at my cousin's in Oxton Road after Colin has gone off to the Army. It would be such a shame to disrupt her plans.'

'Well, I think it will do her good and I don't want any opposition from you, Irene. I'll ring your sister Isabel tomorrow and I'll get Pamela's address off her. With a bit of luck we'll have a bit of peace this Easter, just the three of us, eh?'

I entered the portals of Miss McIntyre's Academy of Dancing, a little nervous but determined to learn the quickstep, tango and waltz. My head was filled with dreams of becoming an accomplished dancer, good enough to travel to Blackpool maybe and dance in the hallowed Tower Ballroom.

My parents used to go dancing at the local village hall and I remembered the hampers of goodies that they had won. I could imagine myself in a sparkly tulle frock, like the one my mother used to wear when she was young.

'Hello, you must be Vivienne,' said a slim dark haired girl in greeting, as I stood hesitantly on the edge of the dance floor. She was a little older than me, dressed in black velvet wide legged trousers and a pretty lace trimmed white Tyrolean blouse.

'I'm Melody,' she continued. 'We're second cousins by the way. Mum said to look out for you, as Aunt Irene telephoned her to let her know you were coming tonight. I take the ballroom classes now, it gives Mum a bit of a break on a Friday with all the ballet lessons she does on a Saturday morning. Funny we've never met, isn't it, but I'm nearer to Gina's age than yours I suppose? How is Gina, I believe she's gone to America to live? Anyway, I mustn't stand here talking, come over here and meet the others, they're all at different stages, Beginners, Intermediates.......There's Janey over there, she's new like you are, you can help each other with the steps.'

Melody led the way across the large rectangular wooden floored room, to where a dozen young people lounged around on the chairs that lined the ballroom. She clapped her hands and announced me as a newcomer, which seemed to make all eyes in the room look at me. Then Melody introduced Janey, a girl with a wide smile and corn coloured hair and we stood together self consciously, watching as Melody went over the steps of a waltz.

'Now, Billy and Renee come over here and we'll watch a couple in action,' instructed Melody.

'That's it, back with your right foot, Renee, forward with your left, Billy, then side to your left, Renee, side to your right, Billy, feet together, close. Good, good, now I'll put some music on and you can all have a go.'

The hour at the Academy seemed to go very quickly and I felt dazed as I walked up the road to wait for the bus. I thought that I had picked up the dance steps very well and resolved to ask my father if he would partner me in the kitchen when I got home. I had danced with Janey and I wanted to try the dance steps out with a man.

'Wait up.'

I heard a voice and footsteps running a few yards behind. It was a boy I had met at refreshment time. One of four of them, there were four boys and eight girls including myself.

'Oh, hi Ricky, do you catch the same bus as me?' I asked, as the tallish, thickset young man came alongside me.

'Why, which one are you going on?' he asked breathlessly, his fair hair slicking greasily to his forehead from his effort of running up the hill.

'The Heswall bus, there's one at twenty past.'

'Plenty of time for me to get to know you then, Vivienne. You're easily the prettiest girl in the class tonight, that's why I decided to come after you. Fancy coming for a drink instead, there's a pub I know a few minutes away?'

'I've got to get home, Ricky,' I said feeling flattered. 'Anyway don't be daft, Melody's beautiful compared to me.'

'Well, aside from Melody then, anyway she doesn't count because she's the teacher. Will you be coming again next week, only I thought you could dump Janey and partner me instead? I've been going to the classes a few weeks now and I'm sure we'd be good together. I noticed how quickly you picked the steps up tonight. You never know we could win some cups!'

'Oh, are you going on the Blackpool weekend at Easter? I don't think I'll be allowed to go though.

My Dad has me on a fairly short piece of rope at the moment, even though it is my cousin that's organizing the trip, he'll tell me I'm too young to go.'

'Well, let's see how we get on together first,' Ricky said linking my arm. 'There'll be plenty of time to put your name down, it's not till a few months time.'

Oh, why did this keep happening?, I thought to myself despairingly, as I came up for air a second time. Ricky had grasped me in a bear like hug as soon as we'd got to the bus shelter and had clamped his sticky lips onto mine, like a bee sucking out honey. All I had wanted to do was learn how to dance that evening, not end up being mauled by a rugby tackler.

I glanced through the window to see if my bus was coming, while Ricky got ready to advance on me for the third time.

'I think I can see my bus coming, Ricky,' I said weakly. 'I'll see you next week if I'm allowed to come dancing again.'

'Oh, let this one go, Vivienne. You can tell your father you missed it, stayed behind chatting or something. Come on, I'm enjoying myself, you're quite a good kisser, you know.'

'No, I'll have to get this one,' I replied firmly and dodged passed him with a sigh of relief.

The bus drew up and I jumped quickly onto the platform, sitting myself down thankfully on the first vacant seat. I rummaged in my handbag for the bus fare, to pretend I wasn't watching as Ricky waved a fond goodbye.

'Darling Vivienne,' Colin wrote.

It has been a week now since we parted and I've missed you every minute of those seven days. I have settled into the routine here. Up at six, square bashing until breakfast, kit inspections, drilling, lectures and sport. I'm really shattered at the end of each day. I've met a good bunch of people and we're all getting on very well. In five weeks time we'll be having our Passing Out Parade and I hope you will be able to travel with Mum and Sarah to see it, then you and I can spend my leave together on my return. I think your parents will allow it, because they seemed very happy to meet me when I came to your house for tea. Do you think you could send me a photograph of yourself? A lot of my mates have their girlfriend's photo' pinned to the wall above their beds. If you want to have one taken at a photographers, I'll send you a postal order to cover the cost. Please go and visit Mum while I'm away, because I know she thinks a lot of you. I've put my address as you can see at the top of my letter. Sherrington Barracks is the place to be! Looking forward to hearing from you.

Love from Colin.

I sat on my bed reading his letter the next morning. It was Saturday and I planned to go into town to look for some glitzy shoes that I could wear for the dance classes. I was feeling very mixed up as I read his words. 'Darling Vivienne.' How romantic, but romance didn't figure in my life at the moment. Romance would get in the way. How was I going to tell him that without hurting him? I only wanted to be friends with Colin, not get into this courting lark and end up married like Gina with a baby on the way? Besides he'd go mad if he knew what Ricky had been doing in the bus shelter and if I was honest with myself, Colin deserved someone better. He needed a girl who would love him right down to his little fingers, not a girl who was already acquainted with the grubby side of men.

He'd be horrified if he knew that I intended going to the Youth Club tomorrow night, to chat with this new bloke who had been there with his cousin Mark, last Sunday. Sean O'Connell had come in his Airforce uniform and on his jacket sleeve was a special badge of wings!

'A pilot?', I asked, the next evening after I had sauntered over to Mark, who had replaced Colin as the provider of the youth club's record player.

'Yes,' replied Mark proudly, 'well, a trainee pilot. My cousin is one of the youngest to be picked for training in his squadron, but Sean has always wanted to be a pilot since he was a small boy.'

'And hasn't he come over this weekend to stay with you then?', I asked feeling a little disappointed. I remembered his happy smile and the lilt of his voice with him coming from the Emerald Isle.

'No, he won't be coming again until Easter. It's quite far to come just for the weekend, as he's stationed in Anglesey, so he has to get on two trains.'

'Where does he live in Ireland then? My family come from the west coast of Ireland, from around Galway, I think.'

'Oh, the O'Connell's hail from Killarney. His father and mine are brothers, but Dad came to live in Liverpool after the War.'

'We're probably related then,' I smiled happily. 'Anyway put a record on will you, I feel like having a dance.'

I didn't reply to Colin's letter. How could I when it would raise his hopes, making him think that we were courting? I would write to him nearer the time of his Passing Out Parade and let him down gently. Tell him I wasn't allowed to travel to Warwickshire, my parents thought it was too far to go.

'I've had a letter from your cousin, Pamela,' said Father, as we all sat around the table a week or so later. 'She'd like you to go and help her at her guest-house in Tenby, Vivienne. Easter is a busy time in the hotel trade and I know how you like to earn a bit of money from time to time.'

'But Tenby's at the other end of the country, isn't it?' I replied,

112

taken aback that my Dad would consider letting me go on such a long journey.

'Well, as far as I know it's on the west coast of Wales, the jutting out bit below Cardigan Bay. It'll take you about eight hours on the train.'

'I don't even know Pamela, Dad. The last time I saw her was at Aunty Isabel's when I was about ten and she'd just finished her teacher's training. I thought she was a strict old misery, telling me off for leaning my arms on the table.'

'Oh, she's lovely,' Mother said. 'We always got on very well together when she used to come to stay with us before you were born. It was a pity she married and went to live so far away. It was his job you know, he used to work for the Diplomatic Corp.'

'He'll probably need to be on hand then when our Vivienne lands in Tenby,' Father joked. 'No, seriously, I've decide you're going, so when the school term finishes you'll be off on the next morning train.'

'But I wanted to go to Blackpool to the Tower Ballroom at Easter. Melody's arranged a trip and I've told her that you'll let me go.'

'Out of the question young lady,' Father scoffed. 'If you think for one moment that I'd let you go off to a place like Blackpool, where you'd be let loose amongst all those fellows that hang around looking for a good time, then you don't know me very well. No more ifs and buts and you're to take a white blouse and a plain black skirt with you. It seems from her letter that you'll be doing a bit of waiting on.'

I mooched up the stairs to my bedroom, misery welling up inside me at the thought of my Easter holidays being mucked up by my Dad. I'd been so looking forward to that weekend away in Blackpool and even if Ricky was becoming a nuisance, I wouldn't have had to spend too much time with him anyway. He was still walking me to the bus stop, still trying to grope me at every opportunity he had, but recently I had come up with the idea of leaving the classes early so that he'd be too embarrassed to ask if he could leave as well.

Nothing seemed to be going well for me at that moment in time. School was a headache as usual, with the teachers banging on about how important the lessons were with the Mock exam's only months away; the youth club was boring and dancing classes were beginning to go that way too. It seemed that I knew all the steps I needed now and my only option was to go to learn Latin American dancing on Sunday evenings. Oh, how I wished I was older and could make my own decisions over things. Two weeks under the controlling influence of my cousin Pamela and she probably wouldn't pay me properly for all the work I did, or just give me a bit of pocket money to cover buying personal things.

My thoughts flew to my small savings account that now only had peanuts in it. I wondered who would be paying my fare, as I had no money for that sort of thing?

Perhaps though I could turn this trip to my advantage, learn the trade as it were and earn some money at a local place on my return? Or even better, tell them at school that I was going to leave at the end of my fourth year. I'd be sixteen at the beginning of August, old enough to be earning a living in this rotten old world.

Another letter came from Colin. He loved me, he missed me, why hadn't I written or had I and my letter hadn't got through? He had tried to 'phone me, but my Dad had told him I was out with one of my friends from school. He didn't know I had any girlfriends, it was a girl wasn't it? I hadn't dumped him for another boy?

His final letter came two weeks before the term was to end for Easter. He would be home the following Friday and he would meet me at the Youth Club on Sunday night. He was really looking forward to seeing me, more than he was looking forward to the Passing Out Parade, even though he had been promoted to a Lance Bombardier.

I shivered as I read it, not sure how I was going to face him. How was I going to tell him that I hadn't missed his presence at all? There was fear in my mind as I looked into a future with Colin. I'd be tying myself down to the domineering influence of a husband, just like my mother had twenty three years before. I wanted to make my own choices when I was old enough, not be accountable to someone who may love me now, but would see me as a possession in years to come. The kindest thing would be to stand him up and then he'd get the message. I was bored with the Church and Youth Club anyway.

The day was drawing nearer to my trip to Wales, Dad had said he would give me the money for the train ticket and I could pay him back from the wages I would earn. At last I would be free of Ricky, as Friday night was the last time I'd be going to dancing. Let him find a girl in Blackpool he could practice his rugby tackles on.

I got down from the bus at the stop on Oxton Road, smoothing my hair down with my hand, as a gust of wind blew it out of its neat shoulder length bob. I had my sparkly shoes in my vanity case and was wearing my black and grey stripey culottes that I had made especially for wearing over Easter in Tenby. Surely even cousin Pamela would allow me some time off and maybe I would find a girlfriend to go to a dance hall with in the local town. Free from the strictures of my parents, I was sure I would enjoy myself wherever I went.

This was to be the last time I would be attending Miss McIntyre's Dancing Academy, at least for the time being, maybe in the future I would return to learn the Latin American dances.

I began to walk down the hill towards the familiar building, when suddenly my heart stopped when I saw who was waiting outside. It was Colin! Dressed in a khaki uniform with a red peaked hat on his head and white puttee bands around his calves. His shoulders looked broad, he had filled out and was looking very handsome, but the first thing I noticed...... he looked like a man! He'd remembered me telling him that I was going to attend the dancing school on Oxton Road and had decided to surprise me on his first evening home!

Well, he had done, I thought, as I turned heel and ran quickly back up the hill. For there was no way I was going to meet him and cause the hurt that was sure to appear on his face.

At last! I got off at the station in Tenby with a sore bottom, from sitting in an uncomfortable compartment for the past six and a half hours. It had been an adventure. I had boarded the train from Chester and found it quite exciting to watch the world go by, as the train chugged through the North Wales countryside, then stopped at various coastal stations on the way down. But excitement had changed to boredom, as I finished the magazine my father had bought me, when he had dropped me off at Heswall Hills to catch the Chester train.

It was late in the afternoon and I had finished off the cheese and tomato sandwiches that my mother had made me for my journey. I was hungry and the smell of fish and chips assailed my nostrils, as I walked up the station ramp into town. I was about to follow my nose and treat myself to a large portion of both, when a man in his fifties drew up in a car.

'Are you, Vivienne?' he asked politely. 'I'm Philip Monroe, Pamela's husband. I've come to collect you and take you home to West Park.'

'Oh yes, Philip, Pamela's husband, pleased to meet you. I was just on my way to get some fish and chips. Would you mind waiting for me a minute or so?'

'Good heavens,' he said looking at me in astonishment, 'I can't have the car smelling of fish and chips, my dear, Pamela would go mad if she smelt them on the upholstery. Anyway, we'll be having supper when we get to the guest-house. It won't be fish and chips, but I can promise you a very satisfying meal. This your suitcase then, I'll put it in the boot, shall I? Doesn't seem to be very heavy seeing you'll be staying two weeks or so.'

I slouched into the passenger seat beside him, thinking how unfair it was that I wouldn't be eating fish and chips for my tea. I'd probably be given liver and I hated liver, but again there was to be no choice in the matter, Pamela would be replacing Father as my jailer while I was staying in her guest-house.

I looked at Philip surreptitiously as he drove his station wagon through the busy streets and headed out onto a country road. He was a big bear of a man with shaggy eyebrows and a large moustache that turned down at the corners. His black hair was quite long considering that he used to be a diplomat, but now that he had retired I supposed he could wear his hair how he wanted to. He was wearing a heavy navy guernsey sweater with black corduroy trousers and on his feet were a pair of Jesus sandals.

'It's a good twenty miles from here, Vivienne, so I'd sit back and relax if I were you,' he said kindly. 'We're buried out in the countryside, but the place is popular with walkers so we manage a lot of bookings from now to September. That's why Pamela asked for your help, there's not many people willing to work in isolation like we do.'

Oh no, I groaned. Not the back and beyond where's there's no nightlife. How was I going to cope buried in a far off place miles from anywhere, especially the nearest town?

'Is Tenby the nearest town to West Park then, Philip?'

'I'd say it was, though you can catch the bus I suppose to Redbarrow, which is a village about two miles away. There's a pub' and a small grocers there, but mostly it's countryside and farmland around our way, though we're probably also nearer to the sea.'

'Oh, how far away is the sea then?', I asked eagerly, thinking that if I had a day off I could sunbathe on the sands.

'Well, it's not in walking distance, it could be a bus ride I think. If there is a bus that travels there.'

So my Dad had set me up then, nothing within walking distance, everything by bus or begging for a lift by car. Had he known all this?, I wondered. Was that why he was so willing to send me so far?

Eventually the car drove up a long tree lined winding drive, the sort of drive you would expect a castle to be at the top of, but West Park sitting in all its splendour in the dying rays of the evening sun wasn't a castle. It was more like a small chateau, with grey coloured walls and shiny green roof slates.

'This looks like the houses I saw in Brittany,' I said, awed that the place that had been described to me as a guest-house, was more like a small hotel.

'It belonged to a gentleman farmer years ago, who before he had settled down to farming had travelled extensively throughout the world. A bit like me really, perhaps that's why I like the place so much.'

'And how many guests have you got staying at the moment?'

'Five doubles are occupied and we have one single chap staying. Eleven guests for you, Vivienne, to wait on hand and foot.'

'Mmm.'

As Philip drew up to the heavy wooden front door, cousin Pamela came shooting through it. She barely resembled the young woman that I remembered. This lady was tall and thin, with her fair hair scraped back into a bunch that lay on her left shoulder. She wore a big white pinny over a long blue dress and she also wore a frown on her buttoned up face.

'Got her then, Philip? What took you so long? Supper's been keeping in the oven for you, I couldn't wait for mine. Hurry up then, the guests are waiting for you to open up the bar. It's too bad, you know, Philip, that I had to serve their dinner on my own.'

'Well, where's Mrs. Slack when she's most needed?'

'She was in the kitchen of course, where do you think she'd be? Oh, hello, Vivienne. Bring your suitcase in and follow me. I'll show you your room, it's on the top floor next to ours.'

Nothing else. No, 'did you have a good journey?' Or, 'you must be tired, come along in.'

My cousin had really changed since she was training to be a teacher. She used to be plump and her fair hair had been curly. I had always thought of her as pretty, but she wasn't now.

'Don't take any notice of Pamela,' whispered Philip, as he got my suitcase out of the boot of the car. 'She's a pussycat really, but she's tired with not having enough people to help her. I'm sure she'll feel better now you have arrived, my dear.'

She'll be more like a cat with claws, I thought, as I trailed up two flights of stairs after my cousin. I wasn't trained to do the work she'd be wanting and by the time she had trained me, it would be time for me to go back home again.

I was glad to get up the next morning and feel the warmth of the kitchen range on my chilled body. My small room on the top floor didn't seem to benefit from any sun and the floor was bare, except for a lambs wool rug at the side of the bed, which had been nice for me to curl my toes in.

'I'm happy to see that you've put your blouse and skirt on, Vivienne,' observed Pamela, 'and taken off that muck you had on your face when you arrived yesterday. Not good for your skin you know, and causes wrinkles in the long run. Anyway, you'll be serving breakfast in the dining room from eight o'- clock. Now it's just gone seven, so I want you to start by pricking those sausages before I put them in the frying pan, then slice the tomatoes and crack a few eggs into that bowl over there.

Here's a pinny and I hope your hands are clean and I've set the tables for you, but that will be your job after today.'

'Don't we get any breakfast before we start, Pamela?,' I asked hungrily, eyeing the bacon that was sizzling in the frying pan. The dinner of beef casserole and vegetables that I had been given for my supper the evening before, had been only enough for a bird to live on and my tummy was rumbling at the sight of all the breakfast food.

'No, we eat after the guests have left the dining room. A quick bite to eat and then we start cleaning out the bedrooms.'

Mmm, I thought. A bit of slave labour here working for my cousin, but if it teaches me the workings of the hotel trade, I'll put up with it while I'm here.

My days then became one long flurry of activity, from the time I got up in the morning until I laid my tired head on the pillow at night. My only respite was an hour to myself in the afternoon before tea was served at four o'- clock and a couple of hours in the evening, once the dinner dishes had been stacked away and the kitchen had been scrubbed until all the surfaces shone.

But to be fair, Pamela and Philip worked just as hard as I did, with Philip manning the Reception desk, keeping the extensive gardens in order and being 'Mine Host' in the Bar in the evenings.

119

No wonder Pamela looked whacked and didn't have a lot to say.

One morning though, after I had finished cleaning five double bedrooms and one single, plus the two bathrooms on each corridor, Pamela said I could have the afternoon off if I wanted to.

Did I want to? I was off like a rocket to my bedroom and after donning my black and grey striped culottes with a long sleeved white blouse and pink hand knitted cardigan, I flew on wings along the drive to the country road that I knew would lead to Redbarrow. I drew in great breaths of crisp clean air and looked with appreciation at the grassy meadows that I could see over the blossom covered hedgerows, and listened to the birds who were singing in the bushes and the trees.

My plan was to find some young company to chat to. I was fed up with the grey hair brigade who made up the residents at West Park and only wanted to talk to me about where they had been that day. Lucky for them that they could sample the delights of the Pembrokeshire countryside, while I was stuck indoors and couldn't feel the warmth of the sun. If I managed to find the pub' that Philip had told me about, surely there would be someone around my age. I knew I was only fifteen, but the makeup I was wearing made me look older and I'd put on some clip on earrings, which made me look very grownup I thought.

After tramping along in shoes that had two inch heels on, I finally made it to the Partridge Inn. It was closed, but the grocers was open and I went inside to buy a packet of Woodbines and hopefully a bottle of beer.

'New round here, are you?', asked the woman behind the counter. I nodded.

'Thought so, not seen you in this neck of the woods before. Ten Woodbines and a bottle of Pale Ale, is it? Do you want a box of matches as well?'

'Oh, yes, thank you, I've forgotten my lighter. What time does the pub' open, only I rather hoped to find some young company? I'm working at West Park and it's rather dull over there.'

'Ah, it's a pity our Maggie's away in Tenby, she's about your age,

120

nineteen in the summer. She has a job in a hardware shop, but lodges with my sister during the week. Pub' doesn't open until seven and they're mostly my age or older that drink in there. Farm labourers and the like that live round here.'

'Oh,' I replied, my spirits plummeting as I paid the woman for my purchases, then stepped out onto the road again.

Dad had really sent me to the back and beyond, hadn't he?, I thought, as I lit up a cigarette, then took a swig of the cool hoppy tasting drink. I coughed as both smoke and liquid hit the back of my throat. I'd not had a ciggie for quite a few months. So this was all I had to escape to, a small country village with a mostly closed pub'.

So I spent the rest of my free time at West Park, walking around the formal gardens and counting the days until it was time to go home.

On the morning of my departure I caused ructions in the kitchen, when I asked my cousin for the wages I felt was due.

'What wages?', Pamela said waspishly. 'You've had your bed and board and I didn't make you pay for any breakages, which I was quite entitled to do.'

'I've worked hard for you, Pamela, you've had my heart and soul and the sweat off my brow and if you don't give me any wages, how am I going to pay my Dad back for my train fare? It came to two pounds, seven and sixpence and I also need money to buy some sandwiches for my journey.'

My cousin looked mutinous for a moment, then after glancing at her disapproving looking husband, she took her purse out of her handbag.

'Here's two pounds, ten shillings then. Now, Philip, get her out of my sight.'

'Pamela, there's no need to be like that with Vivienne,' he retorted angrily. 'From what I've seen, she's worked harder than any of the girls we've had here before, so at least be civil with your cousin before she makes that long journey home.'

'Yes, of course, I'm sorry, come here and give me a kiss. It's because I'm short of help now that you're going back that I'm feeling snappy and of course you've been a great help to me. Call in at that agency, Philip, when you're in Tenby and see if they've got any hotel workers on their books.'

I was glad to make my escape, what an old shrew my cousin had turned out to be.

What her husband Philip saw in her, I would never know? He had taken the trouble to chat with me, mostly over a whisky or two in the Bar when they had closed up for the evening, I had found his wit agreeable and he didn't treat me like a silly little girl.

I waved goodbye to him after he dropped me off at the station. Strangely I felt sad that I might never see him again.

The platform of Tenby station was awash with soldiers, lined up in readiness to embark on the waiting train. Fearful that I would end up standing for most of my journey, I made a dash for a quiet compartment, after handing over my return ticket to be clipped by the man who stood at the barrier.

I sat in trepidation, hoping that the soldiers would be directed to designated carriages, but just my luck, two dozen of them swarmed into my corridor, grabbing seats or squatting on the floor, shouting through the windows at the top of their voices to others of their unit, who were still waiting patiently to board the train.

'Can we come and sit with you?', asked one of the soldiers, as he put his head through the open door of my compartment. 'We won't be any trouble, me and my mate Charlie, we're the most agreeable of men.'

I laughed into the dark eyes of the most handsomest man I had ever seen and my heart began to somersault, as he came to sit beside me. His mate, Charlie sat opposite, quietly thankful to have the company of a pretty young lady who he could feast his eyes on.

'Going far?', asked the young soldier, who if he hadn't got his hair cut so short he was a dead ringer for Elvis. 'Oh, sorry, my name is Private Thomas Dickinson, this here is Private Charlie

Wright and we're returning to our barracks in Shrewsbury, after manoeuvres in the countryside over the weekend.'

'Well, my name is Vivienne Dockerty and I'm travelling to Chester, after having spent the last two weeks employed at my cousin's hotel and I'm going home for a rest.'

'What is it you do then? Are you a waitress, a chambermaid, a kitchen assistant? No, you're a receptionist, aren't you? You're far too pretty to be wasted behind the scenes.'

I dimpled at his compliment and decided to keep up the pretence of being a receptionist. What did it matter anyway, I'd never be seeing this young soldier again?

The three of us sat chatting for about an hour or so, mostly about the latest records or the films that were showing at the pictures, though I didn't have a lot to offer on that score, as I hadn't been to see a film since a tenth birthday treat to see Carousel. Charlie seemingly a bit bored decided to get up and stretch his legs in the corridor a little later.

Thomas offered me a cigarette, then after lighting it up for me, put his arm daringly around my shoulder.

'You know, Vivienne,' he said in a flattering way. 'I've been searching for someone like you for a long time. You're pretty, easy to talk to, you dress smart and I love your hair. Do you think we could write to each other and maybe meet up one weekend in Chester? I haven't got a girlfriend, I'm choosy who I go out with, but I think I should settle down a bit now that I'm twenty one. Come here, give us a kiss to seal my commitment. Have you got a photo' I could put above my bed?'

I shook my head, then settled back to endure his attentions. I hadn't got much choice in the matter and he was the handsomest of men. Surprisingly I enjoyed his kisses, his lips were soft and warm and I felt safe in his arms as he cuddled me to him, doing nothing to cause me alarm.

Then all too soon he drew away from me, to scribble his address on a scrap of paper he had found in his pocket, pleading that I write to him as soon as I got home.

I said I would and blew him kisses from the corridor window, as his platoon marched smartly out of Shrewsbury station.

I settled back in my seat again intending to mull things over, was it possible that the handsome soldier had only been a dream?

Father laughed when I told him that I had been buried alive in the countryside and been treated like a slave. He told me I could keep the money that Pamela had given me as a reward for sticking it out with her. He wasn't so happy, when I let it slip that I had been in the company of a platoon of soldiers on my train journey home and warned me of the perils of being too friendly with people, especially men in uniform.

With a sinking heart I sent a letter to Private Thomas Dickinson at Shrewsbury Barracks. There was no way my Dad would let me meet a soldier for a date in Chester, so I might as well put the lad out of his misery and tell him the truth, that I was only fifteen, still at school and had only been helping my cousin out temporarily. Sorry if I mislead him and hoped he'd find the girl of his dreams soon. I didn't put my address at the top of the letter, because it looked as if I was expecting a reply.

CHAPTER 6

It was back to school on a rainy Tuesday and I squelched my way through the puddles to the main building where the Headmistress had her study. I had come to a decision about my future and I had bravely made an appointment to see the dragon in her den.

The office lady had booked me in to see Miss Preston after the dinner break, which had given me the whole morning to go over the plan I had in mind.

I was going to give notice that I intended to leave school at the end of the summer term. What was the point of prolonging the agony, when I hated the place and the constraints it put on me? I knew I was going to do badly in the mock exams', except maybe for English and Religious studies, but those two subjects would be the only ones I would get a pass in.

I had made a mental list of my talents, in order to see what kind of job I would be suited to. I was friendly, though could only tolerate people in the short term, I could tell a good tale and liked a joke, I was punctual and extremely honest and thought that I would be hardworking if I was interested in the job.

Mother had once suggested that I look for a job as an Almoner in a hospital, seeing me as a sympathetic person to those less fortunate than myself, but that would entail passing five O' levels and I hadn't told my mother of my plan. I knew there would be outrage on my parents part, especially as they had gone without to pay for school uniforms and equipment for both me and my sister, but I was determined to leave the school as soon as the term was over, even if it meant taking an unskilled job.

'So, Vivienne, to what do I owe this pleasure?'

Miss Preston waved me into her study and told me to make

myself comfortable on a chair.

'I've decided I want to leave here at the end of term, Miss Preston,' I said quickly. 'I've never liked it here and I think it's a waste of time staying on for my O' levels.'

'Oh, I see,' the headmistress said, looking quite taken aback.

'But I think you are perfectly capable of passing all five subjects if you were to put the effort in.'

'Well, I don't think so and it's me that has to sit the exams. I don't want to wait around for another year when I could be out earning money.'

'And what do your parents think of this, Vivienne? I'm sure that they won't be happy with your decision and neither will the Education department.'

'What has the Education department got to do with me leaving?' I asked, surprised at them having anything to do with it. 'I'll be sixteen in August and I can finish school if I want to then.'

'Ah, but you are not sixteen until August 2nd and according to our superiors you can only leave school this year if you were born before August 1st.'

'That's rubbish,' I replied scornfully. 'Just because I was born a day later means I've got to come here for another year?'

The headmistress nodded.

'Well they won't make me, I just won't turn up in September and then what will they do?'

'They will send a truancy officer around to see your family and probably the matter will go to court and your parents will be fined. Give it a chance, Vivienne, I know you can pass your O' levels if you put your mind to it. I have every faith in you, you know.'

'Mmm, we'll see about that. Thank you for seeing me, Miss Preston.'

'Right,' said Father, after he had received a letter from the headmistress telling my parents of the interview she had recently had with their daughter.

'I'll tell you what I'm going to do, Vivienne. Your Mum has enough on her plate at the moment, what with her Aunty dying and having to arrange the funeral, so I'm going to take you in hand myself. You'd think you would have learnt some lessons at your cousin's in Tenby, on what kind of work there is for people without qualifications, but I'm going to arrange some interviews for you and then you can see for yourself. I'm going to telephone Miss Preston and arrange some time off for you and first we'll go to the hospital in Heswall and see what you have to do to become a nurse. Then I'm going to take you to the Army Recruiting office seeing as you like dallying with soldiers, then perhaps we'll go to the Co-op and see what they'll offer you there. If you're still determined to turn your back on your education after all that, then so be it, but don't moan to me when you realize what chances you've thrown away and all you've got is peanuts in your purse.'

'I don't want to do any of those things, Dad. I thought maybe something in selling, perhaps have my own business one day.'

'Pipe dreams, Vivienne. Look at me, I'm self – employed now and you don't see me with great amounts of money rolling in. No, maybe after I've taken you around these places you'll come to your senses and see what a good position you're in.'

The Matron at the hospital was very pleasant. Yes, they did have vacancies for Probationer nurses, but was it possible that a girl with my education would want to start her career by swilling out bedpans? I would be better off finishing my studies and then if I was still determined to work at the hospital I would be able to apply to be an SRN.

The Recruiting Sergeant at the Army office was askance at the very idea of me considering joining up as a Private, when with five O'levels under my belt I could train to be an Officer!

I was only given an application form at the Co- op, but by that time I had decided I didn't want to end up with a lifetime of stacking shelves.

So with a heavy heart I went back to the County Grammar school, still determined to leave at the end of term, but not sure now how I was going to achieve my aim.

Once again the house was in mourning, because Mother's Aunt Jenny had passed away. Like most young people I viewed her death with sympathy, but the old lady had been eighty five anyway, so I couldn't understand why my mother was full of misery.

I was feeling bored and frustrated. My studies were a nuisance, because each time I went over a subject I couldn't seem to retain the facts in my head. I toyed with the idea of running away somewhere, perhaps up to the Outer Hebrides where my father would never think to look for me, but I would need some money for the train fare and I hadn't got any. I needed a job, but my father wouldn't hear of me taking casual work while I was studying for my exams.

Rejoining the dancing classes was out, because that Ricky would probably still be lurking there. Maybe I should look for a girlfriend, so that we could do things together, like swapping clothes or making up each other's faces, or perhaps spending the day on Hilbre Island. I'd never got my wish to go over there. But since Sally had moved with her family to Liverpool, I'd never really been comfortable in another girl's company. At school they were swots or too toffee nosed to want to be friends with someone like me. They mostly lived in posh houses and their mothers drove them to school in the car. I did have girls to sit with at lunch time to discuss boys, makeup or fashion with if I wanted, but no one I could put my trust in and tell them all my cares.

I wondered whether I should go back to the church youth club? Colin would have got the message by now and maybe that dishy Irish fellow had come back again to stay with his cousin, Mark. I asked Audrey would she like to go to the youth club with me, but my sister had her own friends now from her grammar school and got invited to visit their houses to play.

I was welcomed back by the vicar, who had noticed me hesitating after the church service, wondering whether I should stay behind at the youth club or make my way home. He seemed pleased to see me and glad that I could make up the numbers, as not many teenagers from around the housing estate were willing to come.

'We haven't seen Colin for some time, Vivienne,' he said. 'You'll know of course that he joined the Army and I have heard he's been posted to Germany. Pity really, because he was such an exemplary kind of lad, but do come inside and meet a few newcomers and of course there's Mark and he's brought his cousin with him, though I do wish they'd attend the church service first.'

My legs turned to jelly when I saw who was in the church hall. What was it about Sean that fascinated me? Was it the lilt that he had in his voice, or his happy wide grin, or had it been his uniform that first attracted me? He wasn't that handsome really. His short brown wiry hair was beginning to thin over his forehead, he was stocky and of medium height, not tall like the boys I usually admired, but his green eyes were twinkly and he had dimples when he smiled and he had an easy going attitude, as if he hadn't got a care.

Mark came rushing over when he saw me, to ask me where I had been?

'We missed you, Vivienne, didn't we?', he said as he turned to the other teenagers that had been there before. 'Anyway come over and sit with us in this corner. Do you remember Sean, my cousin from Ireland? Well, he's staying at my house on a seven day pass, so perhaps we could do something together during the time that he's here.'

'Nice to see you again, Vivienne,' said Sean. 'I think the vicar is working up to an announcement, but perhaps we could chat later on or maybe I could walk you home.'

Walk me home! I couldn't think of a more agreeable past time, even if it meant getting a shouting at from my father, who I knew would be waiting at the bus stop at the end of our lane at nine o'-clock.

The evening passed in a whirl, I hardly listened to anything the vicar said, kept losing at draughts because I couldn't concentrate and wasn't remotely interested in the discussion of the merits of The Beatles. Who cared about an up and coming band from Liverpool when I had Sean walking me home?

But things never seem to turn out how you're expecting them to, because Mark decided he wanted to keep us company and tagged along at the side of Sean and I, as we walked the two miles back to Whaley Lane.

'Are you off to school in the morning, Vivienne?', asked Sean as Father appeared in the distance, leaning against the bus shelter wall.

I nodded quickly, keeping an eye on my Dad to see if he had noticed me walking along with two lads.

'Then how about if I got on your bus at Arrowe Brook and escorted you there? We could have a chat, just the two of us and make some plans for next weekend.'

'Oh, that would be smashing, Sean,' I said quickly. 'I catch the ten past eight from Whaley Lane, so I guess it will get to you by twenty past. I have to go now you two. Unless you're both good runners, I suggest you don't walk me to my Dad.'

The next morning as Sean had promised, he was waiting for my bus as it came along Arrowe Brook Road. My heart was pounding as he hopped aboard, then came to sit beside me and I hoped that he didn't care I was wearing a soppy uniform.

'That colour suits you,' he smiled, hoping that he would dispel my embarrassment. 'So what have you got in your satchel then, a few nice egg and salad cream sandwiches, or some boring study books?'

'Boring study books. I have to stay in and have the school dinners, as my mother thinks I'm skinny and need building up.'

'You look healthy enough to me, Vivienne. In fact, I'd say you've got a glow about you this morning. Ah, I like mornings, they're the best part of the day.'

'Do you have to get up very early in the Airforce, Sean?'

'Yep, up at six every morning, but I've always been used to getting up early as my parents have a farm.'

'Oh, do tell me about living on a farm, Sean. Do you have any animals or do you grow things like wheat or barley? I've decided that one day I'm going to visit Ireland. It sounds so romantic..... the Emerald Isle.'

So, for the next few days Sean got on the bus every morning, got off with me at my bus change, then travelled with me to school. I didn't inquire what he did with himself for the rest of the day, as I was so delighted to be in his company. We talked of many things, though mostly it was Sean talking, as he told me about the beauty of the lakes in Killarney, of the golden beaches on the west coast, the little villages that he passed through on his way to catch the ferryboat and about the Wicklow mountains where he had taken holidays as a child.

I was spellbound and could envisage a life with Sean, on his parents farm in Killarney. I hoped that he saw me as his girlfriend, especially after that first morning when he started to hold my hand.

He looked so cute in his green and orange striped mohair sweater and I liked the way it tickled, when on the third morning he took me in his arms. In the bus shelter of course, not on the bus.

I was wearing my school uniform and it would never do to bring shame on the County Grammar school.

Then all too soon it was Saturday and after taking me to a Milk Bar in Birkenhead for a coffee, we said a fond farewell. With me waving goodbye, as Sean boarded the Chester train at Woodside station, the scene was reminiscent of the film, 'From here to Eternity'. He promised to write, though he said he wasn't very good at sending letters and said he would be back in a few weeks time to take me dancing. He suggested that I might make myself a dress in Shamrock green, so that he would feel proud to have me on his arm. I promised that I'd see to it, but wondered how I was going to afford the material.

Mother had been to see her Aunty Jenny's solicitor. Everything that had belonged to the old lady was left to my mother in the Will. There was the bungalow in Seaview Lane, the furniture and a little in a bank account. The bungalow was to be valued by an estate agent and eventually put up for sale.

'That is when they get round to this bloody Probate,' Father remarked, when my parents started to discuss what they were going to do with this unexpected windfall.

'Well, I think we should sell up both houses and move to Blackpool,' Mother said enthusiastically. 'We'll get a guest house, Eddie, and you can do the cooking and me and the girls will do the cleaning and waiting on.'

'What!', said Father in astonishment. 'If you think for one moment that I'm going to throw all our money into a venture that could bring us to bankruptcy, you must be crazy. You only have to look at what happened to my father to see you'd be on a sticky wicket right away.'

'A nice bungalow then overlooking the River Dee at Heswall, I can see myself going for long walks every morning with the dog and think of all that lovely sea air.'

'Well, I think you should hand over the money to me, Irene, if you're having such flights of fancy. I think we should pay the mortgage off on this place, then spend some money on visiting Gina in America.'

That swayed it for Mum. 'Oh, could we, Eddie, visit Gina, I mean? You can have the money anyway, you know I'm not very good at that sort of thing, but to see our Gina and our little granddaughter. Would we fly in an aeroplane or would we go by sea? Do you think I could give our Gina a ring tonight and tell her she might be seeing us soon? Oh, just think, now they've moved to San Francisco we can go at any time of the year, because they have sunshine all the time. Though what about the girls, Eddie, Vivienne has got her exams coming up and Audrey's far too young to be left alone?'

'Both of them are too young to be left alone, Irene, but I'll have a word with my mother who can come around on a daily basis to keep an eye on them. Anyway, it could be months before we get to see our Gina, don't forget there's this Probate thing to deal with first.'

I was coming home from school one afternoon, when a cheeky bus conductor began to give me a chat up line.

'I see you've lost your boyfriend then. What's up, had a tiff or has he gone off to pastures new?'

'None of your business,' I replied huffily. 'Anyway, I'm not talking to bus conductors, you're only here to take our fares.'

'Oh, dear, someone's in a bad mood, aren't they? Well never mind, if you're ever looking for a replacement you can ring my bell anytime.'

Cheeky monkey, I thought. Ring his bell indeed and I'll be stuck up against a shelter in Arrowe Park like I was last time. If I knew who to report him to, I would do. I'd get a later bus home tomorrow and then I wouldn't have to put up with this sort of thing.

But the same bus conductor was on duty again when I boarded the bus at Singleton Avenue and as I was dying to get home to use the loo, I had no option but to get on his bus again.

'Are you doing anything on Friday night, Vivienne?' he asked cheerily. 'It is Vivienne isn't it, only I heard your ex-boyfriend calling you that when he got on the bus at Arrowe Brook?'

'He isn't my ex-boyfriend, we're still going out together, but he works away so I don't get to see him very often.'

'So you'll be free on Friday night then? I thought that perhaps we could go to watch a film together, they're showing G.I. Blues again at the Ritz.'

'I never saw it the first time, but anyway I'm not allowed out without my father meeting the person I'm going with and he certainly wouldn't be happy if I was going out with you.'

'Ouch, you've got a way with words, haven't you, Vivienne? Anyway, don't forget if you need a shoulder to cry on when your boyfriend chucks you over, let me know.'

'Why would you think he's going to chuck me?'

'Because if I had a girlfriend like you, I would never let you out of my sight and you don't know what he's up to when he's away from you.'

I tossed my head and refused to speak to the conductor for the rest of the journey, but his words had got me rattled and I wondered if Sean had got a girlfriend back in Ireland, or even in Anglesey? He hadn't written, though I had put that down to him flying about all over the place, but I resolved to ask his cousin if he indeed had a girlfriend tucked away somewhere?

Mark was at a loss for words, when I asked him over a cup of tea at the youth club. I had made a special journey that Sunday, because without Sean being there, it would be a very boring place.

'Well, I don't really know, Vivienne. He hasn't talked about anybody to me, though before he went back to Wales this time, he said his next leave was being spent at his parent's farm. Did he tell you he was coming back at all to stay at our house? You never know with Sean, he pops up at a moments notice, though of course he's welcome to stay at anytime.'

'But does he have a girlfriend in Ireland or Anglesey, Mark?'

'I'm the wrong person to ask, Vivienne, you should ask him yourself. Do you want his address, you can ask him in a letter?'

'I've got his address and I've already written to him, but he hasn't replied yet, so I can't send him another one or he'll think I'm chasing him.'

There was a letter waiting for me one Saturday morning as I came down for breakfast, but it wasn't from Sean, though it did have a Welsh postage stamp on the envelope. It was from a girl I had met on a Sunday school trip when I had gone for the day to Prestatyn.

Dear Vivienne, (the girl had written).
I don't know if you'll remember me but we met at Prestatyn when you were on a trip with your Sunday school. We had a great couple of hours together didn't we, playing rounders on the sands and eating our sandwiches in the dunes, then spending all our money on the one armed bandits until your teacher came and told you off for playing on a gambling machine? I remember that day so vividly, because we had such fun together and I found your address recently in my old gabardine mac and thought I must get in touch with you.

I'm leaving school in July and start working in a hotel as a trainee receptionist at the beginning of August, but I wondered if you would like to meet me in Chester one Saturday? We could catch up with everything we've been doing since we were twelve years old and perhaps have lunch in the Market Hall. I'd love to see you again as you made me laugh.

Write to me at the above address.

From your friend.

Kathy Taylor.

A girlfriend at last, I thought, fancy Kathy writing to me out of the blue like that. I tried to visualize what Kathy had looked like. Did she have brown hair in a pony tail or short fair hair and buck teeth? No matter. I'd show my Dad the letter and see if he would allow me to go to Chester one Saturday.

'Well, I can't see the harm in it seeing as she was on a trip organized by the Sunday school', my dad said. 'So when do you want to go, Vivienne? Here take this fiver and treat yourself, but I don't want you chatting up lads when you get there. The day is for renewing your friendship with this girl and doing a bit of shopping. I'm trusting you, Vivienne, to behave yourself so don't let me down.'

I wrote to Kathy immediately and dashed down to the local Post office so that the letter would reach her first thing Monday. I said that I would meet her outside the cathedral at eleven o'clock the following Saturday and if I hadn't received a reply in the negative, then I looked forward to seeing her then.

Strangely enough the absence of a letter from Sean didn't seemed to have lowered my spirits, now that I was to have a girlfriend my life had brightened up.

I paced up and down the cobbled street in front of Chester Cathedral the following Saturday.

I was dressed in a summer frock I had made herself, a round necked sleeveless A- line in a black and white cotton fabric that came just above the knee. With it I wore a black edge to edge long sleeved jacket that was waist length, a work of art that had taken weeks to make because of the fiddly insertion of the shoulder seams.

My watch said it was twenty past eleven and I scanned the crowds of people who were passing, worried that I wouldn't recognize Kathy as it had been nearly three years since we last met.

My feet had begun to ache in my shiny black stiletto heels and I looked for a bench that I could sit down on. I would give Kathy until half past and then have a look around the shops on my own.

Suddenly a tall girl wearing a red polka dot halter necked dress, came dashing up the street from the direction of the train station.

'Viv', it's me, Kathy,' she shouted, oblivious of the curious stares from people who were passing her by.

'Sorry, Vivienne, the train was late, there must be a football match on today because it was full of men with scarves and rattles,' she said breathlessly. 'I'd know you anywhere, you haven't changed a bit. Well, maybe you're more grownup, Viv'. Oh, I say, I love your hair, it's so neat and perfect.

Mine wants cutting so I just put it up in a pony tail.'

'Well, you've certainly changed,' I replied, glad that this wasn't the short fair haired girl with the buck teeth. 'You've grown taller and dare I say it, filled out more?'

'Yes, I've done rather well in that department, haven't I? 38DD last time I measured myself.'

'Oh well, can't have looks and boobs I suppose,' I countered, looking at my own 34B chest. 'Anyway, what do you want to do first, go for a coffee or have a mooch round the shops?'

'Let's have a coffee first at Cottles, eh Viv', then we could have a look in Brown's, though I have to say I can't afford their prices, the Market hall is more my style?'

'I love your halter neck, Kathy, did you make it yourself?'I asked curiously, looking at the neat stitching.

'Yes, I made it myself, can't run to buying off the peg until I earn some wages, but my Dad said I look a tart in it, because it only just covers my bum.'

I smiled, as we walked together through the crowds onto Eastgate, that was just the kind of remark my own Dad would make if I appeared before him in a short dress like Kathy's.

'Well, seeing as we both like to make our own clothes then, how about helping me to choose some material that I need for a dance that I'll be going to in the next couple of months?' I asked. 'It has to be in a shade of Shamrock green, as this boy who has invited me comes from Ireland and he has asked me to wear his favourite colour when we go on our date.'

'Oh, how exciting! Have you got a boyfriend then, Viv'? My Dad said he'll shoot anyone who comes near me with his shotgun. I can't wait until I'm older then I can go on dates.'

'I think he might be my boyfriend, but I'm not so sure about him. Anyway let's have that coffee and I'll tell you all. His name's Sean by the way and he's stationed in Anglesey.'

I had a lovely day with Kathy. We got on so well together that when we parted, each going to a different platform to catch our trains home, it had been decided that I was going to ask permission for Kathy to come and stay at my house for a weekend in the summer. Before or after the French girls' return visit it didn't really matter, as I had decided to ignore them anyway and let Audrey take care of them.

Meantime, Kathy and I were going to keep in touch by letter and exchange each other's news; while in my shopping bag there was a length of green satin material. The assistant had said it was Shamrock green and that was good enough for me!

Finally a letter came from Sean, full of apologies for not writing before, but he had whizzed over to Killarney on his last leave to see his folks and thought he would wait until he knew when his next leave would be before he wrote to me. There wasn't much to put in a letter anyway, as all he was doing was putting in the flying hours he needed to get his pilot's license and once done, he was going to put in for a posting abroad, as he fancied somewhere hot like Dubai or Singapore.

That would be even better than living in Ireland, I thought in my naivety. I could just imagine swanning around in a yashmak or a sari, having cool drinks ready for Sean at our apartment when he came home to me tired from work.

I pulled out all the stops to get the dance frock finished. It was to have a low necked rounded bodice, gathered at the waist and then falling in flouncy folds down to my knee. I decided on a cap sleeve, then changed my mind and made a matching bolero instead.

His letter had said he would be taking me to the Mecca Ballroom in Birkenhead on the first Friday in July. I counted the days off on mother's calender, it was the Friday after my exams!

'So why the rush to finish off this dance frock, Vivienne?' Father asked, as he heard me one evening pleading with Mother to help me line the bolero with a darker shade of material.

'It's nothing to do with that boy who wrote to you from Wales is it, because you've got your exams soon and you should be studying instead?'

'No, Dad, it's for the celebration dance that we're having when we've got the exams over with. It's on the first Friday in July and it's being held in the Town Hall.'

'It seems a funny place to invite a lot of youngsters to. You'd think they'd hold it in the Main Hall at your school. It's got a wooden floor hasn't it, just the place for a Social I would have thought? I bet you're glad you went to dancing classes, Vivienne. I suppose they will have invited the lads in from the Boys school, so you watch yourself young lady and don't make a fool of yourself. Do you want me to run you down to Birkenhead that night, so that you don't get your nice new frock creased from sitting on the bus?'

'No, you're all right Dad,' I said hastily. 'I don't mind going on the bus and I'll have my coat over my outfit so I'm sure it won't get too creased.'

'Well, here's a couple of pounds to buy yourself some refreshments and I want you home on the last bus, so that you're in here for twenty past eleven. Remember, I'll be waiting on the corner of the lane to meet you off it, so don't be letting me down.'

Finally the great day arrived, though it came at the end of a lot of pen sucking for me as I sat my five mock O' levels that week in the school's Main Hall. I thought I'd done all right in English Lit', English Language and Religious studies, but what was all that about 'Contour lines in Europe' and 'Population Growth' in my Geography paper and where the heck was the 'Sugar Loaf Mountain', was it in Africa or Argentina? My History paper would be borderline, I knew little about the Battle of Agincourt or the kings who had reigned before Henry V111, but never mind I was free at last and counting the hours until I could put on my beautiful satin dress!

I wore it with silver peep toe sandals and rinsed my hair in a beer solution, so that when it dried it shone. I went sparingly with the pan stick and the black penciled lines round my eyes, as Sean had said he liked a girl to look natural, not like a whore on the game.

My heart was beating madly, as I tottered on my high heels down to catch the bus and buttoned up the front of my coat so that he wouldn't see the dress straight off. Tonight was going to be magic, Sean would look at me and be blown away. He'd probably tell me that he loved me and couldn't wait until the day we got hitched!

Sean was waiting outside Central Station as I got off the bus at Argylle Street. He gave me a wolf whistle, then ran across the road to envelop me in a hug. Oh, it was so good to see him again. I leant against him, breathing in his masculinity and admiring the black evening suit he was wearing with a white frilled front shirt.

'Well, let me see it then,' he said, trying to tug at my coat buttons so that he could see the dress.

'No, you must wait until I've put my coat in the cloakroom and then you can see it,' I said giddily. 'Come on, I'm dying to get to there, I've never been inside a dance hall before.'

We walked together holding hands and I thought I must be the happiest girl in the world. We were going to enjoy this evening together, especially as he had just given me a present. It was a brooch etched beautifully in silver work on a burgundy coloured background. He told me that the picture on it was from the Book of Kells, an ancient manuscript written by monks from medieval times. So he had even thought to bring me a present, that sounded like commitment from my point of view.

I put my coat with the cloakroom attendant, then made my way to the Ladies so I could tidy up my hair. Sean was going to the Bar to get the drinks in and I was looking forward to his reaction, when he saw me in my Shamrock green dance dress that I had made just to please him.

I took a deep breath and walked confidently to the table where he was sitting, taking no notice of the silver ball that was suspended from the ceiling, I just wanted his reaction to my beautiful dress. He must have really liked it, because he was giving me a cool appraising stare.

'So what do you think?', I asked, giving him a twirl so that he could see how snugly the bolero fitted. It had taken hours of mine and Mother's time to get it just right, so that it didn't strain across my chest.

'It isn't the colour I asked you to wear.'

'What? Of course it is, you said wear a dress in Shamrock green.'

'I said Emerald green, you eejit. I come from the Emerald Isle and I wanted you to wear Emerald green!'

'Oh.'

I felt my knees buckle under me and tears started welling up in my eyes. How could I have been so stupid? Of course I should have made the dress in Emerald green, what had I been thinking of?

Though my eyes were blurred with tears I could see the look on Sean's face. It was a mixture of anger and distaste for me. I looked away, wondering whether to run from the dance hall or stick it out, hoping that he would forgive me my mistake. He got up from the table, picking up his pint of Guinness and wandered off to the Bar again, as if he had come out for the night on his own. I sank down into the chair that he had vacated, rummaging around in my handbag for a hanky to wipe the tears from my eyes.

'Do you feel like a dance?', a quiet voice asked. I looked up to see a man staring down at me.

I shook my head and said 'No, thank you'. He smiled at me shyly then walked away.

'Hey, who was that?', asked Sean, as he came over to me minutes later, after he had watched the man from his position at the Bar.

'I don't know him, he just came over and he asked me did I want to dance.'

'Well, I'll be the one who does the dancing with you. Come on, let's bop to 'Bye Bye Love' by the Everley Brothers, though it might be appropriate in our case.'

'What do you mean by that?', I asked bristling with sudden anger. 'I worked long and hard on this dress and if it's not good enough for you, then bugger off and find someone else who's got a dress on that's more to your taste.'

I got up and ran across to the Cloakroom. How could an evening that I had looked so much forward to, turn out to be such a disaster? Well, I wasn't going to be treated like a child by him, I had enough of that at home.

I threw my coat on and walked back to the dance floor to let him see that I'd had enough of his behaviour and that I was going to leave. Sean was standing by the Bar, talking to a girl with red shoulder length hair and would you believe it, she was wearing a slinky evening dress in Emerald green!

I ran down the road to the bus stop full of indignation, with angry thoughts leaping around my head, as I thought of the way I had been treated by men. Why did I keep falling for them, I hated them? I'd become a nun and dedicate myself to a convent! No more listening to men's silvery tongues and succumbing to their advances.

I felt calmer now as I waited for the bus, my fingers feeling the coolness of his brooch in my pocket. Well, at least I'd had a present from him, which was more than I'd had from any other man.

My bus came in view and I breathed a sigh of relief when I saw it. I'd go home and take off my finery, then sit on the sofa with a blanket around me and watch a bit of late night T.V.

Then suddenly there came the sound of running footsteps. I looked over horrified to see Sean running full pelt along the road, as the bus drew up before me.

'Vivienne, wait, I'm sorry. Stay and we'll talk it over,' he shouted breathlessly.

'Get stuffed,' I shouted back, as I swung myself onto the platform, watching as he slowed his pace and shrugged his shoulders at me.

'I see you've dumped him then,' said a cheeky voice from the top of the bus staircase. 'Well done, Vivienne. I knew it would happen, now perhaps you'll let me have a date with you.'

CHAPTER 7

The French exchange students had gone back home, thank goodness and I excitedly arranged a weekend for Kathy to come and stay with me.

Mother had said that everything felt flat now that Renate and Mireille had gone back to France, but that was because she had practiced her school- girl French on them and had taken them to the pictures and to Liverpool on the ferryboat. Father had done his part too, he had driven them in the car to Chester Zoo and over to the sands at Southport, but I hadn't gone with them. I had left it to Audrey to accompany the girls, as I still felt annoyed at the way I had been treated, after I had walked in on that orgy that afternoon in France.

The end of the school term was in sight and also the dreaded exam results. I kept looking for signs from my teachers, to see if they knew whether I had passed or not, but none of them were willing to give the game away.

Anyway, I didn't really care, I was still intent on leaving, but I hadn't come up with a plan. I decided to relax and look forward to Kathy's visit, especially as Father had said he would treat us to a hair do each, at his cousin's hair salon.

The long awaited day arrived and I went with my father to Heswall Hills station to meet Kathy off the Chester train. I could barely breathe from excitement, as I saw my friend come walking through the station gate, holding her vanity case in one hand and a small suitcase in the other.

Kathy looked so poised and confident. She was wearing wide legged trousers in a creamy coloured fabric and a cowl necked blouse in a pretty peach; she had pinned her brown hair up into soft curls above her head and was wearing cream and gold strappy sandals upon her feet.

I ran up to hug her, then introduced Kathy proudly to my waiting Dad.

'Oh, we're going to have such fun together, Kathy,' I said, as Father put my friend's cases into the boot of the car. 'Mum is treating us to fish and chips from the Chippy, we're to pick them up on the way home. I thought tonight we could listen to my L.P's on my record player and then tomorrow we're going to my Dad's cousin's hair salon and she's going to do our hair. Then, we can go shopping in Birkenhead and in the evening we can go to the pictures and on Sunday we can go to Hilbre Island. Dad says it's going to be a sunny weekend.'

'Phew, it doesn't sound very restful, Vivienne,' Father exclaimed, as he listened to me chattering to my friend in the back of the car. 'Perhaps Kathy would like to do something different, maybe go for a nice walk in Arrowe Park?'

'No, I'm happy, Mr. Dockerty, with everything Vivienne has said. I'm going to be starting work in a few weeks time, so I'll be pleased to do all the things that have been arranged for me. It'll be something to look back on if I have boring days.'

'Boring, Kathy? I wouldn't be bored if I was training to be a hotel receptionist,' I said enviously. 'I can't wait to leave school, but I'm not allowed to yet, am I Dad?'

'No, certainly not, Vivienne. It would be a waste of your education to get a job as a hotel receptionist. Now let me concentrate on my driving or I'll never get you home.'

The first part of the weekend was perfect, we sat and listened to music in the bedroom, while Kathy cut out two bikini's from some of my black and white flowery material that I had left over from my summer frock. Then she sewed them on Mother's machine while I looked on in awe; each bikini was made in half an hour and was a perfect fit for Kathy, but my top made me look flat.

Then on Saturday we went to my second cousin's hair salon and I had my hair cut into a shorter bob, that I could wear either behind my ears or in front of. Kathy only had a trim because she liked her long hair the way it was.

In the evening we sat through Dr. Zivago with Julie Christie and Omah Sharif, eating choc' ices and giggling at the couples that were necking on the back row. Then came Sunday morning when I was about to achieve my dream.

Father ran us in the car to the West Kirby Marina, with dire warnings of what would befall us if we got caught by the incoming tide. We took cheese sandwiches, fizzy pop and sun hats in case the sun got too fierce over on the island. Kathy had bought some sun tan oil, when we had visited Boots the Chemists, in Birkenhead.

There was a crowd of people setting out for Hilbre Island that morning, mostly teenagers with their minds set on a sun tan and the adventure of sitting on an island while the sea swirled around them for eight hours. It was going to be fun and many had brought their transistor radios. The music was blaring out so loudly, that people passing by were putting their hands to their ears.

The Marine Manager stood with his pocket watch in his hand and after receiving some sort of signal from the island, he let it be known that it was safe to travel over. The crowd set off with a whoop of joy, Kathy and I amongst them, and within minutes the beach was clear of young people, leaving just a few little children making castles in the sand.

It took twenty minutes of sloshing through the puddles and mud flats that had been left by the outgoing tide, but first Little Isle was passed, then Middle Isle, until we reached Hilbre Island at last.

Oh, the joy of it, as we all eagerly clambered up the rocky cliffs to find the best positions on the grassy mounds that covered the island. We shouted to the people that were lagging behind to be quick, as we could see the gully's filling up. Breathlessly we all collapsed into assorted groups, friends people had come with or ones that they had made on the way.

Kathy and I found ourselves with a group of boys, who had seemed to tag along with us as we had been walking across the sands.

'Aren't you Vivienne Dockerty?', one of them said to me. 'You live in Whaley Lane, don't you? I live in Thingwall Drive, just up the road from you.'

'You're not Alan Roberts, are you?', I said, recognizing the boy suddenly. 'I haven't seen you for years, not since you went to Primary school. You were only there for a short while though, weren't you?'

'I'm at University now,' Alan replied. 'I've just finished my first year at Leeds, I'm studying to be a solicitor. I get home at the weekends now and again and here I am trying out the Hilbre Island experience. This is Dave by the way, he's come over with me from Uni'; this is Mick, we went to Caldy Grammar together and this is Freddie, he's at Cambridge. Quite a swot aren't we, Freddie? And who is your gorgeous friend, Vivienne?,' he asked, appraising Kathy. 'Oh, Kathy, pleased to meet you and where are you from, I've not seen you before?'

I watched as Kathy came over all girly and silly and before I knew it Alan was making room on his towel for Kathy to sit beside him. It made me feel resentful. Kathy was my guest and I didn't want to share her with some four eyed lad that would be here today and gone tomorrow. He wasn't even handsome, he wore glasses and he had a big nose, he had spindly legs and had stupid calf length shorts on. I got up in a huff and went for a walk to the far end of the island, where I sat on the cliff with my legs dangling, looking out to sea.

It was pleasant sitting there looking over to the Welsh Hills, trying to decide where Prestatyn was and if I could pinpoint the seaside town of Rhyl. There were seals bobbing up and down in the sun dappled water, they looked like shiny up side down black wellingtons and they brought a lump to my throat as I watched them. I lay on the grass in the warmth of the sun and dozed off, until I was awakened by a concerned looking Kathy. She was desperate to go to the toilet and she asked me where she could go for a wee?

'I don't know,' I answered. 'I've never been here before, perhaps we just have to hold on to it until we get back to West Kirby when the tide goes out.'

'Oh, surely not,' grimaced Kathy. 'I'll wet myself before too long. Alan's given me half his pop and Tizer always makes me want to wee. Haven't you noticed what the others have been doing, someone else must be wanting to wee by now?'

'I'll keep a look out and let you know,' I yawned. 'Now are you going to sit with me or are you going back to lover boy? Trust you to land yourself a trainee solicitor, that's something I'll never be able to do.'

'No, you won't, will you?', remarked Kathy and walked back to sit with Alan again.

What did she mean by that?, I wondered. Oh well, I'd ask her later when we're going home.

The problem of toileting was solved, when the tide began to ebb away from the island and the bottom part of the cliffs revealed some little caves, just big enough for a body to crouch into. It was dangerous climbing down, but it all added to the excitement and there was loud applause and much yah hooing when a blushing girl desperately slithered down the side. I held on, it was too embarrassing to show myself up in front of all those grinning boys. I sipped at my bottle of cream soda and made myself eat my share of sandwiches.

The time passed quickly in the afternoon, as some boys had brought a ball with them and so we all had a kick around for an hour or so and then played catch with a circle of other girls.

All too soon a signal came from the mainland and everyone launched themselves back onto the wet sands, to hurry over to dry land again. We all looked at one another to spot degrees of sun burn and Kathy covered herself with a beach dress, as she had been wearing her bikini all day.

I hadn't been able to wear a bikini, because Kathy had been a dab hand at making her own bikini, but had failed miserably in a creation for me. Kathy said it was because I hadn't got enough up top to put in it and I was better off in a bathing costume instead.

Dave had a car and so we all piled into it when we got back to West Kirby. Alan and Kathy cuddled up on the back seat, while I sat with Dave in the front. I thought how unfair the day had turned out to be. I had got my wish to visit Hilbre Island, but I was seeing Kathy in a new light and I didn't like what I saw.

'Do you think your Mum would allow Alan to come in for tea with us, Vivienne?', Kathy asked, as we drove through Caldy. 'Only Dave is going home to his mother's and Alan and me would like to spend a bit more time together if you don't mind.'

'It's only beans on toast, Kathy,' I answered reluctantly. 'With us being out all day and Audrey staying at her friend's house over the weekend, Mum won't have gone to any trouble.'

'Beans on toast is fine, Vivienne,' said Alan. 'I can eat beans on toast anytime.'

Mother seemed quite rattled when we all walked through the kitchen door. She recognized Alan Roberts straight away and knew that he lived in a big house on Thingwall Drive.

'Oh no,' she groaned to me in the kitchen, after Alan and Kathy had settled themselves on the settee in the front room. 'Couldn't you have telephoned me to say that he was coming, I've only decided on beans on toast for tea?'

'He said he doesn't mind, so stop worrying. Though I do think it's a bit much of Kathy asking if he could come for tea, when she's our guest and she's only met him today.'

'Pity you couldn't bring someone home like Alan Roberts,' Mother hinted. 'He's going to be a solicitor you know and he'll live in a great big house one day.'

'According to Kathy I'll never get someone like a solicitor. I'm going to ask her later what she meant by that?'

Alan went home at eight o'clock, leaving Kathy with his address and pleading with her to write. I got my chance then to ask about that earlier remark, when we'd settled down together to watch some T.V.

'Well, I was talking to Alan and I was asking why none of the other boys or even himself was making a play for you, Vivienne,'

Kathy said frankly. 'He said you were a tart and no one would touch you with a barge pole.'

'What!', I cried, hurt to the core that somebody thought that about me. 'The bloody sod and on what facts has he based that on?'

'He said his mother has seen you talking to bus drivers, and she once saw you necking with some fellow in a bus shelter.'

'But it's all right for you to lay out all day on Hilbre Island in just a bikini, with a crowd of boys fawning all over you?', I spat out angrily.

'I'm only repeating what Alan said, Vivienne.'

'And are you seeing this pompous twit again?'

'Well, yes I thought I would. He seems very pleasant and I'd like to get to know him better. We'll keep in touch, letter writing like I will with you.'

'Oh no, Kathy, there'll be no more letter writing to me, if you don't mind,' I replied, vindictively.

'You've ruined my day and I'd been looking forward to this day for a long time. You're supposed to be my friend, you didn't come here to go messing about with Alan bloody Roberts! When you go home tomorrow I never want to hear from you again.'

'Girls, girls,' said Mother, coming into the living room, seeing me angry faced and my stricken looking friend squaring up to each other by the window.

'What ever is the matter with you both, I thought you'd had a lovely day?'

'She said I was a tart,' I shouted. 'She can go to Hell as far as I'm concerned.'

'Now, that's not very nice, Kathy,' Mother said reprovingly. 'Better to be a little tarty than sweet and sugary, my dear.'

I got my exam' results. I passed in all subjects, but only just. My teachers said I could have done better, but these exams were only a rehearsal for the O' levels to be taken in the Fifth year.

I didn't care, I was still hoping to have left school by then and defiantly threw my hat away, hoping I would be expelled for not wearing it.

The summer holidays beckoned, long and lazy days to fill with absolute nothing, but I knew I must get a job as there was only peanuts in my savings account again.

I haunted both the grocer's and the local post office windows, searching for part time employment on the postcards that were displayed. Maybe baby sitting or walking a dog; I'd been round to Laurel's house but the family appeared to have gone away.

And then I saw the notice...... 'Agent wanted to canvas door to door.'

I can do that, I thought and looked at the address on the postcard. It was only a ten minute walk away. I rushed immediately to a house on Cornelius Drive and was met at the door by an elderly man, who was putting odd shaped parcels into his hallway from an old battered van.

'It's selling household goods to the public,' he said, after I had inquired what an agent's job entailed?

'You give booklets out to the housewives and they order an item or items from it. Then you bring me a list of what is wanted. I bring them to your house and you take them out to the customer.'

'And how much do I get for doing that?'

'You get 10%. You can make a lot of money if you put the effort in. Have you got a garage or somewhere to store the products if you take a lot of orders, 'cos I haven't got much room here if I'm storing your goods as well?'

'Oh, I'm sure Dad will let me use his lean to,' I replied airily. 'Have you got some booklets then and I'll make a start right away?'

'I'll just get a list of those streets that I haven't canvassed yet,' said the man, looking relieved that his postcard advert' had been taken up so quickly. 'If I keep to to my side of Heswall and you stick to around where you live, I think we'll do very well together. I've seen you around Whaley Lane, am I right in thinking that's where you live?'

So I became a door to door saleslady, though there was initial opposition from Father when I told him I had a job.

'You're working for a brush company?', he exploded. 'No, I'm not having that, what will people think when they see you on their doorstep?'

'Oh, leave her alone, Eddie,' Mother said in my defence. 'She's making an honest few bob and she'll soon get tired of it, you wait and see.'

But I stuck it out for the whole of the six weeks holidays and was £10 richer when I went back to school.

How was I going to get out of taking my O'levels?, I pondered, as I searched through the Birkenhead News job advertisements, one Thursday evening after school.

Did I dare go to Miss Preston's study again and ask if I was allowed to leave now that I was sixteen? I knew the answer already and wondered if I'd get anywhere if I wrote a letter to the Education department and point out that their rules were stupid, because I was being penalized for just one day.

An advert' caught my eye for a cashier in a Kardomah cafe. I could do that. I'd had experience handling cash at Woolworths, when I was a Christmas assistant and surely that would stand me in good stead.

I'd apply for it, there was no harm in asking for an application form and the advert' said 16+ and I was sixteen years old and one month! I dashed a letter off there and then and sent it next morning to the Head Office in Liverpool.

Meantime, my parents were making plans again, on how to spend the money that they would be receiving after Aunty's bungalow had been sold. As luck would have it, the house next door to them had come up for sale because the old lady next door had died. Father said that if everything went to plan he would put an offer in and they would get an income from renting it out. He hadn't forgotten though about their trip to San Franscico, they would definitely be going there early next year.

I was being hassled again by the cheeky bus conductor. I finally gave into his plea for a date and went to watch 'Blue Hawaii' with him. He was courteous and only held my hand when he took me to the bus stop after we had seen the film together, but he was very insistent that I went out with him again.

His name was Harry and he lived with his widowed mother, sister and brother on a newly built council estate. Before that, he said they used to live in Rock Ferry, until their home was compulsory purchased by the council to make way for a new road.

A letter came for me from Kardomah. Would I go for an interview in a few days time? Would I go, try and stop me? I told my mother that I felt poorly on the morning of that red letter day.

I felt better though by ten o'clock and as my parents had gone off to the estate agent's, I was able to dress myself carefully in my black and white summer dress, then throwing on my matching black jacket, caught the bus in time to make the half past eleven interview.

'I'm actually still at school,' I told the Personnel woman, who was reading through my application form. 'But if I were to get a job I'm sure they will let me finish, because I am passed the leaving age of sixteen.'

'It says here you have had experience working in Woolworths,' she said kindly. 'Tell me about working there. Did you have to handle money, did you operate a cash register?'

'Oh yes, all of that, I'm very good at adding up and I got on very well with the customers.'

'Well, that's fine then. You look a very personable young lady and you can have the job if you are able to leave school like you say you can. Telephone me if you have any problems, but otherwise I'll expect you at our Moor fields branch at eight forty five on the first of next month.'

Dear Sir or Madam, (I wrote).

I am a pupil at the County Grammar School for Girls and now that I'm sixteen years of age I am wanting to leave full time education. I understand from my headmistress, Miss Preston, that I am not allowed to do this, as I seem to have been born on the day after your cut off date, 1st August.

As I have found myself a job I think it would be in my interest for your department to bend the rules a little, as I am sure you won't want to send the Truancy officer to Liverpool to look for me, nor spend rate payers money on taking my parents to court.

I await to hear a favourable decision and meantime I will present myself to school each day until the end of September.

Yours faithfully,

Vivienne Dockerty.

'So this is a copy of the letter that Vivienne sent, Mrs. Dockerty,' said Miss Preston, as Mother once again sat in the headmistress's study, with me standing resolutely by her side. 'She's obviously intent on leaving. No words from me will make her reconsider, though I've told her she's perfectly capable of passing her O' levels and going to University in time.'

'And what have the Education department said?' I asked, knowing that my future would soon become clear to me in the next few minutes or so.

'They've left me to make the final decision and all I can say is, you can take a horse to water but you can't make it drink. So, Vivienne, I wish you all the best in the future and hope that you won't come to regret the abandonment of your studies in the long run.'

I gave Miss Preston a glowing smile and thanked her for her patience, then Mother and I left quietly, without any goodbyes to anyone and caught the bus back home.

'You're Dad will go mad when he hears what you've done, Vivienne,' Mum said worriedly, as we sat together on the Bebington bus for the very last time. 'I'll just have to ask him if I can have some money and enrol you in secretarial college. We can't have you taking any old job, so I'll see if you can go to the same place that Gina went to. At least her qualifications have stood her in good stead.'

'I don't want to be a secretary, Mother,' I said feeling irritated. 'Why won't you and Dad just let me get on with my life and let me do what I want to do? If you had let me go to secondary school in the first place, I wouldn't be in this position now. I would have been happy to work hard if I had been a bigger fish in a smaller pond.'

'Don't be silly, Vivienne, you wouldn't have liked it there. At least you can now say you've had a grammar school education to future employers and that should open a few more doors.'

'Well, nobody's going to stop me from starting work next Monday. I've got myself a job at the Kardomah in Liverpool. So no matter how angry Dad is, I'm still going to start next week as a cashier there.'

As it happened I didn't have to explain myself to Father. He had suffered the first of his heart attacks and was in the hospital when we got home!

Mother was beside herself when she found Mrs. Miller, a neighbour, hovering on her doorstep, waiting to give the news that Father had been rushed to hospital, while Mum and I had been out.

'Oh, what am I going to do, Mrs. Miller?' my Mother said worriedly. 'I haven't passed my driving test yet and there's no one to drive the car for me to Clatterbridge. Was he bad, Mrs. Miller, did you call the ambulance for him? He's been getting pains in his chest recently, but he wouldn't go to the doctors. Said it was just indigestion after something he'd ate.'

'He managed to telephone the ambulance himself, Mrs. Dockerty,' the neighbour replied. 'I happened to be watering my plants in the garden and I said to my Albert, 'there's an ambulance over there.' My Albert can sit beside you in the passenger seat if you want to go to visit Mr. Dockerty. He learnt to drive in the army but we've never been able to afford a car.'

'Oh, that would be so kind of him. Vivienne, go inside and put the kettle on, I could do with a hot cup of sweet tea.'

So I was left at home to wait for Audrey, with the news that our father had been taken into hospital with a heart attack. Strangely enough, Audrey took the news much as I had. It was all his ranting and raving that had caused it and neither of us were in a hurry for him to come back.

Mother's twice daily visits to the hospital gave both us girls the freedom to do what we wanted. I went out with Harry and Audrey was able to see The Beatles, who were playing in the Cavern with other bands of the day. We cooked for each other in the evenings, scrambled eggs on one day, beans on toast on another and assured our mother we were behaving ourselves and to give our father our love.

I caught the ten past eight bus on the morning of the 1st of October. I was neatly dressed in a white cap sleeved blouse, a short black pleated skirt and two inch black court shoes. I carried a lightweight coat over my arm, as the days were getting chillier and it might be cooler when I was coming home.

I was looking forward to starting work and although I had decided to catch the underground train that day to Liverpool, on future days I would catch the ferryboat, as there was a great deal of difference in the price of the fares.

By nine o'- clock I was being shown the ropes by Rose Millet, the Manageress. A pretty blonde haired young woman who did her job with pride. There were two cashiers, as the cafe was self-service and the customers could choose which side they took their purchases from. There was hot food on one side and cold food on the other.

The first morning passed quickly, as I learnt the rudiments of the job with Rose Millet by my side. We ate a quick lunch with food chosen free from the cold section, then I was told I would be on my own for the rest of the day. The job was easy, too easy really, I thought, as I added up a plate of cheese sandwiches, a wedge of apple pie and a small cup of coffee. I gave out the man's change with a ready smile, then realized he had been leering at a gap in my blouse.

'Don't take any notice of them, Vivienne,' advised Rose, who had been watching the man out of the corner of her eye, while checking something on the section a few feet away. 'They'll ask you out, they'll slip you notes, they'll declare their undying love for you, but at the end of the day you have a job to do. Though it is your decision who you see after work, of course.'

'Oh, I've got a boyfriend,' I replied. 'He'll be coming to pick me up from here later on.'

Though I did wonder if I wanted Harry to come over to collect me, he was becoming possessive and I didn't really want it to be that way.

'I thought that perhaps you'd like to come and meet my mother on Sunday,' said Harry, as we sat side by side on the top deck of the ferryboat that evening going to Woodside. 'Now that you're working she'll be pleased to see you and you can meet my brother Bobby and sister Freda, while you're there.'

'Why did I have to be working before I could meet your mother then?' I asked innocently.

Harry coloured slightly, then looked away.

'Oh, I may as well tell you, Vivienne. When she heard from me that you were still at school she accused me of baby snatching. I am twenty three and I suppose I should have picked someone closer to my age, but you know how much I've always wanted you to go out with me. I just didn't want to start a courtship with anyone else, in case one day you'd say yes to me.'

I looked at him guiltily. The only reason I had gone out with him in the first place was because he had pestered me to have a date. He was nothing special in my eyes. He was only four inches bigger than me, he had yellow teeth because he smoked a lot, his clothes were old fashioned, he was still wearing a tank top for heavens sake and his brown hair was receding, leaving him with a widow's peak across his brow!

'I don't have to go and meet your mother,' I said, suddenly nervous at the way things were going. 'Why can't we leave things the way they are?'

'Because one day I'm hoping you'll marry me, Vivienne and I

think my intended should meet my mum.'

'Oh, Harry, don't you think you're racing ahead a bit? I'm only just turned sixteen, just got my first job and hoping to have control of my life.'

'Ah, you're saying that now, but when you really start falling in love with me you'll change your mind. You'll want me as your husband and have my babies too.'

He kissed me tenderly on the mouth, so that I wouldn't have anything more to say.

CHAPTER 8

Father came out of hospital two days after I had started work at the Kardomah. He had been given some small white tablets, to put under his tongue if he felt he was going to have a heart attack again; he was told to rest and not get himself in any angry states.

He wouldn't speak to me, he sat staring morosely into the living room fire. That is until the Friday evening when I was getting ready to meet Harry. I had taken a quick peek at myself in the mirror that hung over the mantlepiece and pulled at my sweater, because it had ridden up around my waist.

'I suppose you've got all dolled up to meet that bus conductor, haven't you?' Dad suddenly said.

I was startled! How did my father know I was going out with Harry?

I said as much.

'I have my ways and means of finding out about things,' he said snappily. 'So, this is what it has come to? Left a damn good education to work in a cafe and the next thing will be that you'll get pregnant and have to marry that 'No Mark.'

'Dad!'

'No, let me finish, Vivienne. The way you're behaving you're going to have me buried in Landican Cemetery. Out of my three daughters, you're the one who has caused me the most trouble. Now, I'm warning you, this man will be no good for you and if I was you I'd finish it and find yourself a decent young man.'

'But you don't even know Harry,' I replied, red faced with anger at what he had just said.

'And I don't want to neither. Now get of my sight and think of what I've said.'

I slammed out of the front door all fired up because of my father's attitude. Well, I wasn't going to give up Harry just because father had told me to.

Though when I was sitting with Harry in the pub' drinking a lemonade shandy, my father's words came back to me. I looked at my boyfriend, who was beginning to drink his third pint of Black and Tan and didn't like what I saw. Earlier, before we had visited the pub' on the rough council estate where Harry was living, he had taken me to meet his mother who was getting ready to go to work. She was a nurse at the local geriatric hospital, doing the night shift because it paid so well. She looked old for her age, her face was creased with worry and I thought that thirty years on, I might end up looking like that. Harry's brother and sister were ignorant people, who had looked me over then turned back to the television. His mother had been distant to the point of rudeness and Harry had been embarrassed at her lack of sensitivity.

That was why we were sitting in the pub, because Harry had said we wouldn't get any privacy at his house. He'd have to wait to invite me back there when he knew we could be alone.

I sighed. What was I going to do about the situation? Maybe I could run away to Scotland when I'd got some money saved?

My job at the Kardomah was still very pleasant. I had made friends with another cashier called Joanna. She was pretty in a doll like sort of way and liked to spend her lunch times walking around the clothing shops.

We never managed to have lunch together though, because we had to cover each other's breaks, but sometimes our shifts would finish at the same time, if one of us was working an hour's overtime.

Joanna was only working at the Kardomah until her papers came through to join the Navy. She had applied six months earlier, but she couldn't begin her training until she was seventeen and a half. I was so envious and toyed with the idea of applying to the Navy also, but Joanna put a dampener on it when she told me I would have to learn to swim. I was fearful of water and had been ever since my swimming lessons in the icy baths near my school.

When Harry was on the late shift at work and if Joanna's and my finish time coincided, we would go to the pictures together or make up a foursome with any fellows who asked us out on a date. One of the dates was with a couple of handsome Swedish sailors, who had called in for a coffee on a cold and rainy day. Their ship was docked in Liverpool while the cargo it was carrying got unloaded, then something else was loaded on to be taken to Gothenburg. The sailors spoke good English and we girls were totally smitten by them.

That was when I decided that I was having the time of my life! Why should I give all this excitement up and settle for Harry? He didn't take me dancing, never treated me to the pictures anymore, because he was saving up to marry me and going to the pub' was all he could afford.

Now he was trying to get a deposit together so that he could move into a bedsit'. His mother had been nagging him to give up going out with such a young and innocent girl.

Innocent wasn't a word that would describe me any more. If Harry had known about the dates I was having behind his back, then he would have chucked me over there and then!

He managed to find a bedsit' in a large Victorian dwelling, that had been converted into two self contained units on the first floor, while the landlady lived downstairs. He proudly invited me to come and see his little love nest. It would do for now, but he was going to save even harder so he could put a deposit on a house.

It was a Saturday afternoon when I knocked on the door of Number 26, Glasgow Terrace. A woman answered and announced she was Mrs. Johnson, the owner of the flats.

'I've come to see Harry, I'm his girlfriend,' I said confidently.

'I thought I'd made it clear to your young man that I don't allow women in the bed sitting rooms.'

'Well, I'm only staying for a minute or so, he wants to show me around, but then we'll probably be going out for a mooch round town.'

'And who am I speaking to, I can't let just anybody in?', she asked suspiciously.

'My name is Vivienne Dockerty and I live with my parents near Heswall. Harry and I have been friends for a long time now, so it's not as if you're just letting anyone in, is it?'

The woman stood aside to let me pass and pointed to the steep stairs behind her.

'His room's up the stairs and first on the right.'

I ran up the stairs two at a time, thinking what an old battle axe the landlady was.

'Viv', come in,' Harry said, delighted to see me. 'I'm just making a cup of tea on this Baby Belling so I'll make you one as well, shall I? You'll notice that I've got the place furnished, though it's not much to look at I'm afraid.'

I looked around at the dingy furnishing in the rectangular shaped room. The brown velvet curtains at the tall bay window, the high yellowy ceiling with the paint flaking off, an old green moquette sofa and a creaky looking table, with a couple of plastic chairs painted in a horrid lime green. The floor was bare, except for a large Persian rug that had seen better days and at the back of the room under a soot marked sash window was a double bed, with a grubby bed cover thrown over it.

That was where Harry was leading me to and asking me to sit.

'We'll leave the tea 'til later shall we and make ourselves comfortable on here, then we'll get ourselves down to some serious loving, because it's just been fumbling when we've been alone at home.'

'But I've just met the formidable Mrs. Johnson and she doesn't allow young women in her bedsits.'

'Oh well, she'll have to get used to it, I've paid the rent until the end of next month. Come on, Vivienne, that's why I moved out of my mother's house so you and I can be together. Don't tell me I've wasted my time and you're going all frigid on me.'

'It's not that, Harry, I'm not ready to do things with you in a bed. We're not even engaged yet and I'm not sure that I want to,' I ended desperately.

'So you don't love me, is that it, Vivienne? I've gone to all this trouble to get this place for us and now I find you don't love me.'

'But Harry, I've just told you why.'

'Well, if it's an engagement ring you're after, we'll go to the jewellers this afternoon.'

So I meekly took my dress off and got under the grubby covers of the distinctly smelly bed.

I sighed and closed my eyes, as Harry took his shirt and trousers off and got in beside me.

If I thought of something nice, whatever he was planning to do to me would soon be over, so I thought of sitting on Hilbre Island feeling the sun on my face.

Two weeks later, a thunderous looking Father stood waiting for me when I came in from work.

'Do you know a Mrs. Johnson?', he asked sternly.

'Er, a Mrs. Johnson, why Dad?'

'She's your boyfriend's landlady, so you should know her.'

'Oh, that Mrs. Johnson. Why, do you know her as well Dad?'

'I do now, she's been on the telephone telling me about what you and lover boy have been up to in his bed. It seems she warned him not to have young women in his flat, but he seems to have gone against her rules.'

'Bloody old tittle tattle.'

'What did you just say?'

'Well, she must have rung up every Dockerty on the telephone in Heswall, just to get back at him.'

'Anyway, he's getting a month's notice. It's her house and her rules and she wants him out.'

'And what's my punishment?'

'You, young lady, have been booked into a Clinic in Birkenhead and if I find out you've lost your virginity, I'm going to have you sectioned and put into a Mental Home. You're promiscuous, Vivienne, so I might decide to have you locked up until you're twenty one.'

I sat down with a clump onto the settee and looked at my father disbelievingly. This was the 1960's, we weren't living in the Dark Ages anymore.

'You can't do that!' I shouted, when the import of his words began to sink in. 'I'm sixteen now, I'm working, old enough to leave home if I wanted to.'

'That's true, Vivienne, though I can have you made Ward of Court if you don't agree to go to the Clinic.'

'What does Mum think of all this?' I asked looking for an ally. 'Surely she's not willing to let you do this and make a show of me.'

'Irene, get in here where I can see you, I know you're listening by the kitchen door,' my father said triumphantly.

My mother came into the living room. She looked as if she'd been crying and she wouldn't look me in the eye.

'Are you going to let him send me to the looney bin, Mother? Are you in on this too?'

'Well, Vivienne, we think it's for your own good,' my mother said quietly. 'You have been a bit naughty lately and if you're father thinks his actions will be for the best in the long run, well I'll go along with him.'

'And what if I say I won't go to your rotten clinic?'

'You've no choice in the matter,' Father shouted. 'If you're not willing to go in the morning with your mother, I'm going to telephone the Police and have that man you've been seeing hauled up for interfering with an under age girl.'

'You don't have to do that,' I replied icily. 'I take it that you won't be allowing me to work at the Kardomah either if you're intent in putting me in a Mental Home. I'll go to my room now, but before I go let me tell you this, Dad and Mum, I'll never forgive you for as long as I live.'

After a sleepless night, alternatively raging inside over my father, then worrying myself sick about what would happen the next day, I emerged from my bedroom to vomit in the upstairs toilet.

'What's the matter, Vivienne?', Audrey said, as she passed me on the way to get her breakfast before setting off for school.

'Nothing that concerns you, Audrey. Just go and be a good little girl, take your O' levels and try and keep out of Dad's hair.'

'Oh,' was all Audrey said. I was often moody and said things she didn't understand, but she hadn't heard me being sick since she was a little girl.

'Shall I tell Mum to come up and see if she can help you?'

'No, Audrey, go and have your breakfast, there's a good girl.'

By ten thirty, Mother and I were sitting in a small waiting room attached to the Maternity section in the Birkenhead Borough Hospital. Our trip in father's car had passed in silence and he was going to wait for us in the car park, as this was women's work.

'Vivienne Dockerty, Room seven, please.'

A nurse dressed in a lilac striped uniform with white frilly hat, collar and cuffs appeared and beckoned us to follow her down the corridor.

We were shown into a white walled sterile looking consulting room, where a man in his middle fifties stood with a document wallet in his hand. The nurse stood quietly in attendance.

'Good morning, I'm Doctor Bratby Holmes, you'll be Mrs. Dockerty,' he said to Mother. 'I understand that you want me to examine your daughter, Vivienne. I believe it is a matter of the utmost urgency, a possible sectioning under the Mental Health Act I understand.'

'Could I possibly speak for myself, seeing as I am over sixteen and in full time employment, Sir?', I asked, feeling annoyed at his attitude. 'It is my life that you will be ruling on and I think I should get a say in the matter.'

The doctor looked at me in disgust, then completely ignored me and turned to my mother.

'If you could ask your daughter to go behind the screen and take her clothes off, then put on the robe and return to me.'

'Go on, Vivienne, do as he says.' my mother said sternly.

'Then what will happen when I've done that, Sir?' I asked feeling afraid now, because I wasn't sure what he was going to do to me.

'Tell your daughter that she will be examined internally, to see if her hymen has been broken.'

My heart did a flip. This was going beyond anything I had

imagined what was going to happen to me. My father had really stitched me up with this on the spot examination. I had imagined a little chat, told I was a naughty girl by someone in authority. Told to wait until I'd got married before I gave myself to my husband, but not this. Examined by a cold eyed stranger who hadn't an ounce of compassion for a nervous teenage girl. I saw red.

'Oh no, you don't, you randy old bugger,' I said rudely, glaring at him whilst I clutched my coat around my trembling body. 'No one sticks his finger up my bum unless I say so. Mother, did you know that this was going to happen?' I couldn't believe that she was going along with it.

Mother nodded her head unhappily, not able to meet my gaze.

'Well, if that is your attitude and you refuse to submit to my examination,' the man said sharply, 'then I will have to send you to the duty psychiatrist, she will decide what to do with you. Nurse, ask Doctor Williams if she is free to see Mrs. Dockerty and her daughter, will you?'

Mother and I were sent to sit back in the waiting room. I was scarlet with embarrassment by now and hating my mum for putting me through all that.

'You shouldn't have said what you did to the doctor, dear,' she said quietly at the side of me.

'What nasty words you used, I felt so ashamed.'

I kept a rude retort to myself, I was only going to make the situation worse if I fell out with her.

'Vivienne Dockerty.'

The same nurse had come back and asked us to follow her down another corridor.

Inside the room we were shown into this time was a woman in her forties, a brisk looking woman with brown hair, blue eyes and and a pleasant smile on her face.

'Ah, you must be Vivienne and this is your mother?' she said kindly. 'Sit down both of you. Can I ring for a couple of coffees, I don't know about you but I'm parched?'

'Not for me, thank you,' Mother replied timidly.

'I'll have one, white with two sugars,' I said. I needed a drink to calm me down.

When the woman had placed her order via the telephone, she sat back in her chair behind her desk and looked at us thoughtfully.

'Now, Vivienne,' she said, 'are you comfortable on that chair or would you like to move to that one over there? Mrs. Dockerty, are you comfortable as well? Yes, well now I will begin. Oh, I'm Doctor Alicia Williams by the way. Vivienne, I believe you wouldn't submit to Doctor Bratby Holmes's examination earlier. Did you know why he wanted to carry out the examination?'

'Because he's a dirty old man?', I said venomously, still feeling intimidated by what was happening.

'No, because he was requested to by your mother. She and your father are concerned that you might have lost your virginity to the man who has been courting you and they are concerned for your safety.'

'So why didn't my parents ask me if I had lost my virginity, though I can't see what it has to do with them?', I replied, disgusted with my parents for what they had done.

'Mrs. Dockerty.' The woman suddenly made her mind up about something. 'Do you think I may have a few minutes alone with your daughter? I'd like to explain something to her and I fear it could be embarrassing if you are still in the room.'

'Yes, of course, Doctor Williams. Shall I go back to the waiting room and Vivienne can join me there?'

'I'll need to see you again, Mrs. Dockerty, to let you know what I've decided. Ah, here's the nurse with our coffees, thank you. Could you show Mrs. Dockerty to the waiting room?'

Doctor Williams fiddled with her pen for a moment, then sipped her coffee while I gulped mine down.

'Vivienne, I'd like to put my cards on the table and speak to you in confidence. You seem to have got yourself into a situation where your parents have over reacted, as far as I am concerned. However, this man that you've been seeing, has been taking advantage of a minor and your parents have every right to protect their daughter, as you are still under age. By submitting to an examination your parents would have been reassured if you were still a virgin.'

'Or if I wasn't they could send me off to the looney bin, you mean,' I said, still full of anger towards them.

'Yes, something like that. Can I ask you if you're still virgin?'

'Well, I don't know really.' And it was true I didn't know.

'When I was talking to a girl at school, she said you had to see blood when you did it for the first time. I've never seen any blood when Harry has made love to me.'

'But you have had intercourse?'she continued delicately.

'I don't really know what you're talking about, he's messed about with me, but so have a few others since I was fourteen.'

'Oh, my dear, if there is anything you want to tell me, then just spill it out.' Doctor Williams looked aghast.

'No, thank you,' I said firmly, not about dig up old hurts in case I broke down and made a fool of myself. 'I'm not about to rake things up that I've buried up here in my head. Now are you going to send me to the looney bin or what, because my father is waiting in the car park and he'll be drumming his fingers on the steering wheel by now?'

'I'll ask the nurse to get your mother, but let me tell you what I've decided before your mother comes in.'

When Mother came into the room, I'm sure she was expecting to be mopping me up after a total nervous breakdown, but not I. I made sure I looked quite calm and collected, as I didn't want her telling Father that I'd been brought to heel, as it were.

'I've decided that Vivienne is to attend Forest Manor on a purely voluntary basis,' explained Dr. Williams. 'She will go every day, have lunch with the residents and will see me once a week for a counselling session. She has promised me that she will not see her boyfriend while she is attending Forest Manor and hopefully the time spent apart from him, will make him look elsewhere for someone of his own age.'

'And is that what you want, Vivienne?', asked Mother. 'Will you be happy with that?'

I gave my mother a scornful look, picked up my handbag and headed for the door.

'I'll see you in the looney bin then, Doctor Williams,' I said cheerfully. 'Come on Mother, mustn't keep dear Father waiting in the car!'

I didn't speak to my parents all weekend, I stayed in my room and played my records over and over again. My favourite singer was Jim Reeves and I heard my father say he would go out of his mind listening to 'I love you because', that he could hear playing overhead.

Meals were taken in silence and when I had finished I darted back to my bedroom. Audrey took herself off to a friend's house, where she complained of the tense and volatile atmosphere that seemed to be dwelling in her home.

On Monday morning, Father was waiting for me to take me down to Forest Manor.

I had dressed myself in a dark blue woollen pinafore dress over a light blue long sleeved sweater that I had knitted myself. The air outside was chilly as we set off in the car in silence, I hugged myself into my brown winter coat as I stared out of the window screen at the road ahead.

'I hope you can see the sense in all this, Vivienne,' Father said suddenly, perhaps feeling that he had to make a comment to his mutinous daughter in the passenger seat. 'Your mother and I think this is the best solution, it will give you a wake up call and make you change your ways.'

There was an uncomfortable silence. I had taken a vow of silence.

'You can't keep the silent treatment up for ever, you know. One day you'll thank me for this.'

There was still silence. No way would I thank him for the way he was dictating my life.

'Well, I'll pick you up at four o'- clock and I'll do the same thing everyday.' He gave up and shrugged his shoulders at what he saw was moodiness.

Father drove though the open gates into a tree lined drive that lead to a large Victorian mansion house that had seen better days. There was room for his car in front of the heavy oak doorway and once I had got out of the passenger seat, he waited until I had walked into the place. I could have hovered in the hallway and waited until he had driven out on to the main road, but with a sense of curiosity I went up to the desk where a sign said 'Reception.'

I gave my name to the middle aged woman, who was dressed in a bright pink overall and wore her hair in a Marcel wave. She looked pleasant and seemed happy to see me, as I stood nervously in front of her.

'Oh, hello, Vivienne, we've been expecting you. I'll take you through to the lounge where I'll introduce you to some of the people there.'

She led me into a large room, which was oak paneled from the skirting boards to the leaded windows. It was a light and airy room with red moquette sofas, comfortable looking armchairs and an open log fire burnt in the marble surrounded fireplace.

The strange thing to me was that the people sitting around looked perfectly normal. They all looked older; two women in their late twenties, a man who looked in his forties and one old codger with a flat cap on that looked like the gardener.

'This is Vivienne, everybody,' the woman announced. 'She's come to join us for a few weeks, hopefully she'll still be here at Christmas and then she can help us with our Christmas show. This is Marion, Josie, Phil and Maurice. Well, you're just in time for a cup of tea, Vivienne, so I'll go off to the kitchen and bring a tray.'

'Come and sit near me, Vivienne,' said the woman who was called Marion.

'Miss Lucas won't be long and she makes an excellent cup of tea. What are you in for, the electric shock treatment or a course of happy pills?'

'Heavens, I hope neither,' I said, feeling a rush of fear at Marion's words. 'No, I'm here to keep you all company as far as I'm aware.'

'Can you play canasta?', asked the old man, displaying gaps in his upper row of teeth as he smiled at me hopefully.

'No, I'm sorry, but I'm a fast learner if you wanted to teach me.'

'Do you knit?', asked Josie from her chair, where she was busy with her knitting needles.

'Yes I do, I made this sweater.' I showed her my sweater proudly.

'Ah, I see you've made yourself at home, Vivienne,' said Miss Lucas, who had returned with a tray bearing six white cups and saucers. 'You'll find we're a comfortable bunch, we all get on well together. Help yourself to sugar if you take it in your tea.'

'Hope you haven't put any bromide in mine,' Philip chuckled. 'A good looking girl like you, Viv', will have the other fellows leering when they come in from the treatment at lunch time.'

'Other fellows?', I asked, suddenly quaking in my boots.

'Don't take any notice of him, Vivienne,' Miss Lucas said quickly, seeing my mouth tremble.

'He's talking about Geoff and Frankie, they'll be well sedated when they get back.'

'Oh.' That made it all right then.

'Do you sing, Vivienne?'

'Well yes, I suppose I can, Miss Lucas. I tried for the choir at school once, but I got rejected because Miss Parkes, the music teacher had her favourite girls, but I think I'm as good as any other.'

'Good, then if you're here at Christmas we'll put you down for a song. Everyone will do their bit, we get an appreciative audience every year.'

'Have you looked in on Pamela, Miss Lucas?', asked Marion. 'Only I saw her going into the bathroom earlier with a pair of scissors and she must have been in there an hour now.'

'Oh no, why didn't you tell me before?'

Miss Lucas ran out of the lounge, pressing a panic button on the wall as she went.

'She's always threatening to cut her wrists,' said Marion. 'She never does it but it keeps the staff on their toes.'

Oh no, I groaned to myself, all feelings of curiosity diminishing.

Where had I come to, how long was it going to be before I felt like slashing my wrists too?

Every day became the same. Father would run me to Forest Manor, I would spend the day with the inmates, Father would pick me up again and I would spend the evening at home. I felt as if I was sleep walking, everything seemed so surreal.

I saw Doctor Williams once a week, when she did her best to get me to talk about my parents, my innermost feelings and my childhood, but I had shut my mind down and wouldn't open up to her.

Somewhere in the dark recesses of my conscious was the promise that I had made to my mother, that I would never tell another soul about that fateful day at my uncle's house. I wanted to, often I was just about to unburden myself to this sympathetic lady, but I was frightened that all my emotions would tumble out and I would crack up like the inmates of Forest Manor.

But I did tell Doctor Williams how much I hated my dad. I didn't hate my mother, I just felt sorry for her, but I hated my dad with a vengeance and would never forgive him for doing this to me.

'I had a good job at the Kardomah, I had a boyfriend who loved me down to my little fingers, now I have nothing and when all this is over I'm going to have to get my life back to normal again,' I said one day at our counselling session.

'What is normal, Vivienne?' she asked. 'Let's talk about this and tell me about the relationship with your dad.'

One morning after I had been attending Forest Manor for three weeks, Father couldn't run me to the place because he had an early start at work.

'I'm trusting you, Vivienne, to go there and back again without getting up to any mischief,' he said wagging a finger. 'I have to be on site at eight o'clock to help with unloading a brick wagon at my customer's house, and I'll have to put a long day in if I want to get paid at the end of the week.'

It was just the chance that I had been waiting for. I rushed up to my bedroom and under the pretence of putting my makeup on, I dashed a note off to Harry to tell him what had been going on. I wrote that I couldn't go into detail, but begged him to meet me outside Forest Manor if it was at all possible at four o'- clock. When I caught the bus at ten past eight, I asked the bus conductor to pass the note to Harry, if he was in the works canteen at dinner time.

It was a long shot, Harry might not be on an early shift, but I could keep my fingers crossed that he would get my note.

It was too good to be true, I thought, as I saw Harry waiting by the bus stop on the other side of the road from the loony bin that afternoon. He wasn't wearing uniform and when I crossed the road to join him, I remember feeling faintly disappointed when I noticed his appearance. He looked shambolic in his worn out shoes, his greasy looking jacket and a pair of denim trousers that were fraying at the hems. So this was my knight in shining armour, who I had put my life on hold for, because I hadn't been brave enough to walk away.

'Vivienne!', he kissed me tenderly on the mouth, his blue eyes shining as he looked into mine.

'I kept ringing your home, but every time I did your dad would put the receiver down. I've been at my wits end wondering what's been going on. How long have you been going to this place then?'

I explained all as we waited at the bus stop, with Harry getting more and more angry as he listened to my tale of woe.

'Well, you've made my mind up, Vivienne,' he said clutching me to him. 'We're going to get married. I don't know how we'll do it, but I'm not having you going through this alone. I'll go and see your father and explain to him that my intentions are serious towards you. Once we've had a talk, I'm sure he'll like me and you won't ever have to come to this place again.'

'No, Harry, don't do that!', I said alarmed at his vehemence. 'He'll probably kill you on the spot and he's just been in hospital with a heart attack. No, leave it and we'll find a way of seeing each other somehow. I'll send you notes via one of the bus conductors if I'm able to see you, like I did today. Have you found somewhere better than Mrs. Johnson's yet? It's her bloody fault I'm at this place. I'm taking it as read that you left her house at the end of the month.'

'I've gone back to my mother's house, Vivienne. I felt like swinging for that old bitch when she told me that she'd telephoned your father.'

'So you knew about it?' I asked in amazement. 'Knew that she'd telephoned my father and said we were at it in your bed?

'Well, yes and I was expecting your father to come and hunt me down or send the cops around. That's why I had to leave Glasgow Road the very next day, so no, I didn't keep the bedsit' on until the end of the month.'

'Oh.' I wondered why he hadn't tried to contact me.

'Anyway, Vivienne, come over behind that clump of bushes where we can't be seen from the road. I'll show you how much I've missed you and we'll hear the bus coming anyway. What's the matter?'

I had stepped back from him, seeing him suddenly for the coward he was.

'Oh, don't say that you're annoyed with me. Did you want me banged up in jail because I went with an underage kid?'

'I'm just thinking of what I had to go through to shield you from the authorities. Anyway, I can hear the bus coming now, so we've no time to go behind the bushes.'

'Miss this one, get the next.'

'No, Harry, I'm sorry but I want to go home.'

I managed to keep my tears at bay until I reached my bedroom. Then I let loose all of my emotions and cried until I could cry no more.

CHAPTER 9

It was the second week of December and the inmates of Forest Manor plus me, were rehearsing for our Christmas Variety Show.

Frankie, who was a Billy Fury look-a-like, was going to sing 'Like I've never been gone.' Phil' was going to play 'Danny Boy' on his violin, Maurice had a couple of magic tricks, Marion and Josie were going to dress up as two spotty school girls and do a tap dance together and I had decided to sing 'If you were the only boy in the world.'

Geoff', said he didn't want to make a show of himself so he would sit in the audience; poor old Pamela had succeeded in slashing her wrists and had been taken to hospital.

As we were sitting having a break, Miss Lucas came to me and told me that Doctor Williams wanted to see me in the consulting room.

'Oh, but I only saw her yesterday,' I said puzzled. 'I wonder why she wants to see me again today?'

'You won't find out if you don't go, will you? I'll save you one of these chocolate eclairs if you like.'

I knocked on the consulting room door politely, then put my head around.

'You wanted to see me, Doctor Williams? I thought I was seeing you again next Tuesday.'

'Come in, Vivienne, I want to talk to you,' she said gaily. 'Sit next to me on the sofa and I'll tell you what I've decided to do.' I did as she asked, feeling baffled.

'It seems to me that you're wasting your time here. When I was talking to you yesterday, I thought, what is this girl doing here? I know you've got a lot of emotional baggage tucked away in that mind of yours, but honestly if your parents had handled the situation differently we wouldn't be having this conversation now. Unfortunately, there are no schools that can teach parents how to deal with their offspring, but if you had been my daughter I wouldn't have brought in outside help to control you, I would have handled it in a different way. Still, you are not my daughter. So, Vivienne, if I said to you that you are free to go, what would you say to me?'

My spirits had begun to soar as I heard her words, though my mind was slow to accept them.

All I could think of was the Christmas Show, and how I would let the others down if I decided not to appear with them. I had a duty to the others who had all become my friends.

'I'd say thank you,' I answered slowly, 'but can I come back for the Christmas Show, because I don't want to let my audience down?'

Alicia Williams smiled at my loyalty.

'What will you do with yourself now that you don't have to come to Forest Manor anymore?'

'I don't know, perhaps run away to Scotland and make a new life there.'

'And your boyfriend? Will you get back with him again?'

'Again I don't know, I'll have to think about it, perhaps I'll get a different one.'

'Vivienne,' Alicia said softly to me. 'Why do you have to have a boyfriend? Couldn't you envisage a life without one?'

'I think because I need someone to love me. I don't mean wanting sex, I mean someone who will hug me and kiss me and make me feel good about myself. Harry was like that in the beginning, but then he got possessive and wanted to make me his wife. I want to be free to do what I want, but I also want some loving as well.'

'Then you'll have to be strong and find a man who will be willing for you to call the shots then,' Alicia laughed. 'But unfortunately there are not many of them about.'

I hadn't managed to see Harry since the day he met me at the bus stop. I wasn't really bothered, I had decided that Harry was all in my head and the real Harry wasn't worth having. So I felt a bit put out when Miss Lucas handed me a letter from him, as I was leaving Forest Manor and saying my goodbyes.

I had mentioned to him that there was to be a Christmas variety show when he had accompanied me on the bus back to Woodside terminus. I had told him the date and that I was allowed to invite a friend. His letter said that he would be there in the audience and after, if my father wasn't there as well, he had a surprise for me.

I began to feel nervous as the following Friday afternoon loomed, I didn't mind singing in front of people I didn't know, but Harry being in the audience was certainly bound to throw me! When I had got into the car with my father, on the afternoon that Doctor Williams had dropped her bombshell, I had decided to keep the news to myself for a while. I needed to think of what my next move was going to be and I didn't want my parents coming up with new solutions for me, that is, secretarial college might be mentioned again, or going back to school. Besides, my father had been dropping me off at the gate of Forest Manor recently, so maybe I could catch the bus into town and visit some of the employment agencies that I had seen advertised.

Next morning, instead of dressing myself in my usual casual indoor clothes, I put on a skirt and jacket, telling my father that I wanted to look smart as we had some visiting dignitaries going to Forest Manor that day. An hour later I was sitting in an employment agency, while the girl behind the desk shuffled some cards in front of me.

'What kind of work are you looking for, Miss Dockerty,' she asked. 'I've a shop assistant, a factory worker and a pools clerk? Oh, and there's another one here, dining room maid in an Outward Bound centre. Oh, but it's in the Lake District and residential so you wouldn't want to travel all that way.'

'But I would,' I said fervently. 'That sounds exactly what I'm looking for. Can you give the details? Where would I have to go for an interview?'

'You'll have to travel over to Liverpool. You go to the Adelphi Hotel, they've hired an interviewing room there.'

'When can I go?', I asked eagerly. No more Harry, no more Father if I got the job!

'The interviews are next Tuesday, you have to be there by 10 a.m.'

'Put me on your list then, I'll be going!'

I could hardly wait until Tuesday and I still didn't tell my parents that I had been discharged from Forest Manor and I continued each morning to be dropped off outside the gate. There was an uneasy truce in our household, at least everyone was speaking to each other but nothing in depth was said. Mother had been in contact with the American Friends and Family Club, as she was desperate to set a date to travel over to San Francisco.

I overheard my parents one evening when they thought I was up in my bedroom, but I had come down for a glass of water and was listening at the living room door.

'I should imagine you'll be able to go in January, Irene,' Father was saying. 'Now that I've got the money through from the sale of the bungalow, there's nothing to stop you. I'll have to stay here and keep an eye on the girls, but what I could do, seeing as you will have to fly out of Heathrow, is get my mother to come round and look after them, while I come down with you on the train, then see you on the flight.'

'Are you sure you don't want to come with me?' Mother asked.

'No, not this time. You and Gina have some time together on your own. I've got to be here to keep my eye on Vivienne, or I'd be worrying what she was up to while I'm away.'

Ah, I thought, as I tiptoed away quietly, knowing their plans will suit me very nicely. With a bit of luck I'll be in the Lake District at the end of January.

The small audience sat in rows in front of the stage, which had been erected by the handyman in the Recreational centre. They had listened to a laid back Billy Fury, hummed along with the violin recital, laughed at Maurice trying to get a live rabbit out of a top hat and were now waiting expectantly for Miss Vivienne Dockerty, to entertain them with her song.

I was standing ready for my cue from Miss Lucas, wishing that I hadn't volunteered and hoping that Harry wouldn't come, but there was no time to back out now and as I stepped upon the stage in my red sparkly top and black wide legged trousers, there was a ripple of polite applause.

I cleared my throat and began.

'If you were the only boy in the world and I was the only girl,'........and then I saw Harry in the audience smiling at me. My throat constricted in panic and I forgot the next line. Oh no, what was I going to do? The audience looked at me expectantly.

'Nothing else would matter in the world today, we would go on loving in the same old way'.........

There was Harry coming towards me and singing as he walked. By the time he got to the stage, the audience had joined in.

'A garden of Eden just made for two with nothing to mar our joy.

If you were the only boy in the world and I was the only girl.'

I stepped down from the stage with Harry holding my hand, while the audience clapped us both cheerfully, then I sat with him gratefully on the back row. I felt such a fool though and my face was aflame!

'I've got something for you, Vivienne,' Harry whispered, squeezing my hand as we watched the tap dancing schoolgirls. 'I'll give it to you when we get out of here. Is your dad picking you up after the show?'

'No,' I said. 'Suddenly he's decided to trust me to go home on my own in the afternoons, though he still drops me off in the mornings. Anyway, I don't have to come here anymore, I've been discharged. I'm going to tell them tonight when I get home.'

'Oh, great,' Harry said, kissing me on the cheek in his delight that I was a free woman again. 'Come on, let's get out of here. We'll have to work out how we can see each other and that makes my present doubly special.'

I stopped mid flight, coinciding with the end of the Christmas performance. I drew Harry into a corner, while the friends and family of the inmates gathered in groups to wait for the refreshments that would soon come out.

'Show it to me, Harry,' I squeaked excitedly. 'What have you got me?'

Harry put his hand in his pocket and drew out a little gift wrapped package. I snatched it from him there and then and tore away at the paper and pretty pink ribbon. I pulled at the lid of the box impatiently and there nestling on a pad of cotton wool, was an engagement ring.

'Do you like it, Vivienne?', Harry asked, when no comment came rushing out of my lips.

'Yes, Harry, I love it,' I lied, looking with gathering horror at the tiny garnet stone set in a circle of diamond chips, watching as Harry quickly pushed it on to my betrothal finger.

'You don't look as if you do.'

'Well, it's just a shock that's all. I was expecting a Christmas present, not an engagement ring.'

'But I told you we were going to get married, Viv',' Harry said seriously. 'Look, let's get out of here, the acts have finished now and we've got some serious talking to do.'

'O.K., I'll get my coat and say goodbye to Miss Lucas and some other people. If you wait near Reception I'll see you soon.'

Instead I went to the Ladies and sat on the toilet seat, twisting the ring around on my left finger, where Harry had lovingly placed it. I felt trapped and wondered how I could get out of the engagement, but I couldn't hurt Harry at Christmas. Not when it was the season of good will to all men. I would wait until the New Year then and see what I could do.

I went to the interview on the following Tuesday, by this time I had told my parents that I had been discharged from Forest Manor and was going to an employment agency, to see if there were any suitable jobs. Mother had mentioned secretarial college like I knew she would and Father had said I should go back to school.

The job in the Lake District seemed to be just what I wanted; the place was in the back and beyond, used by walkers, college students and commercial travellers. It appeared to be a cheap and cheerful hotel and because of its isolation they were desperate for staff. I didn't need qualifications; providing I was hardworking and conscientious, I was good enough for the interviewer. Could I start on the 1st February and was I willing to live in?

Oh yes, very much so, I thought, as I walked on air back to the ferryboat. I hoped I would get some money from my parents at Christmas, because I was going to need some for the train fare. Mother had been giving me a little from her housekeeping for bits and bobs at Forest Manor, but although I had given up smoking and had really no need to spend the few shillings, it wasn't enough to pay for a ticket to the Lake District.

So what was I going to tell my parents? Absolutely nothing. I was going to wait until I knew the date of Mother's flight and hopefully it would tie in with my plans.

On my way back I managed to sneak an hour with Harry, who was doing a split shift that morning and didn't have to return to work until half past two.

We sat in the Woodside cafe drinking coffee and talking about our future. It was there that I told Harry about this company that I would be working for, who owned many places throughout England and Scotland. If I wanted, I could work in Scotland which had always been a dream of mine.

Instead of Harry being sad that I was going away and leaving him, he was ecstatic!

'Don't you see, Vivienne, this is the perfect way forward for us?'

'How?' My spirits dropped as I saw his eager face.

'Well, you do say three months in the hotel they send you to, then put in for a transfer. You can apply to work in Scotland, do your three weeks residency and then I can come up and marry you! Didn't you know that in Scotland you can get married at sixteen without your parents permission? Don't worry, I'll come up and visit so you won't be lonely; perhaps you can smuggle me into your bedroom when I come to stay. So, where is this place that you'll be working at?'

'I'm not sure,' I said, trying to stop myself from giving too much away. 'I've been told to catch the train from Liverpool to Preston, get off there and then get on the train to Windermere, then I take a bus to Ambleside.'

'And what will you be doing?'

'She said they already have two general assistants, so I'll wait on in the dining room. It's breakfast and evening meal and I suppose I'll help out wherever I'm needed in the time in between, but what I liked about it was we aren't required be on formal terms with the guests, we have to be pleasant and helpful and join in with evening activities.'

'What kind of evening activities?'

'Oh, they have quiz nights and card games, dancing and social evenings where I suppose we sit around and have a chat.'

'And I suppose there'll be men there.'

'Well, of course, it's an outward bound centre, silly, there's bound to be men. I can't see a lot of women wanting to do outside activities.'

'Then the quicker you get your feet under the table there, the quicker you'll get to Scotland. But I won't be jealous because I know you love me the best.'

He had such confidence in me, I thought as we kissed goodbye and I caught the bus back home, but already I was feeling the excitement of getting away from Harry and my father. Suddenly I had caught the whiff of freedom and I couldn't wait for that day to come.

Christmas was spent quietly at home, though we had a quick visit to Southport to see Aunt Isabel and her teenage son. Aunt Isabel said that Pamela and Philip had decided to give up the guest house, as the running costs were prohibitive and they couldn't make it pay.

I wasn't really interested, I still had a lot of resentment towards the way my cousin had treated me and hoped this hotel I was going to in Ambleside didn't work me like a slave.

At the beginning of January, Mother was in a frenzy deciding on what she should take in her suitcase for her trip to America. There had been the usual emotional telephone call from Gina over Christmas, with little Mandy chattering at the other end which made the tears from Mother flow.

My parents had been very generous with my Christmas present, though Audrey had been given the same. We both had a crisp ten pound note to spend. I kept mine in my purse as I had a secret agenda, but Audrey caught the bus into town once the January sales began. She brought back shop bought clothes to wear on evenings and weekends, because she had only ever had hand me downs or hand made clothes to wear.

Audrey was beginning to turn into a quietly attractive young lady, she had lost her puppy fat and had grown a few more inches and wore her dark brown hair in a bob cut like Sandy Shaw.

She confided in me, though she swore me to secrecy, that she now had a boyfriend that she met after school. I gave her dire warnings on what would happen if Father were to find out.

Nothing had been mentioned regarding me finding a job. It seemed that my problems were forgotten, while Mother made lists and did a lot of shopping and Father made travel arrangements and got his jobs up to date.

I could only see Harry if I sneaked an hour with him in town under the guise of window shopping. My mind was firmly on my future, so I turned down his pleas of snatching some time in his house while his mother was out, or going for a walk over Bidston Hill. I was determined that nothing was going to stop me getting on that train from Liverpool and if Harry was a little huffy, then tough, that was the way it was going to be.

Mother's flight from Heathrow was on the 29th January and I worried constantly on how I was going to get away without my father finding out. I had decided not to tell him about the job I had got in the Lake District, in case he handcuffed me to the bed or got Nana to stand guard over me. I pondered long and hard on what I could do to get away.

I decided to take my sister, Audrey, into my confidence. Audrey, like me had little respect for our tyrant of a father, ever since she had been punished for playing truant when nipping across on the ferryboat to see the Beatles playing in the Cavern at lunchtime. So, when I explained that I was in a fix because I'd never get away if we were in the care of Nana, Audrey said she would pretend that I was in bed with an infection, and we both knew that Nana wouldn't come in to check.

'I'll ask a friend to come and stay so that I won't be on my own, Vivienne,' she said. 'But if Mum and Dad are leaving on the 28th what are you going to do?'

'Well, I heard Dad say that they'd make a bit of a holiday of it, so he won't be back until the 30th and I'll be miles away by then.'

'But your job doesn't start until the 1st of February.'

'Oh, I'll tell them that I thought I'd travel up earlier, learn the ropes as it were without any pay. If they won't take me in I'll get myself a Bed and Breakfast and then I can look around and have a little holiday.'

'What are you going to do, leave a letter?' Audrey looked anxious.

'Yes, and I can't wait to write it and you know nothing about my plans, do you hear?'

I said a fond farewell to Harry on the afternoon before I was to leave. He stood there bravely waving as I got onto the platform of the bus. I said I would write and send the telephone number of the hotel so he could ring me, but somehow I didn't feel sad. I just felt excitement bubbling up.

I waited until my parents had caught the bus which would take them down to Hamilton Square station, then they would take the underground train to Liverpool, as they were catching the London train from Lime Street station. There had been tears from Mother and strict instructions from Father, that we were to lock ourselves in the house at night and only speak to callers through the letter box. Nana would come round each day to make sure that we were eating properly; there was plenty of food in the refrigerator and money in the old tea canister if we needed to buy anymore.

We waved our parents off from the top of the driveway, then ran back into the house chuckling with glee.

'So, what are you going to do, Audrey?' I asked, though I was too excited really to worry about leaving her. 'Are you going into school or are you staying off today?'

'What do you think,Viv'? I'm going to throw a sicky and go on the bus later into town.'

'Well, I'm going to go through my clothes, see what wants washing, do some ironing and then start packing. I've decided to go tomorrow in case Dad decides to come back a day early.'

'Oh, you are lucky, you know, Viv'. Once you've gone he'll turn the pressure on me and I'm going to have to get my O' levels and make him proud.'

'Tough,' I answered, hugging my sister. 'But never mind Sis', just think you'll be his favourite daughter then!'

Next day I left my letter on the mantelpiece, said goodbye to Audrey and set off on my journey into the unknown. Well, I knew where I was going to, but I felt I was off on an adventure and I couldn't wait to get there.

A few hours later I stood at the bus stop outside Windermere Station. The train journey had been long, as I'd had to wait at Preston for my connection and now I was feeling tired and sooty from my travels and hoping that Ambleside wasn't far away.

The scenery from the compartment window had been breathtaking, changing from scrubby moorland or vast tracts of farmland in Lancashire, to dense forests and majestic hills and lakes that were long and tranquil looking. Now I was standing on the road that lead down to Lake Windermere, where even in the winter there were walkers wearing hiking boots and bobble hats.

A single decker green Crosville bus pulled up alongside me and

I asked the bus conductor if it was going to Ambleside?

'It sure is, Missy,' he said, smiling at me in a friendly fashion. 'That's where we'll be finishing for the day. Hop aboard and I'll take your case and put it in the luggage rack.'

I sat on the side seat next to the platform, paid my fare with a sixpenny piece and settled down to look at the passing countryside. The bus was empty and the conductor decided he wanted to chat, so I spent the next twenty minutes explaining why I was going to Ambleside. He seemed a good listener, though now and again he got out his handkerchief to wipe his spectacles. He also seemed to have something wrong with his adenoids, as when he spoke it was with a nasal sound, as if he had problems between his nose and the back of his throat. But he was friendly and interested in what I had to say, so I thought it was a good start to my new life to talk to someone nice.

As the bus chugged into the depot, he pointed out the road that I had to walk up to get to Tree Tops House.

'I'd take you there myself,' he said, 'but I've got to do my paying in. If you have any problems or need someone to talk to, just call in here and ask someone to contact William Fearns, for you.'

What a nice man, I thought, as I trundled along the main street looking in the shop windows as I passed them by. They were full of gifts from the Lake District, coconut fudge, homemade toffee, jars of honey, Kendal mint cake, postcards, lace work, pottery and knitwear. Everything you could imagine as a souvenir.

William had said that the hotel I was looking for was out of the village on the main road to Grasmere. He said that Tree Tops was set back up a long drive and the grounds at the back led down to Lake Windermere.

It was getting dark by now, and the street lights seemed to end as I walked out of civilization. It was only when a car came by shining its headlights, that I could really see.

After ten minutes of keeping to the narrow grass verge, as there wasn't a pavement, trying to keep out of muddy puddles and tripping over boulders that seemed to be there to upend me, I came to an opening and on the stone post at the side of the gate it read 'Tree Tops House.'

I sighed with relief and pushed open one of the tall ironwork gates, only to slip on a cattle grid that had been put there to stop the local sheep from straying in. I took a minute to recover, then set off up the stony drive towards the lights from a house that shone in the distance. It was eerie passing the dense bushes and stark looking trees that lined the way and every little sound made me jump as I walked along.

Then suddenly I was there and looking in awe at the large stone mansion house that stood before me, with the light from the open door to the hallway brightening up the gloom.

I walked confidently into the Reception area expecting to see someone on duty, but there wasn't anybody, so I sat on an old medieval storage chest in the hall.

Perhaps the hotel wasn't open yet, I thought, but the front door was open and there was a smell of cooked food coming from somewhere. I peeked into the office that was at the back of Reception, the light was on but there was no one in the room, just a desk, a filing cabinet and an old Olivetti typewriter. So I went back to sit on the chest again.

Then I saw a hand bell sitting on top of the Reception counter, a big brass gleaming thing that looked like it should be in a schoolroom. I decided to shake it and see what happened. The bell made a loud clattering sound that made my heart jump into my mouth!

From one of the rooms off the corridor that led from Reception, a little woman in her forties wearing an orange twin set and a short black pleated skirt emerged. She ran swiftly towards me, her small round eyes holding delighted surprise.

'Who are you then?' she asked. 'Are you a guest or one of our new employees? Only if you're a guest we don't open until February and if you're an employee we weren't expecting you.'

'I'm Vivienne Dockerty. I've come up early to Ambleside, because my parents have gone to America and it meant I was in the house alone.'

'America? That's very nice for them. Well, I'm happy to meet you, Vivienne. You'll be the dining room maid?'

'Yes, I hope you don't mind me arriving earlier than I should. I can get a B and B if you'd rather and come back again the day after tomorrow.'

'No, no, I'm delighted you've arrived early, you can help us get the place ready for our guests. I'm Miss Ripon by the way, I manage this hotel for my sins.'

'Oh, and have any other staff arrived or is it just me?'

'Well, Aggie and Gertie have arrived, they're sisters by the way. They've been sent to us from one of our Scottish hotels, they're not Scots though. Then we have Helen, who is a local woman, she'll be coming in to do the downstairs cleaning. Aggie and Gertie are the upstairs maids. There's also Jack and his wife Priscilla, they'll be working in the kitchen. Jack is the chef and Priscilla is his assistant. Oh, and we also have a handyman- cum- gardener who lives out and he also maintains the boats down at the moorings. Keeps them in good condition for our guests to use. Anyway, Vivienne, you must be hungry after your journey, from Liverpool wasn't it? You haven't got a Liverpool accent, have you? I was expecting a Scouser when I read the staff list. Let me take you to your bedroom with your suitcase and then we'll come back and raid the kitchen for you. I've just eaten a very good hot pot, so probably Jack can rustle up some of the same.'

After blasting me without a pause for breath with her relevant information, she led me up a very fine mahogany staircase, onto a landing and up a narrower set of stairs to the next floor. Then just when I thought I was having a room on the first floor, Miss Ripon lead me up another flight of stairs to the upper floor! She opened the door to a bedroom that was very long, rectangular, and uncarpeted, with two high windows, one on the left side of the room and one at the far end. My heart sank when I saw what was in there, four single beds with a small cupboard between each one.

'Sorry, but you have to share the bedroom, Vivienne,' Miss

Ripon said apologetically. 'We don't have enough accommodation for you all to have your own room. You'll be sharing with Aggie and Gertie and the fourth bed is spare, in case we need to recruit another person, which sometimes if we're very busy we have to do.'

'Oh, that's O.K. with me,' I said politely, though I had been hoping for a room of my own. 'Providing nobody snores. I'm a very light sleeper and the slightest sound keeps me awake at night.'

'Well, I don't know if anybody snores, but I'm the same and my bedroom is right next door to yours. So let's hope the girls aren't snorers and we can get some sleep at night.'

I took my coat off and put it on the nearest bed to the door. I could see that two beds at the far end of the room were taken, because one had a doll sitting on the pink counterpane and the other bed had a teddy bear on top. I left my suitcase at the side of the bed I had chosen, then followed Miss Ripon down the stairs.

She took me into the kitchen and introduced me to Jack. He was a big muscle bound fellow, with sparse grey hair and a round doleful looking face. His wife, Priscilla, was washing up at a stainless steel sink. She was a thin nervy looking woman, but her smile lit up her face as she said 'hello' to me. I couldn't help but bring to mind the nursery rhyme, 'Jack Spratt could eat no fat and his wife could eat no lean'. I stifled a giggle and said I was pleased to meet them both and yes, I would be delighted to have anything that was going to eat.

The chef piled up a plateful of stew and potatoes for me, then I was taken through to the dining room, where I met two elderly sisters who were finishing off their dessert.

'This is Vivienne, our youngest member of the team,' Miss Ripon said to them. 'Sit down there, Vivienne, nearer to the fire. You look chilled after your long journey here.'

I did as I was told, then turned to smile at the two women. I couldn't think of either of them as girls, as both of them looked over eighty!

They reminded me of my two aunties who had lived in Seaview

Lane. One was little and round with white curly hair tucked under a navy satin Chinese hat, the other was of medium height but she had a dowager's hump. Her hair was also white, but it was straight with a parting down the middle and she had pinned her hair into cartwheels around her ears and wore a similar Chinese hat. Both women had long black dresses on and blue hand knitted cardigans. They smiled back at me, then continued eating their bowls of tinned fruit and cream.

'They don't have lot to say for themselves,' whispered Miss Ripon, 'and I think one of them is a little deaf. I haven't decided yet who is Aggie and who is Gertie, but I'm sure I'll know after the next day or two.'

'Would you like a cup of tea?', Priscilla, asked through the serving hatch.

'Oh, yes, please, that would be lovely, thank you,' I replied, then felt myself blushing when I realized the woman was looking at Miss Ripon.

'We'll all have one, thank you,' said Miss Ripon. 'Why don't you serve it in the Library room and we can all get to know one another?'

'We're off to bed,' said Jack's gruff voice from the kitchen. 'Priscilla, take a tray into the Library and then I'll see you in our bedroom later.'

'He seems to be a little shy,' confided Miss Ripon. 'Anyway, when you've finished we'll go into the Library and I'll open a bottle of wine.'

'Oh, yes please,' the two sisters piped up in unison. 'We like a glass of wine before we retire!'

The next morning I was awoken by shuffling and mutterings as the two sisters crept passed my bed. I lay for a moment wondering what I was doing there, then switched on the table lamp that was on top of the small cupboard next to me. It was still dark outside and I searched for my watch to see what time it was. It was a quarter to seven. I groaned and snuggled back under the covers, surely I wouldn't be expected to rise at that time, when I wasn't employed until the 1st of February?

The sisters shuffled back again after ten minutes, still dressed in their matching pink long sleeved winceyette nightdresses and stood at the end of my bed waiting for me to open my eyes.

'The bathroom's free now,' lisped the sister with the curly hair, when she saw that I was looking at her in astonishment! 'I'd be quick if I were you or Miss Ripon will be in there first.'

She smiled a gummy smile and I realized that the woman had no teeth in.

'But why do we have to get up so early?', I asked, pulling the bedcovers around me in embarrassment, because I only had a baby doll nightie on. 'We don't have to start work for another two days.'

'Habit,' said the other sister, who still had all her own teeth. 'The sooner we get started, the sooner we'll get our work done and me and Aggie want to have a look around in Ambleside.'

'Oh, O.K. you win,' I said in defeat. 'I probably won't get back to sleep anyway. Do we get breakfast first do you know, or do we have to wait until later? Because at the last hotel I worked in we had to do our jobs first.'

The two sisters looked at each other in horror.

'Of course we're given breakfast before we start work, how can anybody do their job without any food first?' That was from Aggie, who was round like a little tub.

I took my soap bag and rushed along the corridor to the door that was marked 'Bathroom'. Thank heavens, there was still hot water so I could have a soak!

After a satisfying breakfast of eggs, bacon, fried tomatoes and mushrooms, the staff sat around a table in the dining room, while Miss Ripon spoke to us of the work that needed to be done.

I was to check the dining room side board which I was to be in charge of. There were tablecloths, napkins and napkin rings inside and on the top were trays of condiments, coffee and teapots, milk jugs, sugar bowls and a wooden cutlery box that held the knives, forks and spoons. Most of these items were silver or silver plated and my job was to polish each one.

'Then you'll be free for the rest of the day, Vivienne,' the Manageress said kindly, 'but once the hotel guests start arriving then you'll be required to help the others, as and when. Now, who is coming to stay with us this week?,' she continued, rapidly scanning her list.

'We have a group of gentlemen from the Tokyo Tourist Board in Japan, who are touring Britain in a special coach. Jack, they have not asked for any different food, but they would like to eat dishes such as Lancashire Hotpot and Cumbrian Pie. Then, we have two commercial travellers coming to stay two days later, so by that time the Japanese will have settled in. On the first evening we won't have a special event to entertain them, other than I will play the piano to create a pleasant ambience, but on the second night I suggest that we gather together for social dancing. Of course that means everyone but especially, Vivienne. O.K . Jack, you can be excused because of your war wound, but everyone else I'm sure is capable of trotting out a waltz. Do you know how to waltz, Vivienne?'

I nodded. Of course I could waltz.

'I am only singling you out because you'll have more energy than the rest of us and Helen, I'm sure that you would like to help Vivienne out as well.'

'Yes, but what about my children, they need to be in bed by seven o'clock and will I get overtime?' Helen didn't look overjoyed.

'Surely your husband could put them to bed and have you thought you may enjoy yourself?'

Helen sighed and nodded mutely. She was a pleasant looking fair haired woman in her early thirties, who had left her young children in the care of her mother- in- law so that she could earn some much needed cash. Her husband worked for the Lakeland Trust as a forest worker and didn't bring home a lot of pay.

'So, do we all know what we're doing?' Miss Ripon brought our meeting to a close. 'Any questions? No, then let's all get to it. Oh, and Vivienne, I forgot to tell you, you'll be responsible for the dinner gong!'

I wandered into the grounds after elevenses, leaving the other staff to complete their designated tasks. Although it was the end of January, there was a spring like feel to the morning and I listened to the chirruping of the birds in the many shrubs and bushes, as I walked down a gravel path to the gently lapping lake. I took deep breaths of the crisp cool air, then stood on the landing stage looking across the still water to the dense forest, below a brooding mountain on the other side.

I decided I was going to love it there, as I stared at the hotel's boat house where a man was bent, busily slapping white paint on an upturned rowing boat. Everyone was warm and friendly and I seemed to have been accepted for myself. There wasn't any shouting, well none up to now anyway, we were all there to do a job to the best of our ability.

What it must be like to stay here forever, I mused, in a peaceful place such as this and being able to work in that beautiful house? I looked back to the stone mansion that stood there solidly in the weak morning sun, with its windows sparkling and its paint work shining and its mellowed walls covered partly in a creeping ivy. At one time it must have belonged to a gentrified family, where the children would have played in the shrub filled grounds.

Oh well, my time there was only temporary, thanks to Harry and his well laid plan, I thought. I'd better get a letter written and tell him all about it. I had seen some writing materials in the Library the evening before.

I turned to walk back up the garden path, waving gaily to the man who had put down his paint brush for a moment to look my way, then suddenly I stopped in my tracks and sank on a bench by an overhanging bush. I didn't want to write to Harry, didn't want him to share my delight with this new life that was to be fleetingly mine. Harry had been left in my old life, that I had fled from to come up here! Oh, how was I going to tell him that? I would hurt him dreadfully and he wouldn't understand. He'd want to come up and talk it over and I'd weaken as I usually did. Maybe a postcard then, a few lines like you would send from a holiday? Having a nice time in Ambleside and wish you were here. But I didn't miss Harry, I thought, as I twisted his engagement ring around my finger. I was having a nice time without him and I didn't want it any other way.

CHAPTER 10

The coach pulled up outside Tree Tops at lunch time on the day of their expected arrival, a dozen Japanese men alighted with their guide a few steps ahead of them. The men were wearing dark suits, white shirts and yellow ties with their country's emblem on, most wore horn rimmed spectacles and carried a camera holding shoulder bag.

'We've just come up from Liverpool,' the guide informed Miss Ripon, who was waiting at Reception to greet her foreign guests. 'Have you laid on sandwiches as we requested and their preference of China tea?'

'Already and waiting, Mr. Griffiths. Vivienne, would you take the gentlemen into the dining room, while I get Fred' to put their luggage at the bottom of the stairs? Where has he got to,....... Vivienne have you seen Fred?'

'I'm here Missis, can't yer see me?', said a frail and trembling voice. It was Fred, who had been caught up amongst the foreign visitors as he was only five foot three. Fred must have been as ancient as the sisters Aggie and Gertie and he lived with his widowed sister in a cottage near the lake. He grabbed at a couple of suitcases and hauled them along unsteadily, but some of the men took pity on him and carried their own luggage to the bottom of the stairs.

I was wearing my uniform, a white cap sleeved blouse and a black pleated skirt and was feeling very important being asked to greet these visitors alongside Miss Ripon. I had spent the morning helping Priscilla cut mounds of cheese or turkey sandwiches and was ready to pour the tea for them. The Japanese sounded a happy crowd as they chattered away in their lingo, something that I had never heard before, not even on the radio.

Later the group were off again, to do the circular tour around the upper lake of Ullswater, but each man kindly took their cases to their bedrooms before they set off to do their sight seeing.

In the evening, after a meal of Cumberland sausages, mashed potato, cabbage and gravy with apple pie and cream for dessert, some of the men went off to their bedrooms, while a few stayed behind to drink a glass or two of wine. One man, who seemed younger than the rest of the group came over to talk to me, whilst Miss Ripon played some Classical music and looked as if she didn't mind him doing so.

'Do you want a top up, Sir?', I asked, knowing that I was encouraged to socialize but feeling a bit nervous, as this was the first time.

'No, thank you,' he smiled pleasantly. 'More than one glass tends to go straight to my head.'

'How can I help you then, Sir?'

'I'd like you to come and talk with me, do you think that your lady will mind?'

'No, I'm sure it will be all right with her, we are encouraged to socialize with our guests. Can I get you a cup of coffee instead?'

'No, I'd just like you to sit with me. My name is Suni, by the way.'

'My name is Vivienne. Shall we sit over there a little away from the music, then we can hear ourselves speak?'

As we did so, Miss Ripon closed the lid of her piano saying that she was finished for the evening and to help themselves to wine or whisky, but I was not to stay up all night.

'Vivyen,' said Suni, looking mortified. 'Oh no, I must not keep you, you must get up early and you work so hard at dinner, you must be tired! It's just that I've never spoken to an English girl, but it doesn't matter I still have time. I hear there will be dancing, yes tomorrow we'll be dancing. Till tomorrow evening, Vivyen, I'll have the pleasure of your company then.'

I left him then, glad that I had been given the opportunity to do so by Miss Ripon, as the day had been a long one and I was tired.

Nor did I want any followers, especially a Japanese one that I'd never see again.

The following morning I was taken up with serving thirteen breakfasts. I smiled cheerfully at everyone and wishing them all a good day. The guests' coach was taking them to the Scottish border where they would be walking along Hadrian's Wall, then they would be taking lunch in a place that was called Carlisle.

I had decided I would walk into Ambleside, as the sending of Harry's postcard was weighing heavily on my mind and also was the thought that my father would be home and probably talking to the Police by now. I decided that I would send two postcards, one to Audrey as well. Then my father would calm down, accept the inevitable and let me get on with my life.

It was cooler that morning as I walked down the hill to the main street. I was glad I'd put a head scarf on and buttoned up my winter coat. I had noticed a cafe on the corner when I had first arrived and intended to treat myself to some hot chocolate or a bowl of soup.

I was looking at the postcards that were on a stand outside a souvenir shop. I hesitated over the one I would send to Harry. Should I send one with a rude joke on it or a picture of Lake Windermere with pretty swans dotted about?

'I'd send the scenic one if I was you,' said a man's voice behind me. I jumped with fright as I knew no one from the area, then turned round to look up into the smiling eyes of William Fearns. 'Fancy seeing you here, Vivienne,' he said happily. 'I wondered how you were getting on? Now you can tell me, can't you, have you got time for a cup of coffee at Dodds cafe?'

'I was thinking about going there anyway, William,' I replied, pleased that I would have his company. 'I thought I'd treat myself to a cup of hot chocolate, seeing as it's such a bitter cold day.'

'Then join me,' he said putting out his left arm so that I could link him. 'I'm on the late shift today so I won't be starting until later on.'

We crossed over the road and into the warmth of the quite busy cafe and found two seats by the window so we could watch the world go by. William ordered a cup of hot chocolate for us both, though he said with the weight that he had got on him, he shouldn't be drinking it at all.

'Go on with you, a little plumpness suits you,' I said , though I was only being friendly, not trying to flatter him, but he seemed to seize on my remark as if it was a signal that maybe I was interested in going out with him.

'Tell me, how's Tree Tops, you evidently found it or you wouldn't be here today?'

'Oh, I love it, I like the staff, I like the work and the guests are such a joy. We've got a group of Japanese men in at the moment and they're so polite and unassuming, I'm really enjoying myself.'

I could see the interest in his eyes as he looked at me. My actions were animated and I knew my eyes were sparkling at him. I was being flirty, which was foolish of me given the circumstances, but I suppose I was looking for any kind of attention at the time.

'And what did you used to do before, Vivienne, before you came to Ambleside?'

I could feel my spirits plummet when he asked that question and I took my time in answering, while I wondered what to say. He looked troubled then, as if he wished he hadn't been so curious.

'Nothing much,' I answered. 'I've just left school, but I decided to come here because I want to see a bit of the world.' There was no way I was going to tell him about me and Harry.

'Well, you haven't come far,' he brightened. 'Seeing the world is like going to America, Australia or New Zealand. I've got an aunty who lives in Canada, I hope to go there one day.'

'I've got a sister who lives in America, she lives in San Francisco and she married a G.I.'

'There you are then, you'll probably go and see her, that's what I meant by seeing the world.'

We chatted for a bit longer, then William looked at his hunter watch that he carried in the pocket of his uniform jacket.

'I'll have to go now, Vivienne,' he said ruefully. 'I promised Mum that I'd pick up some meat from the butchers, she wants to make a casserole for when I get in from work. But before I go, my day off is on Thursday, would it be possible for you and I to spend part of the day together. Perhaps after you've finished your morning's work?'

Oh no, I thought, I haven't even sent Harry a 'Dear John' letter and here I am already getting involved with someone else!

'I can't, William,' I replied gently, not wanting to hurt his feelings. 'I'm sorry, but I have to work all day next Thursday. We've another coach load from somewhere and they'll be wanting full board this time, breakfast, lunch and tea.'

I hated lying to him and kept my fingers crossed under the table as I said it and felt awful when William took his leave, with sadness written all over his face.

I stayed in the cafe a little longer, writing quick postcards to Harry, then Audrey, with a pen that I borrowed from an obliging waitress.

'Dear Harry,

Arrived safely, the job is very nice, the scenery around here is wonderful. Can't send you a telephone number because the Manageress doesn't like us using the 'phone. Will write you a letter when I get time.

Love from Vivienne.'

Then I wrote a postcard to Audrey.

'Dear Sis,

Arrived safely, the job is very nice, the scenery around here is wonderful. Can't send you a telephone number because the Manageress doesn't like us using the 'phone.

Love from Vivienne.'

Then I walked down the road to the Post Office, considering my task well done!

That evening, after the Japanese men had exclaimed their

pleasure on eating Jack's homemade cottage pie and currant cheese cake, I helped with the dishes in the kitchen, then ran upstairs to put my black and white dress on.

There was a party atmosphere already amongst the guests, as they looked forward to the entertainment that would surely be a one off by the Tree Tops mixture of staff. I pinned the artificial red rose onto my jacket, given me by a red faced Suni who had spotted it in a Carlisle shop.

'A rose for a rose,' he had whispered softly, as he produced the white box with the flower inside.

The others at his table chuckled as he did so, making the poor man blush furiously under his sallow skin.

Miss Ripon had wound up the antique gramophone in the Recreation room and announced that she would be the Master of Ceremonies for the evening. We were going to start off with a local country dance and would everyone take a partner? Although some of the men would have to dance together, because there was only six women including herself. There was a rush for Helen and me, though Suni being the youngest got to me first, then Aggie, Gertie, Priscilla and Miss Ripon lined up with their partners to make a start on the dance.

Miss Ripon explained how to do it; make a bow to your partner then forward, backward turn around, waltz together round and round then grab your partner by the hand. The bottom couple would dance up to the top, while the rest of us would form archways for them to go through.

This would be repeated until the end of the music.

It seemed so simple, but the hilarity in which it was carried out and the whooping joy of the Japanese guests, had everyone laughing by the end of the dance!

The evening passed quickly, with waltzing, the tango and even a little rock and roll; then Aggie and Gertie did their version of a Scottish fling. There were tears of laughter as the two elderly women leapt around like whirling dervish and pirouetted as high as they could on their spangly dancing shoes. What a performance!

Aggie and Gertie made their bows, then collapsed in a heap on one of the settees!

They'll pay for that in the morning, I thought, as I went to fetch a tray of glasses from the kitchen and get a couple of bottles of wine. I was closely followed by Suni who had watched me leave the room.

'Vivienne,' he said. 'What wonderful dancing, so many memories to take back to Tokyo as to how the English enjoy themselves so. Did you like my flower? I meant what I said, a rose for a rose, sweet Vivyen. I wish I could live here and make you mine.'

I looked at Suni in astonishment as he stood there with his floppy black hair, brown almond shaped eyes and something like puppy dog adoration as he gazed at me. I wondered if he had been drinking, as the pupils in his eyes were big and he had a dazed look on his oriental looking face. He was wishing he could live here and what was he saying, marry me?

'Oh, Suni, I think you're lovely,' I said carefully. 'But it wouldn't work, you know? You're a big man at the tourist board in Tokyo and you don't realize it, but I'm only sixteen.'

'Then we'll write to each other. Then, when you're older you can come out and visit me at my home in Japan.'

He took my hands and rained kisses on them, then tried to take me in his arms there and then in the hallway. I firmly pushed him away and suggested that he rejoined his party. There was no way I was going to Tokyo, even if I did want to see a bit of the world!

He was cool with me the next morning, as the group boarded the coach to take them to the Scottish Highlands for the rest of their stay. He waved to me sadly through the window and I was unhappy that perhaps I had broken his heart.

Once the coach had left, we threw ourselves into a frenzy of cleaning and tidying, in preparation for the new guests who were arriving later that day. I learnt a new skill, making butter pats in the quiet peace of the still room. It was time consuming and fiddly, trying to get them all of equal size and making sure the flower shaped stamp was deeply pressed into every one, but I felt very tranquil in that simple white washed room.

It was raining outside, so later I decided to go and lie on my bed. My energetic night having drained me, though I saw the two elderly sisters were still going strong, as I passed them busily cleaning on my way up the stairs to the bedroom.

I must have fallen asleep, because a loud knocking on the bedroom door startled me from my forty winks.

'I have a telephone call for you, Vivienne,' Miss Ripon was shouting outside. 'Hurry up downstairs to my office as it's a trunk call!'

A trunk call, what was a trunk call, I wondered, as I ran quickly from the bedroom and down to her office, where she left me alone to talk in private?

'It's Harry,' said a voice that sounded very far away. 'I had to get the number from the operator. You should have given it to me.'

'Harry, it's a business line, you're going to get me into trouble,' I hissed back at him.

'So, 'no sorry Harry I've missed you.' Do you know I've had your Dad down at the bus depot playing Hell and threatening me?'

'Oh, Harry, I'm sorry. What did you tell him, you haven't given my whereabouts away?'

'No, I haven't, but I did tell him we're getting married just as soon as you can get a transfer.'

I groaned inwardly, that would fuel my father's temper.

'And what did he say to that?'

'Nothing, he was speechless. He gave me a threatening fist in my face and then he walked away.'

'Oh.'

'So, have you put in for a transfer yet? What part of Scotland will they be sending you to?'

'I haven't had time to even think about it, Harry, we've been so busy since I got here. Anyway, Harry, I'll write you a letter. This call will be expensive and my manageress is hovering and she doesn't look very pleased.'

'Right then, I'll wait for your letter and Vivienne........'

'What?'

'I love you.'

I put the telephone down feeling very shaken, I'd forgotten all about Harry and my father. They lived in a different world.

'Are you all right, dear?' Miss Ripon asked kindly as she came back into the office. 'Not bad news from home I hope? We would miss you if you had to go.'

I shook my head, suddenly in the grip of despair. I decided that fresh air was needed to clear my senses and went for a walk in the garden.

It was there that I met Nigel Gresty, as he got out of his very splendid car, an open topped Wolsley tourer, though he had the hood up that day. He was dressed in a burgundy coloured blazer over an open neck white shirt and a pair of grey slacks; his fair hair was slicked back with Brylcream and he had a wicked gleam in his pale blue eyes. In one hand he carried his black sample bag and an overnight suitcase in the other.

'Well, well, who have we got here then?', he asked as he kicked the driver's door shut, after seeing me shivering in the porch way. 'I've been coming here for seven years and I've never seen anyone as pretty as you.'

'I've just started work here, Sir,' I said, blushing at his compliment, though I had heard it all before.

'My name is Vivienne Dockerty and I'll be your dining room maid.'

'Dining room maid, eh? Well, things are certainly looking up, what? So, Viv', I'll see you later, going for a walk are you then?'

I nodded, though I thought I'd go back to my room to put my warm coat on. Then I stayed where I was as another car swept up the drive, this time a sleek silver Rover saloon that drew up to park at the side of Nigel's car.

'Nigel, old chap,' cried the driver. 'I see I've caught up with you again, fancy joining me down at the Fox and Hounds around eight o' clock tonight?'

'Not when there's a pretty little lassie like this one waiting on us hand and foot, old chap. Meet Vivienne, she's our dining room maid. Here to serve, eh, pretty one?'

He followed me with predatory eyes throughout the evening meal, touched my hand when he thanked me and patted my bottom overtly when I had to pass him to serve someone else. When Miss Ripon announced there would be a quiz that night, he winked and asked me would I like to be in the team with him? I was tired, depressed and in a mix up after my call from Harry earlier, so I told Miss Ripon that I had a headache and would like to be excused for the rest of the night.

Next morning he came pestering, would I like to go for a drive? His calls on the local farmers to sell his wares were boring and lonely, would I like to accompany him? My answer was 'No' very firmly, I had a lot of work to do.

Oh, what was I to do about Harry? My mind was in a whirl. Should I write him a letter, tell him the truth, tell him that I didn't really want to marry him? I felt a little frightened though, he might storm up on the train to Ambleside, persuade me to go up to Scotland and then where would I be? I decided to push it to the back of my mind and think on it another day.

Two weeks passed by, there were no more 'phone calls and I began to feel happier than I'd been for a while.

The hotel became quite busy as February turned into March and the weather began to brighten up, bringing weekend guests to walk or climb, or sail on the lake in the ferryboat steamer. I usually had Thursdays off and was saving my wages to buy a shop bought frock. I fancied buying a gypsy dress that had become all the rage, in a brightly coloured cheesecloth with small puffy sleeves.

It was mid week, a Wednesday and I was laying out the trolley for afternoon tea, when a voice behind me made me jump. It was Nigel Gresty.

'Vivienne,' he said as he strode into the dining room. 'Have you missed me, I've missed you? Mmm, what have you got there on the trolley, sandwiches, scones and a gateau. Good, I'm just in time for afternoon tea.'

My heart sank as I saw him, it was going to be a couple of days

203

of dodging again. Never mind, I was off tomorrow and he'd probably be gone again by Friday.

I stood at the bus stop next morning waiting for the Keswick coach, as Miss Ripon had told me she had seen a posh boutique in the town. Not that I could afford a posh frock, but there might be a sale on, or a cheaper dress shop. I'd not been to Keswick yet, nor Grasmere or Kendal, they were on my 'to do' list when I managed the time. I had heard that there was a poet's house at Grasmere; William Wordsworth who had composed 'I wandered lonely as a cloud', and a Gingerbread shop by the side of the churchyard, where the poet and his family were buried in the grounds.

I was lost in thought as a car drew up beside me. The driver tooted the horn to catch my attention, as he wound down his window with a grin.

'Vivienne, where are you off to? Wherever you're going I'll take you there, hop in.'

It was Nigel, oh, why was it Nigel? How was I going to dodge him this time? What excuse could I give to him?

'I'm off to Keswick, Nigel. You don't have to give me a lift there, the coach is due any minute.'

'Nonsense, get in the car, Vivienne, we'll be there in the shake of a monkey's tale. In time for a spot of lunch, no doubt.'

I got in the car with a heavy heart, then he raced along the narrow country road.

Above the noise of the engine, Nigel told me that it was cattle market day and he was going to Keswick anyway for a meeting with some farmers. He dropped me off later at the small country town, saying that he would pick me up outside the bus station on the dot of noon.

I was trapped, I thought, as I walked along, trapped by another bloody man. A guest at that and could be sacked from my lovely job if the man wanted to make a complaint against me. I toyed with the idea of catching the next bus that came along and travel back to Ambleside.

Then I saw the shop window with its display of dresses and all thoughts of Nigel disappeared from my mind.

I waited at mid day with the dress bag in my hand, it was exactly what I had wanted and had cost me two weeks pay, but the thought of how I had looked in the changing room mirror, with the warm peach colour seeming to bring a brightness to my face, had banished any worry that I had spent such a large amount.

'I've got a call to do near Ullswater,' Nigel said as we roared off in the car again. 'Did a nice bit of business this morning, so we'll stop at a pub' on the way.'

I nodded. Whatever, as long as you get me back in one piece, I thought, as the trees and hedges along the road were passing by at an alarming pace!

We stopped at a pub' and had pie and peas and Nigel had a couple of whiskies as well, before we climbed into the Wolsley to speed away again.

He made his call to an outlying farm, then drove back alongside the Ullswater lake. It had begun to lash down with rain by this time and lulled by the swishing sound of the wind-screen wipers, I felt my head begin to nod as the car crawled along the slippery road. It was warm inside, as Nigel had switched the heater on, and before I was aware of it he had turned down a narrow country track, bringing the car to rest in a lakeside park.

He switched off the engine, then sat back to study me disconcertingly.

'I thought you were taking me back to Tree Tops.' I said nervously.

'I am, but I thought we could enjoy some time to ourselves. I'm going home tomorrow and I don't know when I'll be back again.'

'So, what do you want to talk about then?'

'I don't want to talk about anything, Vivienne.'

He leaned over to take me in his arms, though the gears of the car got stuck in an embarrassing place.

I began to shrink back against the passenger window. It had worked with Dezza, it just might with Nigel.

'Oh, come on Vivienne, you little tease,' he said with gritted teeth. 'You've been giving me the eye since I came to Tree Tops. It's a long way to walk to Ambleside, so you might as well enjoy it. Come on, I really fancy you, give us a kiss for a start.'

'Well, that's all you'll be getting Nigel, I'm on my period,' I lied, 'and I'll walk all the way to Ambleside if you think you're going to force yourself on me.'

'Uh no,' his nose wrinkled in distaste. 'Periods. I'll settle for a hand job instead.'

He opened up the buttons on his trouser front and I paid him for my lunch in the way he expected me to.

I hated men, really really hated men. They were disgusting and made me feel dirty and it would be a long time before I trusted another. A very long time.

It was the week coming up to Easter and Miss Ripon had told the staff that a party of young men were coming to stay from a Lancashire college. There were six of them and their tutor and they would arrive on Saturday around the time of afternoon tea.

I didn't take much notice of this information as I had gone off men, even poor old William was given the frozen mitt when I met him on the Grasmere bus, as I travelled there on my next day off. I was polite to the guests, but not as friendly and mostly read or knitted in my leisure time.

So it came as something of a surprise to me, when I walked in that Saturday with afternoon tea and saw the group of students playing a game of cards. They all looked so wholesome, instead of the usual scruffy or shabby, they were all dressed neatly in long sleeved shirts and denims, with jackets hung on the back of their chairs.

They turned around and thanked me politely, as I put the tray of sandwiches on a table within easy reach, then one of them came over as I began to pour out cups of tea.

'Can I help you with those cups or maybe give out plates for the sandwiches?', he asked kindly.

'Oh yes,' I replied flustered, 'that's very nice of you.'

'Think nothing of it, I wait on at weekends so I know what it's like.'

He helped me out for a couple of minutes, then I went to the kitchen to get some cake.

I watched them closely as I handed around the slices, especially the lad who had been helping me out. He was tall, fair haired and had the bluest of eyes and I liked the way his mouth curved up when he smiled.

'Is there anywhere we can get a drink in the evenings?', one of them asked me.

'Well the hotel is licensed and we have entertainment here. Miss Ripon will be playing the piano from about eight o'- clock.'

They laughed at me good humouredly, then got back to playing their hand of cards.

I was on my way back to my bedroom when the telephone in the office rang. Miss Ripon was nowhere to be seen, so I went to answer its ring.

'Tree Tops House, Vivienne speaking, how can I help you?'

'It's Harry.'

'Oh, Harry.' The familiar plummeting of spirits followed.

'I thought you weren't allowed to use the 'phone.'

'Well, I'm not usually, but the manageress is away from the office for a moment.'

'Why didn't you write to me, Vivienne?'

'I could say the same to you, you've never written to me either.'

'I've been busy, I was taking my *P.S.V* and now I've become a bus driver.'

'Congratulations, more money is it?'

'Yes, but that isn't why I'm ringing you. I've been thinking about us, Vivienne. I think my mother was right and you're far too young for me. By now you would have been arranging that transfer to Scotland, but I think you've been having a whale of a time and have just forgotten about me.'

There was a silence, as I struggled to deny what he said.

'Is there another man?'

'Er, no, Harry.' Definitely not, Harry.

'Well, in my case there is somebody else in my life. I've not done anything about it because I've only just got to know her. She's my clippie, but we get on very well. So I thought I'd ring you and see if you want to continue with our engagement, but I have a feeling that the answer's 'No.'

'That's right, Harry,' I said , feeling the relief flooding through my body as I heard his words. 'I'll always have a place in my heart for you, Harry, but it's true, I'm far too young to get married and will be I suppose for quite some time.' There, it was said and it had been easy.

'Then I'll say goodbye, Vivienne. You can keep the ring, I won't be wanting it back again.'

With that the line went dead and I was left with the dialling tone.

'Problem, dear?' Miss Ripon stood behind me, looking concerned.

'Oh, no, Miss Ripon, sorry, I didn't see you there. No, every thing's fine, I'll just go up to my room for a while.'

I lay on my bed quietly, trying not to disturb the elderly sisters who were getting their feet up before dinner. So, Harry had finished it then, did I feel happy or sad? It was hard to judge with him being so far away from me, but there was a sense of relief that I was free again and didn't have to take orders from any man.

That evening after dinner, the students sat politely through Miss Ripon's piano performance, but I could see that they were bored and itching to get out to find a local pub' to let their hair down in. I had offered them drinks of wine or whisky, but most of them said they would prefer a blessed pint! There was an undisguised mutual sigh of relief when Miss Ripon put the piano lid down and they applauded her efforts for the past half hour.

'Are you taking us down to the pub', Vivienne?', one of the lads with curly brown hair and spectacles asked me. 'We'll treat you to a couple of drinks if you do.'

I glanced over to the Manageress in case she had any jobs for me, but Miss Ripon nodded her head and said that I could go.

The students grabbed their jackets, then waited for me while I got my coat from upstairs, even their tutor tagged along as we rushed along the drive down to Ambleside. It took us minutes to get to the Fox and Hounds, where seven pints of bitter were ordered and a lemonade shandy for me.

I found myself sitting next to the tall fair haired guy, who I now knew was called, Andy. The other students chatted at the bar with their tutor called, Phil'. I wondered if they had engineered it between them because I did feel a frisson of something between Andy and me. I sipped on my drink while he just sat quietly and searched my mind for a moment to think of something to say.

'How come you lot are up here at Tree Tops then?'

'Oh, this is a treat from our tutor under the guise of an outward bound course. He'll have us up Helvellyn tomorrow, says he's going to tire us out up Striding Edge and Scarfell. He's a good bloke is Phil', the best teacher I've ever had anyway.'

'So what does he teach you?'

'He takes us for General Studies, we're all working on our *O.N.D.*'

'And what's an *O.N.D*?'

'It's the ordinary national diploma which puts us in line for the *H.N.D.*'

'And what's a *H.N.D*?'

'It's the higher national diploma and if I get that I can apply to University.'

'Gosh, that sounds like an awful lot of hard work to me,' I said, impressed with all these qualifications he was talking about. 'No wonder you're tutor wants to treat you, what will you be doing at University then?'

'Hopefully I'll get on an electronic engineering course and I'll be working for an First class honours degree.'

'Oh.' I lapsed into silence.

I looked at Andy with a great deal of respect. Well, I could forget him as a potential boyfriend for a start , this lad was going to reach for the stars and he wouldn't be bothering with a common tart like me. But he didn't know I was common, my conscious told me, didn't know that I was anybody's bit of fluff if they showed me a bit of kindness. It would be nice to have someone who liked me for myself and not because they wanted to get into my underwear.

'So, why are you up here, Vivienne?' Andy asked me. 'From what I can see you could do a lot better. What are you doing working as a dining room maid?'

'It's a long story. I had a problem with my school work, ducked out of taking my O' levels, then had a falling out with my dad.'

'Well, that's a great pity, I wish that I had known my dad, but he left us when my sister and I were babies, so my mother has had to struggle to bring us up on her own. Do you want another drink? That glass of wine I had earlier at the hotel has made me feel really thirsty. Another one of those then, O.K , I'll be back in a mo'?'

I sat and watched him as he laughed and joked with his mates at the bar. I knew they were ragging him because he was sitting with me, but somehow I didn't care. There was something about him, a goodness, a kindness, a feeling that I had got inside myself that he was the kind of person who would protect me to my dying day. I mustn't make a mess this time, I'd be anything that he wanted me to be.

'So, thoughts for the future?,' he said when he brought back my drink. 'You're not thinking of staying here forever, are you? Maybe you'll think of going back to your studies one day?'

'Oh probably, one day maybe. Anyway, tell me about your family. Have you got a gran'?'

The others came to sit with us later so there was lots of laughter and silly conversation, but we did walk together back to Tree Tops and Andy held my hand.

I caused a lot of oohing and aahing at the breakfast table next morning, when Andy was given two fried eggs and an extra bacon slice instead of the usual one, but the students were all a happy bunch, pleased that their mate had 'pulled.'

That evening they were all feeling weary after being hauled up and down the local mountains and dragged along the country paths, but one of them found the energy to play a trick on me.

I couldn't find the beater for my dinner gong. After searching and searching, I shouted them all in for their dinner, but had to smile when I went to bed later because I found it under my pillow!

The next morning I decided to pay them back and stood in the door of their bedroom with the reception bell. I rang it so loud that they all shot up in alarm and I nearly wet myself laughing at the panic I had caused!

On Tuesday, as the students were getting ready to leave for the day after breakfast, Andy came to me and asked for a word.

'I was wondering, Vivienne,' he said blushing furiously, 'I wondered when your day off is so that perhaps we could do something together that day.'

'My day off is on Thursday, Andy, but aren't you all going back home on Thursday?' I said, elated that he wanted my company.

'Yes, but perhaps Miss Ripon would let you change your day?'

'I could ask her, but she'll need a good reason.'

'Be honest with her, Vivienne, tell her I've asked you out on a date.'

I said that I would and I'd let Andy know when he came back from walking in Wasdale.

Miss Ripon was happy to let me change to the following day.

'Can't stand in the way of a budding romance, can I?' she smiled. 'Though a word of caution, these fellows seem to disappear back into the wood work once they're back home again, but from what I've seen he seems a nice lad, so I'll be happy to cover for you on Wednesday.'

Andy was delighted when I told him and said his tutor had said a similar thing to him when he had asked if he could have Wednesday off, but omitted to say that his tutor had been rather coarse about it!

We set off after breakfast to Kendal. I carried a shopping bag with a packet of egg sandwiches and a borrowed flask with coffee in. I wore my new peach gypsy dress, had brushed my hair until it shone and wore a pair of pretty gold strappy sandals. The weather was quite warm for April, but I took a white knitted cardigan with me in case it got cooler later that day. Andy was wearing a pale green aertex short sleeved shirt, with light brown flannel trousers and carried a dark brown stripey jacket. His short fair hair cut in an Elvis Presley style, gleamed with the Cossack hair spray he wore.

There wasn't a lot of conversation between us, as we travelled on the bus beside the still waters of the lakes and tarns, past the hillsides, the villages and the farmland on the way. We were content to sit and enjoy each others company and sad that it was to be our last day together.

We wandered through the town of Kendal, past the tourist shops and cafe's until we reached the banks of a fast flowing river, found a bench and then sat down.

'Vivienne,' said Andy, as he munched his way through a sandwich thoughtfully. 'Why don't you go back and live with your family again?'

'I don't want to. All my father ever did was shout and nag and try to get me to do what he wanted me to do.'

'But surely if you look at it from your dad's point of view, he was only doing what he thought best. He would want you to have a good education and find a good job.'

'It's too late now, he wouldn't have me back again.'

'Why?'

'Because I got in with this chap and we were going to run away together and get married.'

Andy had to stifle a laugh at my seriousness.

'You're only eighteen, don't you think your dad was right to be against such a young marriage?'

'I have a confession, Andy,' I thought I had better tell him. 'I'm only sixteen, not eighteen, I just look older for my age, I don't know why.'

'If we're having confession time,' he said, trying hard not to laugh out loud, 'then I'll have to tell you the truth as well. I'll be seventeen in two months time.'

We both chuckled for a moment and then Andy said.

'Surely you don't see yourself working as a dining room maid for the rest of your days?'

'No, but I can't see any choices at the moment, so I may as well stay where I am.'

'What if you became my girlfriend, though it's a long way to come to Ambleside from Wigan?'

'You'd like me for your girlfriend?' I gasped in disbelief. 'You hardly know me and if you did you wouldn't like me very much.'

'I think I'll take that chance, Vivienne,' he said in amusement. 'Now let's seal our commitment with a kiss.'

CHAPTER 11

'Edward Dockerty,' his voice said coolly at the end of the telephone.

'Dad, it's me,' I said nervously.

'Who's 'me'?', he asked abruptly.

'Your daughter, Vivienne.'

'Have I got a daughter called Vivienne?'

'Yes, Dad, I want to come home. Can I come home?'

'I don't know if I want my daughter called Vivienne to come home.'

'I've changed, Dad. I'm a good girl now and I'm not going out with Harry anymore.'

'I wondered how long the bugger would take to come to his senses after I had a word with him.'

'I've got a new boyfriend now, he lives in Wigan, so I need to come home so that he can go out with me.'

'So you're not coming home because you miss me and your mother then?'

'Well, yes, you, Mother and Audrey. So can I come home again, Dad?'

'I suppose so but you had better behave yourself, or I'll be packing your bag for you next time!'

I waited until Miss Ripon was on her own in the office next day, then went in and gave her my notice.

The Manageress wasn't very pleased.

'This is most unfortunate, Vivienne. It means I have to get a replacement for you and that isn't easy now that the season has begun. Every hotel has to have a full compliment of staff. Is there some urgency in your departure?'

'No, I can wait until you find someone else. Would you like me to stay for another couple of weeks?' I thought it was only fair to do so.

'Oh, would you, that would be very kind?' she said in a relieved voice. 'I'll get in touch with Head Office and start the ball rolling right away. Meantime, don't say anything to the other staff, will you, dear?'

So I stayed until Miriam, a big, flatfooted young woman, appeared at Reception saying that she was the new dining room maid. I stayed a couple of days to train her and then I quietly disappeared.

'So you're back then?', Father remarked, when he came in for his meal on Saturday evening after I had been home for an hour. 'Mmm, that smells good, Irene, cooking the fatted calf for the prodigal daughter?'

'Something like that,' said Mother. 'Vivienne, would you be kind enough to set the table in the living room, then come back and get the vegetable tureens?'

My mother had gone all posh, I thought, as I did as I was asked. Vegetable tureens, whatever next, we used to have our dinner served up on a plate?'

'Now go easy on her, Eddie,' Mother pleaded once she thought I was out of earshot. 'She's made the effort to come back home and I don't want her going off again. It's enough I have to go to the other side of the world to see Gina and young Mandy, without you giving Vivienne reason to go off again.'

'O.K., O.K., whatever, but she'd best damn well behave herself this time and not make a mug out of me.'

'Oh, she didn't, she's a teenager. Girls sometimes fall in love with the wrong person, they do it all the time.'

'It's good to be back, Mum,' I said, coming through to the kitchen and wrinkling my nose appreciatively. 'Though we had the finest chef in the Lake District, it was nothing like the food you get at home.'

'Flatterer,' said Mother shaking her finger at me. 'You should have seen what I had to eat in America, it took some getting used to, I can tell you. It's a good thing I had my Rennies with me.

The size of those hamburgers and those Texan ribs, with something else I think they called chilli-con- carne. Give me good old fashioned mince and dumplings any old day.'

'So, what's this you're giving us then, are they what you call hamburgers?' Father looked suspicious.

'Adapted, Eddie, I thought I'd have a go at making them, but mine are a quarter of the size you get over there.'

I was tired after my journey that afternoon, so after an hour of watching boring telly, I went up to the bedroom. My sister was out and hadn't been seen all day by our parents. Mother said Audrey had gone to a friend's house and was staying the night.

It was good to be home, I thought, as I snuggled under my bedcovers. No more sharing with the elderly sisters, who seemed to get a lot of wind after eating sprouts. My parents seemed to be happy that I was back again, though of course there would be tension over the next few days, with my mother bound to be on at me over secretarial college. But as long as I didn't have to go back to that horrible grammar school then perhaps things would settle down.

'So, tell me about this new boyfriend of yours,' said Father, as we sat next morning eating breakfast together.

'Oh, he's very nice, you'll both like him. He lives in Wigan, that's in Lancashire and he's studying to be an electronic engineer.'

'So what kind of job will he get with his qualification then?'

'I don't know Dad, I didn't ask him about his future career.'

'And does he say things like 'eeh by gum?', asked Mother, 'I met a woman from Lancashire once and I couldn't understand a word she said.'

'Well, I understood him,' I replied brightly, 'and that reminds me. Is it all right if I telephone him later, well not him personally because he's not on the telephone, but his sister is and I've to leave a message with her?'

'What kind of message?', Father asked.

'I have to telephone to say that I got back home safely and when it would be convenient for him to visit here.'

'Does he work, is he at college? Will it be a weekend or a weekday?', Mother asked.

'He goes to college during the week, he's on a full time course. He says I should go to college and study for a career.'

'Sounds like he's got a good head on his shoulders,' said Father. 'We were going to talk to you about that, but we thought we'd leave it a day or two. You can't go back to the County Grammar, because I rang and asked Miss Preston. She said you've been out of school too long now and you're best going to college to pass your exams.'

'She could go to secretarial college, Eddie,' said my mother. 'It was good enough for Gina as you know.'

'But I don't want to go to secretarial college,' I said trying to keep my temper in. 'I keep telling you that, Mum. Anyway, I can't start anywhere until the September term, I'll have to get another job. Meantime, is it all right if I use the telephone? I want to leave a message for Andy and give him our number here.'

I dialed the telephone number that Andy had given me, with a bit of luck he might be at his sister's house, because he had said he sometimes went there for a meal.

The receiver was picked up virtually straight away.

'Wigan 6394.'

'Oh, hello, my name is Vivienne Dockerty, could I leave a message for Andy with you, please?'

'And who are you when you're at home?', the young woman on the end of the 'phone asked suspiciously.

'Perhaps your brother hasn't spoken about me yet, I'm Vivienne, his girlfriend.'

'He hasn't got a girlfriend.'

'Well, he has now. Am I speaking to his sister, Dorothy, by the way? Yes, then have you got a pen handy, please give him this telephone number?'

I read out the digits from the front of the family 'phone, as I had never had cause to use it before and hadn't memorized it.

'Please ask him to call as soon as he gets the message, thank you. Goodbye.'

What a strange young woman, I thought. I wonder if all sisters are so protective of their younger brothers? Having never had a younger brother myself, I would never know.

Audrey came home later and greeted me in an off hand manner.

'So you're back then. I suppose we'll have to get used to all the shouting and bawling now you're back again.'

'Why, has it been quiet without me?' I asked innocently.

'It certainly has. After you went Dad didn't speak to me for three days, I suppose he thought I knew more than I was letting on. He didn't tell Mum of course, though he rang her in San Francisco a few times to see how she was. Then he got involved with buying next door, so that took the heat off me and since then he's been scraping the walls and decorating, getting it ready for renting it out. When Mum came home she cried a bit, but I let her see your postcard and she cheered up after that.'

'And what have you been up to since I've been away?'

'Not much, I dumped Brian and I'm seeing another chap now, I'm still working hard at school and choosing my options this year.'

'Well, I'm going out with this gorgeous guy I met when I was up in Ambleside. You'll meet him soon, he lives in Wigan, but he's coming all that way to see me.'

Andy rang to say that he would meet me in Liverpool on the following Sunday. He worked on Saturday's at his uncle's bakery shop, then on Saturday evenings he worked in a pub' clearing and washing the glasses. His uncle also had an outside catering firm and sometimes he would wait on at weddings or any functions that his uncle had been asked to do, but he was looking forward to seeing me again and he hoped that everything had gone well with my mum and dad.

'I don't know what I'm going to wear,' I said to my mother, when I told her that I would be bringing Andy home for Sunday lunch. 'I can't wear my gypsy dress again because he's seen me in it. Can I borrow that nice blouse that you brought from America?'

'But you turned your nose up at it when I said you could have it,' Mother said craftily.

'I know, but I've nothing new to wear, I'm going to have to get a job.'

'I saw two jobs in the Birkenhead News that might suit you. I was going to mention them but your mind seems to be caught up with this Andy.'

'Well, where's the paper and I'll have a look. As long as it's not in an office, 'cos I don't want to be in a stuffy office for the rest of my life.'

The jobs that Mother had circled seemed to be suitable, one was a clerk in a Pools company and the other a trainee telephonist for the *G.P.O.*, but I thought it would be similar to what I had just said. It would be working in an office and that was one thing I didn't want to do.

'You don't know that, Vivienne, you might work in a big office and it won't be stuffy. Send for the application forms, at least you can give it a go,' Mother pleaded.

'All right then, I'll send for them, but I'm still going to have to look for a temporary job in the meantime.'

I caught the bus on the Sunday morning foregoing a lie in that day. I wore the American pink linen blouse with two patch pockets and a plain black skirt. My heart was beating nervously as I caught the Mersey ferry and hoped that Andy would be waiting for me. I didn't want to look conspicuous standing alone at the Pier Head as if I'd been stood up.

'Vivienne,' Andy shouted as he saw me walking down the gangway, looking around to see if he was there.

'We can catch this boat back if you want,' I shouted to him. 'It'll be off again in a few minutes time.'

'No, wait, come up the ramp with me, there's someone I'd like you meet up here.'

Feeling mystified I followed him. Had he brought his mother with him? Would she want to go home with us for lunch?

A rather plump young woman, stood with a slim built man at the top of the walkway, the woman had a green tent like dress on and light gingery coloured hair.

'This is Dorothy, my sister, and her husband, Len',' Andy said proudly. 'They decided to drive me here then spend the rest of the day in Liverpool.'

His sister raked her eyes over me. 'Giving me the once over,' as I told Mother later on.

She shook my hand and said she was pleased to meet me, but I noticed there and then that her smile never quite reached her eyes. Len' smiled and I could see that it was genuine. He said he was also pleased to meet me and perhaps they would see me again.

'Now we'll get off and have a look around,' Dorothy said. 'Which way is it to the Cavern, Vivienne? We may as well go down Matthew Street, seeing as we've come all this way.'

I directed them and the couple walked over to their white Mini van, that they had parked a little way off near the bus station. It had been arranged that they would wait for Andy at four o'- clock near the Landing Stage.

'It doesn't give you very long with me, does it?', I said, as Andy and I walked hand in hand back to wait for the ferryboat.

'But it saved me the train fare and she wanted to meet you, so that was two birds killed instead of one.'

'Mmm,' I said.

'So what would you like to do now?', I asked Andy, after we had eaten a delicious roast dinner and a lemon meringue pie for Sunday lunch.

'Perhaps the lad would like to rest before he sets back on that long journey?', Father said.

'No, you're all right, Mr. Dockerty, I think me and Vivienne have got some talking to do. So perhaps we could go for a walk, eh, Vivienne?'

'Yes, of course, Andy. We'll go round the block, we've got an hour and a half before we need to catch the bus back to Woodside.'

'Nay, you don't have to do that, I'll make my own way back to the Pier Head. Nice to have met you Mr. and Mrs. Dockerty and of course you as well, Audrey. Keep them studies up won't you and make your parents proud of you one day.'

'What did you say that for, Andy?', I asked as we walked along the pavement linking arms.

'What did I say?' He looked puzzled.

'About Audrey keeping up her studies, now you'll have them on my back as well.'

'But I thought you were going to take up your studies again.'

'Well, I'm not so sure, there were two good jobs in the local paper so I might be applying for them.'

'Dead end jobs?'

'No, you get training, one is with a Pools company and the other's with the *G.P.O.*'

'If it was me, Vivienne, I'd go for the one with the *G.P.O.*'

'Why?'

'Because if you get a training with them you can work anywhere. Lots of places want switchboard operators so you'd have a job for life, as it were.'

'And why not the Pools company?'

'Seasonal I would have thought, also it would depend on how many swimming pools they sell.'

'No, silly, it's checking pools coupons. You know, dependent on the football results!'

'Oh, it was a joke, Vivienne, don't you think I knew that.'

We said goodbye at the bus stop, as Andy was very insistent that I didn't waste money on the fare. He arranged to come over again the following Sunday and said he would make his way to our house himself, rather than we meet in Liverpool. He kissed me goodbye chastely on the cheek and told me to take care of myself and to take a long, long look at my future and not do anything rash.

My parents were over the moon that I'd found such a great bloke like Andy, especially my mother who seemed to have fallen in love with him herself, but something didn't feel quite right to me somehow. I didn't know what, but there seemed to be something lacking in my heart.

The following week it was the same routine, though Dorothy and Len didn't bring him to Liverpool in the car this time. Instead Andy looked tired, after an evening spent helping his uncle with a wedding buffet, then the journey down from Wigan when he'd slept on the train.

I didn't tell him, but I had found a part time job in a petrol station, pumping petrol into people's cars for the princely sum of five shillings a day.

'What about you coming up to Wigan next week?' he asked, as we sat in the living room after Sunday lunch, because it had begun to rain.

'Sounds a good idea, Vivienne,' said Father. 'You can have a look at that famous Wigan Pier that people are on about.'

'Didn't George Orwell write a book entitled 'The Road to Wigan Pier'?', Mother asked.

'Yes, I've not read it though, have you?', said Andy.

'So when do you want me to come?' I asked, thinking it would be another adventure.

Andy met me off the train at Wigan station. I had found the view depressing, as we had chugged into the town via cotton mills and houses that were back to back. All the streets seemed cobbled, everywhere looked grey, only a canal with brightly painted barges on it stood out amongst the disappointing view.

He seemed pleased to see me and politely asked about my journey, then said we would catch the bus to Whelley, which was where his family had their home. It seemed that day we ran out of conversation, though Andy asked me had I heard from the pools company or the *G.P.O.*?

We got off the bus outside a petrol station, which brought to my mind that I was working at one just like that, but I decided to say nothing. He'd only go on about a long term plan.

'This is my Mum,' said Andy proudly, as he introduced a slim fair haired lady in her middle forties, dressed in a yellow twin-set and a brown A- line skirt.

'Pleased to meet you, Vivienne,' she said, though she didn't look as if she was pleased. 'I can't say I've heard a lot about you because Andy keeps his girlfriends to himself.'

'Mum,' said Andy warningly, then turned to the other woman waiting for an introduction.

'And this is my Granny. This is actually my Granny's house, she's lived here for nearly sixty years.'

A small lady with white hair tied neatly back with hair grips, dressed in a navy calf length dress with a white pinny over it, came forward to shake my hand.

'Ah, but he told me all about you, Vivienne,' she said brightly. 'You live on the Wirral and you've got a nice mum and dad.'

The house that I had been led into was a three up and two down terraced house, with a wooden extension on the back that held the kitchen sink and a few cupboards, which you walked through if you wanted to go to the outside lav'. I did on two occasions and was fascinated by the newspaper squares hanging up for toilet paper and the paraffin lamp in a corner, which was supposed to keep the draughty place warm. I learnt that the house didn't have a bathroom, but now that Dorothy had got married and moved, they were thinking of changing one of the bedrooms into a tiny bathroom. That was when the family got some money though, as Granny only had her pension, Andy's mother only had a cotton mill worker's wage and of course Andy was saving up to go to university.

The conversation was desultory while Granny rushed about getting the joint out of the oven, basting the potatoes and keeping an eye on the Yorkshire puddings. Eventually we sat round the table in what was called the kitchen, as opposed to the back kitchen and I noticed from the clock on the mantelpiece there was only two hours to go.

My heart sank as I realized that it would be another week before I saw Andy again, another week of staying in and watching boring telly, while Andy sat in his home studying for his exams. Still, if that was what it took to have a nice boyfriend, then I was willing to give it a go.

We walked back to the station together hand in hand, after I had been invited to come again anytime by Andy's granny and mum. Then as the we were saying goodbye, when the train was about to leave the station, Andy said that he'd have to leave it next week as it was the beginning of his exams!!

A few days later a letter came for me from the *G.P.O.* I was to attend an interview in Liverpool on Friday morning, at the Post office chambers in Clayton Square. Then in the post the next morning came a letter inviting me to attend an interview at the Pools company in Canning Street, Birkenhead.

I was suddenly very popular and decided to tell the boss of the garage that I would be leaving his employment on Thursday night. It was cold standing on the forecourt dressed in a donkey jacket with the name of the garage embroidered on the back, even on the warmest day my hands felt chilled and chapped. I was bound to get both of the jobs, all I had to decide was which one?

On Friday morning I sat with other girls of a similar age, in a small room which held a switchboard and a woman supervisor. We were instructed to sit at the board with headphones on, while the woman rapped out numbers in quick succession, to be written down as fast as possible on the examination papers in front of us. We did this for a quarter of an hour, then waited in turn for a face to face interview.

I was asked three questions.

'Why do you want to be a switchboard operator?'

'Because I think I would enjoy being busy answering calls and helping people.'

'What do you think you can offer the General Post Office?'

'I am hardworking, trustworthy and reliable.'

'Would you be prepared to join our training scheme?'

'Yes.'

'Well, Miss Dockerty, thank you for attending the interview,' the supervisor said to me. 'Do you have any questions?'

'Could you tell me what the wage will be?' That was most important.

'Five pounds per week once you have completed the training. We will let you know if you have been successful.'

So that hadn't been too bad, I thought, as I walked along Church Street, looking into the shop windows as I passed them by. I decided to treat myself to a sandwich and a coffee, then wander through Blacklers and perhaps buy myself a pair of shoes.

I sat morosely in my bedroom that following Sunday. It was no fun waiting around for Andy.

He had sent me a letter saying that he was sorry that he couldn't see me, but he really needed to put in some last minute studying before the exams that he was taking next week. He hoped he would be able to see me the following Sunday, but up to then he didn't know.

On the Tuesday morning I set off for my interview at the Pools company. I wore my new black court shoes with two inch heels and my black and white summer dress with the black edge to edge jacket. I always felt smart in that outfit, but was thinking that I really needed to buy or make something else, especially if at the pools company I needed to wear a suit.

This was more of an informal interview though. Eight young ladies sat at desks with a pile of past football coupons before us. We had to check for draw matches as quickly as possible and if we found a minimum of six on a coupon, they had to be put in a separate pile. That was really easy and at the end of so many minutes the supervisor told us to stop. This done, we went for an interview and similar questions were asked to the ones at the G.P.O. I asked about the wage again and it was a whopping seven pounds a week!

'And it could be more with overtime,' I explained to my mother that evening. 'If you work past five o'- clock each night, it could be as much as twelve pounds a week!'

'But it isn't a long term career, is it, Vivienne?' Mother replied worriedly. 'A pools company could close at any time and you know you would always have a secure job with the *G.P.O.*'

'I do know that, Mum, but seven to twelve pounds a week is not to be sniffed at and I'm sure that coupon checkers will always be in demand.'

'Whatever, Vivienne, you'll not listen to my advice anyway. So when is Andy coming to visit again, such a nice boy isn't he, dear?'

I hadn't heard if I had got either job by the time I saw Andy again. He arrived at my house the following Sunday, looking tired and very washed out. We walked together to Thurstaston Hill while he told me of his difficulties in some of his exams.

'But I think I've passed them, Vivienne,' he said eagerly. 'In fact, I'm sure of it, so I'll be taking my Highers at the same time next year.'

We sat on the sandy rock that overlooks the River Dee and to the Welsh hills beyond, it was so peaceful and so tranquil, but Andy seemed very nervous and kept lighting up a cigarette.

'It's getting to me all this studying and working, I'll be glad when it's all over. I mean all the exams, not the ones I've just taken, but I've another six years of it as far as I can see.'

'Six years of me only seeing you on a Sunday, Andy?', I asked with a sinking heart.

'Well, I suppose so, Vivienne, because I have to pay my way by working on Saturdays and I will have to work through the summer holidays, because my mother can't support me through university.'

'I don't know if I can wait that long, Andy. I'm finding it hard sitting around at the weekends doing nothing. I should be out having fun at my age.'

'Fun comes later, Vivienne, when you've got a good career ahead of you and the money starts rolling in. Anyway, if you love me, don't you think it's worthwhile waiting for me?' He looked at me seriously, waiting for my reaction.

'I do love you, Andy,' I said sadly, 'but obviously I don't love you enough. Perhaps I'm not cut out to love anybody. I've not had good relationships in the past.'

'So you want to finish it then, throwing our love away because you don't want to sit at home waiting for me to visit on a Sunday?' He started to look a little angry.

'Yes, Andy, I think that is what I'm saying, but I'll always be grateful to you for making me come back to my family and looking for some better job to do.'

'I don't want your gratitude, Vivienne, I want your love,' he replied grabbing my hand in his, 'but I also want a job with good prospects so that I can provide a decent living for my future wife and kids. I'm not prepared to let my chances pass me by. If you change your mind, Viv', you know where I am and I'll always have you in my heart, because you are my first love.'

Andy caught the bus with me from Thurstaston, but he stayed on it when I got off and carried on to the ferry crossing at Woodside. My heart was full of misery as I walked back along Whaley Lane. Was I a fool for giving up his love, would I regret it in time?'

My mother thought so, when she asked why Andy hadn't come back with me for a meal?

'I'm no fortune- teller as you well know, Vivienne,' she said in a disappointed voice, 'but I can tell you about your future. By finishing with Andy, you silly girl, you've just made the biggest mistake of your life!'

CHAPTER 12

Both letters of job confirmation arrived on the doormat on the very same day. Mother brought them down the hallway, when she brought in the bottles of milk and watched me as I opened the one from the *G.P.O.* Yes, I had passed the exam, would I go for training on the first of the month?

The letter from the Pools company said the same thing, would I go for training on the first of next month?

I didn't know what to do and spent all day thinking about it. Both my parents thought I should train as a switchboard operator, but me with that innate rebelliousness against any parental advice, decided that I would rather earn seven pounds a week. Apart from having to travel to Liverpool for my training, the job would eventually be in Birkenhead which would save on the ferryboat fare as well.

My parents shook their heads over my decision, but kept their mouths shut on this occasion and let me have my way. They both believed that I would return to full time education one day and perhaps this job that I had chosen would show me what hard work was!

I decided to overhaul my wardrobe while I waited for my big day and bought lots of material from the market, to make skirts and pretty blouses to wear at my new job.

Another man had been pestering me, a bus driver who was six feet two, slim with dark curly hair and a permanent smile on his face and he always seemed to be on my route. I ignored him at first, but being the fool that I was, decided to have a laugh and a joke. It lightened my day, took me out of my misery, as I still thought of

Andy and whether I had made a terrible mistake.

One evening, as I was waiting at the terminus after coming off the ferryboat from Liverpool, the bus driver came up behind me, put his hands on my shoulders and asked was I willing to have a date with him?

'I don't go out with people who work on the buses,' I replied scornfully. 'You're nothing but trouble, you're all rotten blokes.'

'Well, if I was to give up the buses and find something else, would you go out with me then?' he asked, smiling disarmingly.

'Don't be daft,' I giggled. 'You don't even know me, why should you go and do that?'

'But I want to get to know you. My name's Ronnie, by the way.'

'My name's Viv'. Let me know when you've changed your job and I'll think about going out with you then.'

I smiled at his audacity when I climbed aboard the bus. Change his job for me, what a joke, that was the corniest chat up line I had ever heard!

On the Friday evening I was going out with my new friend, Janet. We had met on the training scheme in Liverpool and like me, Janet had to travel across the Mersey each day. We had decided that we would have a bite to eat after work, then try out a bit of dancing in the Grafton Ballroom.

Janet was a pretty girl, slightly built with a heart shaped face, blue pussycat looking eyes and natural blonde wavy hair. She normally wore her hair up in a pony tail tied with a different coloured ribbon, to match whatever dress or blouse she had on that day. We had both brought clothes to work in our vanity cases and changed into them in the Ladies Powder Room at the ballroom.

I had on a red sparkly bodice with a plain red satin swirly skirt and Janet had on a black low cut top with a matching A- line skirt. We both wore silver sling backs and an inch of mascara on our eyelashes, but we thought we both looked wonderful in the mirrors above the sinks.

'Well, I'm out to have a bit of fun tonight,' Janet said as she put the finishing touches to her makeup. 'What if we find a couple of fellows, get them to buy us our drinks then ditch them around ten o' clock? We'd still have time then for last orders at the Bear's Paw?'

'Sounds good to me, Jan',' I answered. 'As you know I'm off men at the moment, so if they think that a couple of drinks will pay for a few privileges, they'll have another think coming as far as I'm concerned.'

So we spent a few hours dancing and flirting and two young men fell for our charms, thinking they were on a winner if they kept plying us with drinks, but at ten o'clock we disappeared into the Ladies and made a quick exit through the fire doors there. Laughing and breathless we arrived at the pub' called the Bear's Paw and did the same again after half an hour.

'Can you imagine their faces?', I said gaily. 'Sitting waiting for the two of us to appear. I think we should stay in Birkenhead next time though, or they'll find us in the Mersey floating face down.'

'Oh, it's only a bit of fun, Viv',' replied Janet who had enjoyed the evening as much as I had, 'but O.K., let's go to the pictures next Friday. There's Blue Hawaii with Elvis at the Odeon and we'll have a drink or two after.'

The training weeks finished as I was coming up to my seventeenth birthday. Unhappily Janet had a family commitment and wasn't able to celebrate it too, but some of the other girls I had also trained with, came to the Edge Lane pub' after work and had a few drinks to keep me company. I was quite sozzled, as the girls left me to travel alone across the river in the ferryboat!

'Whoops, nearly fell then,' said a familiar voice, as I swayed up the ramp to walk to my bus stop.

'Oh, Ronnie, got yourself a new job yet, I'm still waiting for that date you know?' I chafed happily.

'No luck yet, Vivienne, and where have you been to? It looks as if you've been on the pop from the looks of you?'

'Just celebrating my birthday and the end of our training in Liverpool. Got to get home to my family, they're sure to have a birthday cake.'

'Look,' he said in a concerned voice. 'I'll stay with you until the bus comes along, in fact I'll ride home with you so that you don't come to any harm.'

'No, don't bother, I'm perfectly able to get home myself. Just tell the driver where I want dropping off and I'll be fine from the bus stop.'

My seventeenth birthday, what a joke, I thought, as I let myself into the house. So where was my family, presents and cake? In fact where was my family, there was no one but myself?

Looking back on that summer made me feel rather ashamed of myself. I was like a cork bobbing in a puddle or a boat set adrift without any paddle. I was smoking and drinking, having one night stands, looking for love where there was none to be found. Then Janet found a boyfriend, a local boy to where she lived and I felt lonely and terribly bored with my job.

My mother persuaded me that September, to enrol on a secretarial course in the evenings. I had agreed in a weak moment when I had come in tired from work. It still wasn't what I really wanted to do, but I supposed if I learnt to type, it would be another string to my bow.

But the learning part was fiddly and boring. I found I had no coordination when it came to the 'quick brown fox jumping over the lazy hen'. Nothing seemed to stay in my head and trying to make my fingers work the keys, made no impression on my mind at all!

So I bunked it, met up with a chap who had been hanging around me. Out of six weekly lessons I turned up for four, until my mother got a phone call from the tutor saying, 'Vivienne is a waste of time'.

One October morning, as I was waiting for the bus that would take me to work, Ronnie poked his head out of the driver's cab' as he drew up at the bus stop.

'Off to work then?'

'Yes.'

'Not seen you for a while, what have you been up to?'

'Nothing much.'

'Fancy doing something this weekend, we could go for a drink on Saturday night or go to the flicks together?'

'If you want, I'm not bothered. You can choose if you like.'

'O.K., then meet me outside the Odeon at seven and then I'll treat you after to some fish and chips.'

I got onto the bus and stared out wanly at the passing scenery. What was the point of refusing a date with him, one man was like another? I had dumped one only last week. He'd been a married man, a rotten lying bastard who had said that his wife didn't understand him. And how did you know that they were married anyway, when they first started spinning their yarns?

My parents had been right for once, my job was proving boring and repetitive. It was great having all that money in my pocket, but I spent it more than saved it on booze and cigarettes.

That week Mother had been scanning the job section of the Birkenhead News again. She had known that I had given up on the secretarial course, because the tutor had telephoned to say that I was wasting my time. Mother found a vacancy for an Invoice clerk, keeping up the records for an insurance firm. Typing was involved, but not essential and must have a good telephone manner on the 'phone.

Vivienne can do that, she had said to herself and telephoned the company to request an application form.

Well, why not?, I thought, when Mother told me what she had done. It can't be any worse than what I'm doing at the moment and it's a little nearer home anyway. In fact I could walk to the office when it wasn't raining, as it was only two miles up the main Heswall Road.

I had never felt so bored with my life, even the date with Ronnie failed to put a smile on my face. He did his best but I was like a puppet, as he confided in his mate Davie when they went for a drink.

'Why don't we go on a foursome then?,' Davie suggested. 'I'll introduce her to my girlfriend, Julie. Perhaps that's what Vivienne is in need of, someone to confide in, do a bit of shopping with? You know, do all the girly things they like to do?'

So I met Julie and the girl did put a smile on my face. We all went dancing at the Mecca Ballroom and had a lot of fun.

One day, Ronnie suggested that he take me home to meet his mother. I didn't want to go because I felt I was being hauled into Ronnie's net. He lived in a council house in Wallasey near the new Mersey Tunnel.

The family had decided to have a party. It was somebody's birthday, one of his two other brother's maybe? I didn't know, nor cared, but Julie was going so it would probably be a laugh.

It was like walking into a brewery, with the two downstairs rooms packed with crates of Guinness and bottles of brown from the floor up to the ceiling! There was music blaring from a record player, ironing piled up in a corner, coats and jackets all over the place and people sitting around on the floor.

'This is my Mum,' Ronnie shouted, bringing forward a slender woman with peroxide hair and a cigarette between her lips, 'and over there is Marty and Gerry, it's Gerry's twentieth today.'

I blanched when I saw the birthday boy. He was one of two that Janet and I had run away from that night at the Grafton Rooms! Still he might not remember and he looked half cut, as he fondled his girlfriend who was sat on his knee.

I jumped with fright though, as a heavy hand slapped me on my shoulder! When I turned around quickly, my father was standing in the living room doorway glaring at me angrily.

'Get out of this place now,' he raged, 'my car's over there and I'm taking you home. You're not staying in this den of iniquity a minute longer.'

He walked out of the house to where he had parked his car and waited for me there, with disgust written all over his face.

'How did he know you were here?', Ronnie said, looking over at Father with daggers in his eyes.

'Are you going with him or stopping here, because it's the finish of us if you go, you know?'

'I'm stopping, he's no right to follow me.' I was so angry that he had showed me up in front of my boyfriend.

I shouted from the doorway, making my displeasure very clear.

'I'm not coming, Dad, you may as well go. I'll see you at home off the eleven o'- clock bus.'

My father took off straight away and I joined the party with blinkers on my eyes.

There was hell to pay when I returned home later that evening. It was 'pack your bags time' and 'never darken my door again', but Mother eventually calmed my father down from his ranting and raving and told me to go off to my room. It was a tense and unhappy atmosphere in the house for a few days after, with me wishing I had stayed in the Lake District.

It was coming up to Christmas and I had settled down quite happily with two other girls in the Insurance firm. Joan was a shorthand typist, Anne was the office manager and I was the invoice clerk. My job was to answer the telephone, make the tea and type up invoices with one finger.

There were two partners in the firm. The Senior partner was in his sixties and the younger man was in his forties. They were amiable and liked to think that we were all one happy family.

Just before Christmas, the Senior partner asked me if I would like a lift home in his car? It was raining hard and it was after dark and he said that giving me a lift wouldn't be out of his way.

'Besides,' he said, lowering his voice so that the other girls wouldn't hear him, 'I've bought you a little something for Christmas, to thank you for all the work you've done.'

'Oh, you shouldn't have done that, Mr. Lennox, but it's very kind of you to think of me,' I said, flattered that he had singled me out.

So we set off in his Zodiac car, which was very spacious and comfortable and made me feel very important in the scheme of things. He began to drive out of the village and not through it, but I thought in my innocence, that he was taking a shortcut. One that only he must know.

After ten minutes of driving along and not seeming to be

anywhere near my home, I asked him where he was taking me, because I was expected in for my dinner and my mother would be wondering where I was?

'Just down here, Vivienne,' he said kindly. 'Be patient, I want to see your reaction to my Christmas gift that I've got for you.'

Mr. Lennox turned down Landican Lane and drew into a lay by, he switched the engine off and settled back in the driver's seat. He produced a small box that was beautifully wrapped and handed it over to me with a smile.

'There, Vivienne. I think you will really like it and after, when you've put some on, you can play with Mr. Bobkin if you like.'

The poor old man's going senile, I thought, looking behind me onto the back seat to see where Mr. Bobkin was. Then I turned my attention to my beautifully wrapped present, which turned out to be a small bottle of Worth Je Reviens.

'Oh, thank you, Mr. Lennox,' I said, my eyes shining in gratitude. 'It's so expensive, I've never had anything like this in all my life. Thank you very much!'

He proffered a cheek for me to give my thanks, then he started to unbutton his flies.

'Would you like to play with Mr. Bobkin now, Vivienne?' he said, taking my hand in his. 'There you are,' he continued, as he drew out his limp and pinky member, 'now give me another kiss!'

So there I was at Christmas time sacked and jobless! There was no way I was going to fondle a dirty old man's willy, for the sake of a bottle of Je Reviens scent and I couldn't tell my father because he would have broken the Senior partner's jaw. When I told my parents that I had lost my job, their reaction wasn't very nice.

'It's because I can only type with one finger,' I said in my defence to Father. 'I wasn't what they wanted really, they needed some one who can touch type.'

'Then you'd better be looking for another job as soon as New Year comes,' Father said furiously, 'because I'm not having you hanging round the house all day!'

January found me searching in the Birkenhead News for some

occupation that I fancied. Things weren't good on the home front, because Father still blamed me for losing my job. I had also been banned from seeing Ronnie, as it was thought I was mixing with the dregs of society and hadn't I been raised in a far better way!

I turned to Julie for advice, when I was able to slip out and meet her. Both my parents were now in poor health and I didn't want to cause them more trouble, as Father was suffering again with his heart and Mother had problems with her hiatus hernia.

'You could always come and stay at my house in New Brighton,' Julie suggested. 'It would give you all a break and you'd be free to see Ronnie again. You could look for a job locally with there being so many hotels and guest-houses along the front, or travel on the bus to Birkenhead.'

So I packed a bag and headed off to Julie's house, though not without a few harsh words from my parents before I went. But it was great to get my freedom, well some sort of freedom anyway.

Though I was made welcome at my friend's home, it wasn't without strings at the end of the day. The mother wanted payment for her bed and board, though I slept on a mattress beside Julie's bed, had tea and toast for my breakfast and ate out for the rest of my meals.

It was a relief when I saw an advert' for a Mother's help, live in, start immediately. I rang the lady there and then and asked could I have an interview?

The house was an old Victorian semi, in a good area called Oxton near Birkenhead. It had four bedrooms, a lounge and a dining room, a study and a sun filled morning room. The lady was the wife of a dentist, with two children and one on the way. She was looking for somebody capable and I looked as if I'd fit the bill.

'Do you have any references, dear? Have you done this kind of work before?' the lady asked me kindly.

'Oh yes,' I replied enthusiastically. 'I used to look after some children for a lady named Laurel, but unfortunately she's moved away and I don't know where.'

236

'Well, we'll just have to take each other on trust, perhaps a month's trial on either side? You'll have bed and board and two pounds weekly and if it's at all possible, could you start today?'

Looking back at this part of my life, I find it hard to remember my emotions. It was like I wasn't really conscious, as I carried out the daily tasks in the ways that I was expected to. I drifted through my dates with Ronnie, held his hand and kissed a little, sat in the pub' with a Cherry B and got to know his family better. It came as no surprise to me when he suggested we got married, produced a ring and set a date. It wasn't what I wanted but I'd lost the will to change my life. He loved me, or so he told me, would cherish me for the rest of my days and it was time for him to marry, as he was nearly twenty three.

The snag was that I needed my father's permission to marry, so with a sinking heart I decided to visit my home.

'No, no, no,' shouted Father, when I nervously asked his permission to wed.

'You're not going to waste your life on someone like him, I'll make you a ward of court first. You weren't brought in to this world to be thrown away on the likes of Ronnie Hopkirk. You've been seeing him behind my back again, so now you'll come home and live here with me.'

Mother heard the commotion from the open living room window, because I had spoken to my father as he dug over the garden at the house next door. She groaned to herself when she heard his harsh words, he was going the wrong way about it because she knew I would only rebel again.

She rushed out through the front door and told us both to come inside.

'Do you want the neighbours knowing all our business, Eddie?' she cried. 'I'll put the kettle on and then we can discuss this calmly.'

'Don't know about discussing anything calmly with Vivienne,' he muttered, as he did as he was told. 'You'll have me in Landican Cemetery, young lady, the way you're carrying on.'

'Now Vivienne, sit there with your father while I make a cup of tea,' my mother said calmly. 'How's your job with the kiddies anyway, still enjoying looking after them?'

'It's all right, I suppose, it's a job anyway,' I said, glad of being able to change the subject, as my father was still glowering. 'The new baby is a little sweetie, but I'm not allowed to do much with her, just change a nappy now and again.'

'Well, her mother will be very protective towards her in the first few months, especially if she's breast feeding. What did they call her by the way?'

'Genevieve, but she's already getting Jenny. May as well have called her that in the first place 'cos Jennifer is a nice name to have.'

'I named you all after film stars, Gina Lolabridgida, Vivienne Leigh and Audrey Hepburn.'

'She knows that already, Irene,' said Father exasperated. 'What I want to talk about is this bloody wedding that she's on about.'

'Language, Eddie. Now, Vivienne, is there a reason for this marriage? Are you expecting this man's baby? Is that what all this is about?'

'No, Mum, I'm not expecting, Ronnie's asked me to marry him and I've said yes.'

'Why?'

'Because I'm sick of being told what to do. I want my own place and someone who loves me. Once I'm married I can make my own decisions, do what I like'.

'I don't think so, Vivienne,' Mother smiled wryly. 'Once you're married you'll have a husband to answer to.'

'Oh, Ronnie's not like that,' I assured her. 'He says I can make the decisions about money, where we live, if I want to stay home and have kids. It'll be great being able to do just what I like and be able to close my own front door on the world.'

'And where do you think you're going to live,' Mother ventured. 'Places don't come cheap, you'll both have to work if you want a decent place?'

'Next door's vacant isn't it, I'm sure you'll let me have it at a reasonable rent?'

'Over my dead body,' shouted Father. 'I'm not having a no mark bus driver coming to live next door to me. Forget it, Vivienne, you'll just have to go and live in a slum.'

'So, you're going to give me permission then?,' I said eagerly.

'No, I'm bloody well not, you can wait until you're twenty one!'

'Then I'll get pregnant then, just like our Gina had to do.'

I picked up my handbag and ran crying down the lane to wait for a bus.

'You've done it now, Eddie,' said Mother sadly. 'You're going to have to give her permission once she's expecting a baby.'

'Oh, who bloody cares,' said Father and took himself off to his lean-to to drink a bottle of wine.

I sat in my bedroom that evening, after I'd put the two children to bed, cross with myself but still defiant, though I felt my life was in a mess again. It wasn't as if I was in love with Ronnie, we had nothing in common, in fact he was a bit of a bore. Always going on about how many minutes it took to get from the terminus to a destination and how long it took to get back again.

What was I going to do? Should we plan to elope to Gretna Green like I had with Harry or should I get pregnant and force the issue? Dad was so unfair, he had never let me do what I wanted to do, everything had been a struggle since I could walk and talk! I clung to the hope that maybe Mother would bring him round, sometimes in the past she'd been able to.

Mother was in fact at that moment trying to talk some sense into Father, but he sat morosely in the living room watching the telly without any sound.

'I'm not giving my permission, Irene, and that's an end to it. Gina was different, her bloke was going back to America and let's face it, now they're living away from his parents, he's a jolly good husband. What kind of life is Vivienne going to have, married to a chap with Hopkirk's background? In a couple of years she'll be wanting out, just like your sister did with her husband.'

'Don't you think we should let her make her own mistakes, Eddie? She's young and romantic and thinks that being married will give her the freedom she desires? She'll soon find out life's not like that and want to leave her marriage in a couple of years.'

'No, I'll not let her do it. In fact I'm thinking I'll pay for her to go to America with you. If she gets out of his clutches for a month or so, she'll do what she did to that Harry and give him up.'

'She won't want to go. I know our Vivienne, once she's got her mind set on something she'll want to go through with it.'

'Well, write her letter and ask her if she'd like to go.'

The answer came back 'No', I didn't want to visit my sister. I knew what my parents were up to by suggesting it and if my dad was prepared to spend that kind of money on me, he could pay for a nice wedding instead.

'No chance,' said Father, 'if she's not going to America, well that's it.'

'Look, Eddie,' said Mother, 'I don't want to go off to see Gina again like we've planned, with this not being resolved. Let her get on with it for heaven's sake and let us get on with our lives.'

'O.K. then, but tell her if she wants permission she's got to come back here before the wedding. We'll still have time then to try to get her to change her mind.'

I was delighted when my mother replied that I could have the permission. I rushed round to Ronnie's house all excited and full of joy.

'And what kind of wedding is your Dad giving you?' asked Mrs. Hopkirk. 'I love a good do, I'll go out and buy a fancy hat.'

'From what I know of Vivienne's father, it'll be the Registry Office,' said Ronnie moodily.

'Isn't that right, Vivienne, he'll not shell out a penny if you're marrying me?'

'Oh, I was hoping we'd be able to have a white wedding in a church,' I replied feeling excited at the thought.

'I'll bet my life on it that it'll be at the Town Hall and your father won't even come,' Ronnie prophesied with foreboding.

Ronnie was right in his prophecy. Father wasn't even prepared to meet the man and told Audrey and Mother that they weren't allowed to go.

'If you're going to do this, you'll do it on your own, Vivienne,' he said when I came back to stay, having left my job at the house in Oxton, much to the dentist's wife's dismay. 'This way I can turn round and say I told you so, when you come crying to me and say you're divorcing. Then perhaps you will have learnt your lesson when you come running back here to me.'

Throughout all this I was adamant. I'd go through with this marriage if it was the last thing I would do. I got the Birkenhead News to search for cheap accommodation, now that I had given up my job we would only have Ronnie's wage to live on.

One day I found just what I was looking for, a one bed-roomed flat with living room, kitchen and shared facilities. It was in a nice area in Oxton, only fifteen minutes walk from Ronnie's place of work and the rent wasn't exorbitant. It was two pounds a week plus an electricity meter.

I got on the bus the very next day, then rang the doorbell of the semi – detached Victorian dwelling. The place was up a leafy drive with lots of pretty flowers in the garden. It wasn't too far away from where I had just been working, so I thought I might be able to earn some money baby sitting.

'Yes?,' said an elderly man, who had taken his time coming to the door. 'Is it about my advert? Are you wanting a place to rent?'

'Yes, my name's Vivienne Dockerty and my fiance and I are getting married in a few weeks time, so I'm having a look around for somewhere to live.'

'Is he black?'

'Who?'

'Your fiance.'

'He wasn't last time I looked at him. Why would that make a difference?'

'They've got different ways than us, that's why I'm wanting to be careful.'

'Well, can I see the flat? I've got a deposit if I like it, my fiance has given me two pounds to put down, because we'll probably need to decorate before we move in.'

'Yes, it'll want decorating, the last tenants left it in a bit of a state. I had to get the Police to shift them.'

'Oh!'

I followed the man up two short flights of stairs and he pointed out the areas where I wasn't allowed to go.

'Our bedroom and those two bedrooms there are out of bounds, but you can use that separate toilet and the bathroom.'

He lead me up to another floor and showed me into a large front facing room.

'This would be your living room. See there's the fireplace but we don't allow cooking on it. I'll show you the kitchen later, after I've shown you the bedroom.'

The bedroom was a bit smaller and had a slanted ceiling, because it was positioned under the eaves of the roof, but it had a lovely view over the pretty laid out garden and large trees screened it from the house at the bottom of it.

He then showed me the kitchen, which was big enough to put a cooker in, a fridge and a small table and chairs. The stainless steel sink looked clean enough and there were adequate fitted cupboards lining the walls.

'My wife did the cleaning herself after those rotters left, but you'll need to replace the wallpaper,' he said. 'There's quite a few tears and stains as you can probably see.'

'Oh, my fiance will fix that, he's looking forward to decorating. So, shall I give you the deposit now and perhaps you'll have a rent book you can give to me?'

I walked down the path gleefully. With the rent book in my hand, I was now on my way to being mistress of all I surveyed!

CHAPTER 13

It was the day before the wedding and I was returning from the flat, where I had been putting the finishing touches to the buffet I had planned for the guests, who had been invited to the party after the ceremony. There wasn't many coming, mostly Ronnie's relatives, Davie and Julie and Mrs. Fearnley, the dentist's wife. Davie was to be Ronnie's best man and Julie was to be my bridesmaid. Though nobody was getting too dressed up for the event, just wearing their best clothes.

It had been an exciting couple of weeks for me and Ronnie. We felt we were pools winners, as we went from store to store ordering carpets and furniture, a fridge and a cooker. Everything had been delivered the day before and I thought it looked very nice. Of course we were now up to our armpits in debt, as Ronnie didn't have any savings and I didn't have a job. There had been a sticky bit when Ronnie had asked for credit in the carpet shop. It seemed he was on a list of bad debtors, something to do with some items he had purchased a couple of years ago. He had hotly denied the charge and said it must be some other member in the family, but as I was now eighteen everything was put in my name.

I had been eighteen for a month now and somehow I was beginning to feel my age. There was a subtle change in my thinking, it was time I became more mature. But how much more mature could you become, when you were about to marry and possibly start a family? No, this was what I wanted to be, a responsibly married woman who would have her own front door.

So I was a bit reluctant to listen to the bus conductor who was on my route back home. I had seen him a lot of times over the years, but had only smiled and said 'hello' like any friendly person would.

'I hear you're marrying Ronnie Hopkirk tomorrow,' he said, waving away my money for the fare.

'Yes, that's right, eleven o'clock at the Town Hall in Birkenhead.'

'I think you want your bumps feeling. If you were my daughter I'd lock you up and throw away the key.'

'That's not a very nice thing to say,' I said, feeling a sense of disquiet.

'Chalk and cheese the pair of you, I'll give it six months, love.'

'Oh, thanks for that, so you'll not be wishing us the best for tomorrow?'

'I'd like to, but take it from me, it's not going to last.'

'Well, you're a real Job's comforter.'

'Well, whoever Job is he's got the right idea.'

I refused to listen then, he had no idea what he was talking about. Ronnie loved me and if there was anything in Ronnie's past that the conductor might be hinting at, well the same went for me, didn't it? I wasn't as pure as the driven snow.

Father seemed to be on edge when we sat around the table eating what was to be my 'last supper.' Nothing had been mentioned over the wedding. It was as if I wasn't going to become a married woman at all and the talk at the table was Mother's holiday clothes.

I was sitting on an angle so that I could watch the T.V and eat my meal at the same time.

I'd done this many times before, as it was easier than having to turn my chair around.

'Sit round properly at the table, Vivienne,' said Father. 'I don't know where you get your sloppy habits from, but I'm not having them in my house.'

I looked in amazement at him. Wasn't I getting married tomorrow? He couldn't make me do as I was told on my last evening at home.'

'Make me,' I said cockily.

'What did you just say?'

'I said 'make me'. I'm getting married tomorrow, you can't treat me like a child.'

The force of his blow across my face made my head bang on the wall behind me. I stood up unsteadily, with shock in every pore of my face!

'I'm bloody glad I'm leaving this sodding place tomorrow,' I shouted. 'No wonder I'm going, it's to get away from you.' And trembling with outrage I left the room.

My mother came after me, trying to pour water on the overheated situation, but I was having none of it, as I sat on the bed in my room.

'You asked for that, Vivienne,' she said gently. 'Didn't you see what he was like when he was eating his dinner? His hands were shaking as he used his knife and fork, a sure sign he's worked up about your wedding.'

'Well tough, I'll be out of his hair tomorrow and then he can have peace and quiet without me.' I replied, still smarting from his blow.

'Oh, Vivienne, why must you and your father be like this? He's been a good father to you, better than some fathers around here.'

'Because he's never once said that he loved me, never put me on his knee and kissed me like other fathers do. All I've had since I've been born is that bloody war. He's tried to bring me up as if I was one of the squaddies. Yes sir, no sir, three bags full sir and I've had enough of it. At least Ronnie loves me and he never tells me what to do, just let's me get on with it.'

'You'll soon get tired of being faced with all the responsibilities. A man must be master in his own home, Vivienne, and not told what to do by his wife.'

'Mmm.'

'You know, Vivienne,' she said, 'I wish you'd tried harder with that young man from Wigan. He was a lovely person and if you had waited and married him, you could have had a big fancy church wedding. Your Dad liked him as much as I did and we've always said what a lovely couple you'd have made.'

'But Mum, he didn't want me. He preferred his studies and his ambitions and the bloody work he had to do to get him through university. If he had loved me he would have given all that up, or at least seen me more than just on a Sunday. Anyway, he'll have met someone else by now, a Wigan girl who can see him more than I ever could.'

I tried to get to sleep that night, but it was difficult because I was wearing hair curlers. My navy and white checked suit was hanging from the picture rail and it had an eerie look to it, because of the fingers of moonlight that was coming through the crack in the curtains. There was no comforting breathing coming from my sister's bed, because Audrey had taken herself off to stay at a friend's house. My sister and I hardly spoke two words now, as Audrey was seemingly disgusted with me.

'I know I don't get on well with Dad either, Vivienne,' she had said, 'but when I think of the advantages we've had compared to others and you've just gone and chucked them all away. Catch me getting married at eighteen. I'll be twenty eight by the time I consider it and that will be after I've got a career.'

I love you too, I thought and dismissed my sister from my mind, as Audrey didn't know what she was talking about, when it was certain that I did.

My Dad looked as if he had had a sleepless night also, when he came in the bedroom next morning to wake me. I had set my alarm clock though for eight o'clock and had been to the bathroom to put the boiler on. I was sitting in my dressing gown taking my curlers out and feeling less than pretty because I had a spot on my nose.

'I've come in to say I'm sorry for hitting you, Vivienne, but you deserved it. That was no way to speak to your father.' His eyes were full of tears as he gazed upon this errant daughter of his.

'Yes, I know, I'm sorry, it was childish and I'm trying to be an adult.'

'Is that your outfit, it doesn't look as if you're going to a wedding in it? You've worn it before haven't you, I saw you once wearing it for work?'

'I can't afford a new outfit, Dad, all our money is tied up in the furniture at the flat.'

'I'm sorry for you, Vivienne, it could have all been so different if you had waited and married someone like that chap you brought home from the Lake District. What time have you got to be at the Registry Office, anyway?'

'The ten past ten bus will get me there in time.'

'Look, Vivienne, I'll take you in the car,' he said, 'to make amends for last night and so that me and you will still be friends. I'll drop you off near the Square and you can walk through the gardens.'

'You don't have to bother, Dad, I'm sure there's other things you want to do with your Saturday.'

'It's what I want to do, Vivienne,' he said firmly and wiped his eyes with his sleeve as he walked out of my bedroom door.

I got out of Father's car later outside the gardens of Hamilton Square. He had asked me on our journey, did I really want to go through with it?

'It's not too late, Vivienne, I can go in and tell Ronnie that you've changed your mind.'

'Dad, I've promised him and it's time you let me make my own mistakes. I'm eighteen now, nearly an adult, and I'll make the best of this marriage, see if I don't.'

'But you shouldn't be going into a marriage with that attitude, you should be totally sure that this is the man you want to spend the rest of your life with, not think that you're going to be making the best of it.'

'Dad, we're here now, at least try to give me your blessing.'

'No, Vivienne, that is something that I will never do.'

The ceremony lasted ten minutes. Only Mrs. Hopkirk, Martin and Gerry, Davie and Julie witnessed us tying the knot. It was raining as we all caught the bus back to the flat and there was no atmosphere of celebration, it was like a business deal done or a partnership.

'How many are you expecting?', Mrs. Hopkirk asked, as she surveyed the table that I had set out with an array of sandwiches, sausage rolls and a shop bought one tiered wedding cake.

'There doesn't look much here, Vivienne. My lads will get through that in no time, there'll be nothing left for anyone else.'

'Well, I'm not expecting more than my mother and Mrs. Fearnley and my mother's only coming if my dad lets her out.'

'Shame on your father, no matter what he thinks of our Ronnie, this is your wedding day and he should be here putting on a brave face. I shall tell that to your mother when she turns up and perhaps she will pass my message onto him.'

'Oh, don't go causing any upset, Mrs. Hopkirk, let's all try and get on well today.'

'Is this all you've got to drink, Ronnie?', his mother continued, surveying a bottle of whisky, six bottles of Guiness and one of sherry.

'Where's the bottles I told you to get, I said I'd pay for a crate of ale?'

'We ran out of money, Mum. By the time we'd paid this weeks rent and paid something off the Provident check, me and Vivienne are stony.'

'But it didn't stop you going on your Stag night, did it? You came in last night drunk as a mop?'

'Give it a rest, Mum, will you, Davie said he'd nip to the offy if we run out. What's a best man for if he can't lend a pal a bob or two?'

'Are you changing out of your suit, Vivienne?', Julie asked hastily in case there was a family row.

'I thought I might put a dress on later, Julie,' I replied. 'Do you think you could help me get some glasses so everyone can toast the bride and groom.'

'Are you not waiting for your mother and Mrs. Fearnley?'

'No, I can't see either of them coming now, they knew that the wedding was at eleven so they'd be here by now, wouldn't they?'

The rest of the afternoon was spent opening the wedding presents and getting drunk. There wasn't many packages to open, just a cut glass bowl from Davie and Julie, and a bedding bale from the Hopkirks'. Mrs. Fearnley turned up briefly, drank a sherry as a toast and left, leaving four very pretty lace edged towels that were really too nice to dry yourself on. Then came Mother who stayed while I made a fresh plate of sandwiches. She then drank a glass of orange juice and fled downstairs to Father's car, where he was waiting rather impatiently.

'Well, that went well, didn't it?', said Ronnie, after he had said goodbye to his family and friends and climbed unsteadily back up the stairs to the flat. 'Put the kettle on will you, Vivienne, and make me a coffee or I won't be any fit state to carry out the nuptials.'

Oh no, I'd forgotten about them, with me bustling about making sure everyone had something to eat and if their glasses wanted refilling. I put my forehead on the cool glass of my kitchen cupboard while I waited for the kettle to boil. Still it wouldn't be a problem, we'd had sex twice before and it was just a fumble and a lot of striving, so with a bit of luck it would only take five minutes and I'd get a good night's sleep. As long as he didn't snore.

Two months went by and I was finding it very hard to make ends meet on Ronnie's wages. I knew I should really find a job, but I was enjoying the pleasure of being a housewife. I kept our small flat clean and tidy and learnt to cook what I thought were delicious meals. Still, I would have to do something soon, as already we were a week behind with the rent, two weeks behind with the Provident check, and the payment on his Dansette that he had got before our wedding had been left for Ronnie to pay. I knew though he wouldn't be bothered paying a weekly visit to the electrical store.

One Thursday morning I decided to call in to the bus depot, where I knew Ronnie would be waiting by the time office for his weekly wage. It would be a good week, because he had been doing a lot of overtime so that he could pay off a little on the arrears. I planned to ask for the money for my housekeeping there and then instead of waiting until he got home, then I could check with the electrical store where he'd got the Dansette from and pay some of what he owed.

Ronnie didn't look too happy when he saw me, as he stood in

line waiting for his wages in the bus depot office.

'What are you doing here, Vivienne, you're showing me up you know?' he said to me belligerently.

'How so, I've only come for the housekeeping?' I replied. 'I can go into town and pay something off what we owe.'

'Wives only come here when they can't trust their husbands to bring home their pay, they're frightened they'll go in the ale house first, but that won't happen to me.'

'Hopkirk,' shouted the timekeeper from his window, 'got your wages here, come and get them.'

'I'll be back in a minute, Vivienne.'

I waited while he laughed and joked with the other men who had been waiting with him, then he accompanied me down the office steps and asked would I like a coffee with him?'

'I would really rather get off into town if you don't mind.'

'Oh, come on, we'll go into the canteen and you can have a coffee while I have my dinner, we'll be out in half an hour.'

'But I've got a home made steak and kidney pie at home for our dinner. What are you spending hard earned money on canteen food for?'

'Oh, what you give me wouldn't feed a sparrow, Vivienne,' he said walking up to the counter to place his order. 'Come on now and I'll sort out my wages while I eat.'

I felt so angry. I had spent weeks poring through the cookery book that, Pamela, my cousin had sent me as a wedding present and he was dismissing my efforts as if they were nothing! Well, I intended to give him short shrift when he came home that night. I wasn't going to let him get away with disparaging my efforts.

I sat at the table after he had ordered a roast dinner with a side portion of chips, then watched him as he sorted out silver and a couple of ten pound notes from his pay packet.

Good, I thought, we'll be able to pay double on everything, then felt quite startled when he gave me one ten pound note and twenty shillings in silver.

'This is the usual money Ronnie, what about making up the

rent and the Provident check?' I asked.

'Oh, they can wait another week, Vivienne, I've got things that still need paying, you know?'

'Like what?'

'I've got my Union dues, that suit and mac' I bought for the wedding was on tick, your wedding ring of course and the insurances I pay to my mother. Then I have to have money for cigarettes, the odd pint of beer at the Carlton and then there's my dinner money. It all adds up.'

'It certainly does, Ronnie, and it's obvious I'll need to get a job to pay some of these debts off. I'll go straight away and look in some of the shop windows in Grange Road. Maybe they'll be taking on staff with Christmas coming up.'

I stalked off in a huff, leaving behind the ordered coffee. Let him drink it I thought, pity I hadn't spat in it first!

I managed to get a job as a shop assistant in a furniture store. Not the one where we had got our sofa, display cabinet, table and chairs and bed from, but another one further down the road which was a bit more up-market. The work was boring and dull and I seemed to spend my time opening heavy packages and rubbing things with polish. Every day became the same, but I did come home on Saturday night with two pounds, ten shillings in my purse. Perhaps things would be different when I had a baby, I kept thinking, Ronnie would be bound to tip up more if he had a little baby to support? But up to now there was no sign of one and I began to wonder if we were doing it right!

One lunch time as I came out of the shop entrance to walk outside to get some fresh air, a voice hailed me from across the way.

'Vivienne, it is you, isn't it?'

A young man of about twenty, solidly built, with dark hair and spectacles came rushing up to me.

'Remember me, Barry Williams, we used to go to the County Grammar together on the bus? A couple of years ago?'

'Oh, Barry, yes, I remember,' I said, trying to put the name to the face of the man who stood before me. 'What are you doing here, I thought you'd be at Uni' by now?'

'Failed my A' levels, then couldn't be bothered to do my re-sits. I'm hoping to become a journalist, but I've not had much luck up to now. Are you off for a walk, can I come with you? I thought I saw you the other day. I'm working across the road in Saltbury's department store.'

'Yes, come along if you want to. Do you fancy coming to Sayers for a coffee and then we can talk some more?'

So Barry and I began to meet quite regularly. He was a nice bloke and a good listener and he had to be, because I was always bending his ear!

One lunch time when we had settled into a couple of seats at Sayers and were busily munching on our sandwiches, Barry asked me if I would do him a great favour. I replied that I would be delighted to if I could.

'It's just that we have a Christmas do planned at the end of next week and I've told everyone I'll be bringing my girlfriend. As you know I haven't got one, because I only have eyes for you.'

'Oh, Barry, you know that I'm married, how can I be your girlfriend as well?'

'But you're not happy with him, you're always moaning to me about him. Why don't you leave him and we'll get ourselves a place together somewhere?'

'I can't do that,' I said gently. 'I've only been married to Ronnie for two and a half months, I can't just up and leave him. It would be like jumping out of the frying pan into the fire!'

'Meaning you don't care enough for me to want to leave him and I thought we were getting on so well.'

'I do care for you, Barry, but as a friend and I've got to give my marriage a chance.'

'Then I'll just have to pretend I'm ill on Saturday, because I'm damned sure I'll not find anyone else in time.'

He left me then and I felt unhappy, but I wasn't going to put my marriage on the line for him.

It was a few days before Christmas, it had been busy in the

furniture shop and my legs were aching from rushing about all day. I was looking forward to a relaxing bath and my feet up in front of the telly. We had recently got one on the 'never never', as a Christmas present to each other. Another two days of working then we could relax for a couple of days. We had been invited to his mother's for Christmas lunch and on Boxing Day I was going to visit my parents alone. Mother and Audrey were back from America and they were sure to have brought some nice presents for me.

As I traipsed up the stairs to the flat, I could hear the sound of men laughing. The landlord was hovering on the landing, as if he was about to have a word with them.

'They've been like this all afternoon, Mrs. Hopkirk,' he said when he saw me. 'Shouting and laughing so that my wife couldn't settle for her afternoon nap. I was just going to knock on the door and ask them to keep the noise down. It isn't the first time either, your husband had his friends in there a couple of weeks ago.'

'I'm sorry, I'll go up and deal with it,' I replied feeling annoyed at Ronnie's behaviour. 'Give my apologies to your wife and I'll ensure it doesn't happen again.'

I flew into the living room ready to give Ronnie a piece of my mind, but his mother and brothers were sitting there and two of his friends from the bus depot.

'Here comes the worker,' Mrs. Hopkirk said, slurring her words as she spoke. 'Come in and join our Christmas party, Vivienne, there's still some whisky left.'

'No, thank you,' I replied stiffly. 'You're going to get us thrown out of here, Ronnie, the way you're carrying on.'

'Ooooooh,' my mother- in- law said sarcastically. 'Hey son, you're wife's in a bit of a strop.'

'Don't take any notice of her, Mother dearest, doesn't know how to enjoy herself. All she does is worry about the damn bills.'

'Well, someone has to,' I said stung by his criticism. 'If it was up to you we wouldn't have a roof over our heads.'

With that I walked into the bedroom and lay on our bed, until I heard the party stumbling their way down the stairs.

'Don't you make a show of me again in front of my mother, you little cow,' said Ronnie coming into the room and glaring down at me on his wobbly legs.

'Moo,' I said calmly. 'Now can I make myself a cup of tea?'

Christmas came and went and I found myself helping to prepare for the January sales at the furniture store. It was back breaking work, humping settees into carefully thought out positions in the display window, to tempt all customers who were passing by.

Ronnie had hardly spoken to me after I had come back from visiting my parents on Boxing Day. I had been wearing the pink and white floral jacket that Gina had sent me and the cowboy boots that Mother had brought me as well.

'You'd think that they'd have a bit of good will to all men at Christmas, Vivienne,' he had said to me plaintively, when he saw that he hadn't been sent a present. 'I bet that was why my ears were burning, they'd be pulling me to pieces while you were there.'

'You weren't even mentioned,' I said wearily. 'They were too busy telling me about their trip and how Gina and Mandy were.'

'It's all right for them who can afford to go piking off on sunshine holidays. Your parents only got that money through being left it in your aunty's will.'

'Oh, for heaven's sake, stop begrudging people. If you stopped swilling beer down your throat and eating all that food in the canteen, maybe we could afford to go on holiday.'

'Piss off, will yer,' he snarled, 'you're getting on my nerves.'

I trudged along to the bus stop one evening, looking forward to some peace and quiet because Ronnie was on the late shift. He wouldn't be home until around twelve thirty, because his bus was the last to come into the depot from the margarine factory. I was planning to wash my hair, read a good book and have an early night.

I had just hung up my coat and taken my hat and gloves to the chest of drawers in the bedroom, when the doorbell rang downstairs. There were muffled voices below, as I opened the living door to see if the caller was somebody for me. Then I heard heavy footsteps coming up the stairs.

'Barry!,' I said. 'What are you doing here, how did you know where I lived? You'd better come in.'

'I've come to tell you something, Vivienne. I followed you home on the bus tonight, I jumped on the platform when you went upstairs.'

'Why couldn't it have waited until tomorrow? You could have called into the shop and arranged to have gone for coffee.'

'I wanted to be alone when I told you, Vivienne. I've decided to go away.'

'Oh, well, come in, sit down and tell me all about it. Shall I put the kettle on and we'll have a cup of tea?'

'No, I've brought a bottle of cider with me. I thought we could drink it together, a farewell drink as it were, because you probably won't ever see me again.'

'Oh, Barry, you sound so down. It's a good job Ronnie's working this evening or I wouldn't have been able to invite you in. I'll just go and get a couple of glasses and then we'll make a toast to your future happiness.'

'It won't be a happy future without you in my life, Vivienne,' he said mournfully.

Unfortunately, the first glass to toast his future was filled up again and then again and again, until I could hardly see. I kept nodding as Barry told me that he loved me and was only leaving the area because he didn't want to have to see me every day. I found myself in his arms comforting him like a mother would, as he poured out his loneliness and envy of Ronnie. If only I would love him he would be a happy man. It was inevitable that we ended up in the marital bed where I committed adultery, but somehow that knowledge passed me by as I lay in Barry's comfortable arms, feeling furry tongued and comatose, but totally sated, which I never had with Ronnie.

I moved back the blanket so that I could go for a glass of water, then search for my watch to see the time in case Ronnie's return was imminent, but as I did so Barry began to look in dismay at a patch of blood on the bed!

'What's this?', he said looking at me in astonishment. 'I thought you were a married woman. What's this I'm looking at, Vivienne?'

Thoroughly embarrassed, I turned away, mumbling that I must have started my period.

'Well, I know I don't have much experience, but I think you were a virgin, Vivienne!'he said bluntly.

I breathed a sigh of relief when a week later I got my period. I had been astounded when Barry had said what he had, but couldn't really believe it. But maybe that was why I'd never got pregnant?

Nobody had ever broken my hymen! Not that I knew what a hymen was, it was just what Barry had explained to me. I had pretended to be asleep when Ronnie had come through the bedroom door, having bathed and brushed my hair after Barry had gone. The bath had woken me, got rid of my groggy head and made me aware of my foolishness, but I was pleased that Barry hadn't looked quite so sad as I waved him off from the front door.

Ronnie came home one evening and announced that a pal of his could get a car for him cheaply, but he needed to borrow some money. Would I be the guarantor?

'I won't, Ronnie,' I said crossly. 'We're up to our necks in repayments. What do you want a car for, you're only a quarter of an hour from work?'

'It's these winter mornings, Vivienne. It's all right for you snuggled up in bed until eight o'- clock, but I sometimes have to be up at four o'- clock and it's usually freezing or raining.'

'You've been getting up and walking to work for years, even when you were living at your mother's house. Can't you wait until we're on our feet a bit, get something behind us then we can get a little car then?'

'No, I want it now. Graham is bringing round a smart little M.G on Sunday morning and we'll have a trip in it, just you and me. I'm sure you'll fall in love with it.'

'And what about the insurance? When I worked in that office in Heswall, sports car insurance was very high'

'Oh, for heaven's sake, Vivienne, why do you have to keep moaning on about money? If I like it I'm having it. I'll get someone else to be the guarantor.'

On Sunday Ronnie was up early, buzzing with excitement because he was going to buy a car.

'Have you worked out how much this is going to cost, Ronnie?,' I said, as I joined him in the kitchen where he was making himself a slice of toast.

'No, whatever it costs, I'm having it. You're working, aren't you and I can do more overtime?'

'Well, I've looked at the figures and if it's brand new it'll cost at least one thousand pounds. Repayment over, say five years will be around six pounds a week.'

'Oh, trust you, six pounds is nothing. I only have to do some overtime for a couple of days.'

'Then there's the tax and insurance, that will cost a pretty penny. What if I were to get pregnant, I won't be able to work then you know?'

'You haven't got pregnant up to now, Vivienne, and even if you did you could work up to seven months, then stick it in a nursery.'

'Oh, please yourself, Ronnie, but I won't pay a penny towards it. You're on your own with this one.'

Graham eventually arrived, parking the dark green M.G with a flourish on the road outside.

He was a shifty looking fellow and I asked him where he had got the car from?

'My brother- in- law has a garage over in New Brighton. He has a glut of these, bought them cheaply off the manufacturer.'

Somehow I didn't believe him and asked could I have a look at the log book.

'You don't get one of them until we've done the paperwork,' he said, not looking at me in the eyes.

'How were you going to pay for it anyway, Ronnie, he'd like cash if you can?'

'Cash,' I hooted uproariously. 'Ronnie will have to go through a finance company and even then he might not get the money if he needs a guarantor.'

'Vivienne,' Ronnie said warningly, 'get back in that bloody house and leave the talking to me. Can I have a test drive, Graham, to see if I can handle one of these?'

They drove off with a squeal of brakes after Ronnie had put his new sunglasses on. I walked back up to the flat, he was a fool to himself that man.

Ronnie came home later looking disappointed and thoroughly fed up with my attitude.

'Why did you have to put your two pennies worth in,' he glowered. 'I could have got the car through the finance company? She's a little beauty.'

'Men who want cash in their hand are up to no good, Ronnie, but if you really want to get a car, do it properly through a dealership.'

'We'll see,' said Ronnie morosely. 'I'm off to my mother's now and I'll be having my dinner with her.'

He didn't speak to me for days after. I didn't really care because he was beginning to get on my nerves anyway. I was fed up with this life of hard work and no benefit and it began to dawn on me that my father had been right.

A month later I didn't get my period. I was always regular so I knew I'd been caught. The years with Ronnie living like we did and tied with a child forever, loomed ahead of me endlessly. Oh, how I wished I had listened to my parents and taken my exams instead!

CHAPTER 14

I decided to go and see my mother. I took the day off work thinking that if my father wasn't in when I got there, it would be better all round for everyone. I had told Ronnie of my suspicions that I might be pregnant, but he didn't seem bothered either way.

Mum wasn't very happy when I told her.

'Oh, Vivienne, you're far too young to be having a baby and you're in that poky flat in Birkenhead. How are you going to cope with a baby there?'

'Not very well probably,' I answered with a sigh. 'I'll have to leave the pram at the bottom of the stairs and it'll be in the way of the other family.'

'Maybe you're not expecting,' Mother said hopefully. 'Perhaps it's just a false alarm and you'll come on in a day or two. Then if you do, get yourself up to see Doctor Roscoe, see if he'll put you on that new pill that stops babies from coming.'

'Do you know I've never thought of going on the Pill,' I said, 'but I'll do as you say if I do come on. I'm not too happy about expecting a baby myself.'

I went to work the next morning, apologizing to the Manager, saying that I had felt unwell.

'You're not pregnant are you, Vivienne?' the elderly man asked. 'Because with all this bending and lifting you're doing, it would be wrong to carry on.'

'I think I might be, Mr. Bird, that's why I was off work yesterday because I was feeling rather sick. But I can stay if you need to find a replacement, that's if you don't mind me not helping with the deliveries.'

I stayed for another week at the furniture store and by that time

I was certain I was pregnant. The mornings were the worst time, when just smelling coffee made me want to put my head down the toilet. It was with a leaden heart that I said goodbye to my work colleagues, especially when Mr. Bird gave me my final wage packet. Now I would be really relying on Ronnie, what the hell was I going to do?

'You'll have to get a different job now, Ronnie,' I said, in a moment when he was looking quite happy and not got on his hangdog face. 'The baby will start costing money, so you can forget going into debt for a car.'

'I've seen one I want, Vivienne,' he said determinedly. 'It's a small Austin A40. It'll cost me five pounds a week.'

'And where will the money be coming from, you only give me eleven pounds housekeeping?'

'I'll work more overtime, ask some of the men if I can do their shifts. I really want a car, Vivienne, and if I want it I'll get it, no matter if you do nag me over it.'

'If you got a different job, say on a night shift, you'll be quids in and still be able to afford a car. Kraft's are taking on in Bromborough or there's Fords or Vauxhall, they're always advertising for staff in the Birkenhead News.'

'I'll think about it. Anyway, it's not as if you're having the baby tomorrow,' he replied stubbornly. 'I've eight months at least to pay the car off without having to find another job.'

'Mmm,' I said, not wanting to start off a row.

I found myself with a lot of time on my hands, so I started visiting my mother every Monday. It was something to do and up to now I hadn't met up with Father, so I spent an hour with my mother, usually arriving before lunch time, then I could share a meal with her.

One morning as I walked up the drive way, I saw my father's car parked at the top of it.

'Oh no,' I groaned to myself. Had my mother told him about the baby and he was waiting to see me?

It seemed so. My parents were sitting at the kitchen table, both eating a bowl of mushroom soup each.

'There's still some in the saucepan, Vivienne,' Mother said. 'I've nearly finished, so you sit with your Dad.'

'Vivienne,' my father acknowledged, 'you don't seem to have much weight on. You're having a baby, I hear.'

'Looks like it, Dad,' I answered despondently. Here we go, I'm going to have my ear bent now.

'What would you say if I offered you next door to rent from us?'

'Next door?' I squeaked. 'But you've already got a family in it. Do you mean it, are they leaving or something?'

'Yes, they've given me two weeks notice. Apparently the husband has a job in Liverpool so they're going to find a place nearer to her mum.'

'And are you sure you're prepared to have Ronnie living next door, you've never even spoke to him. I don't want you falling out all the time?'

'I'm doing this for the sake of my unborn grandchild and my daughter, not him. If you came to live next door on your own I'd be happier, but I suppose better a father for the child than none.'

'Well, I'm sure I don't know how to thank you both. It'll be great bringing it up in the country and I'm sure you two will come in handy for baby sitting, but there is one slight problem, what about the rent?'

'It's six guineas a week, Vivienne,' he pointed out sternly, 'but as you know it is three bedrooms and they're not cheap to rent around here.'

'I don't know if we can afford that, Dad, it's a lot of money and as you know there's only Ronnie's wages coming in.'

'Well, talk it over with your husband and see if he can come up with that sort of money.'

I was over the moon when I told Ronnie the news that evening and he was certainly very happy with the thought of becoming a 'country gent'.

'Just wait until I tell my mates at the depot,' he said excitedly.

'Ronnie Hopkirk, eh, living in the countryside? I'll have to get that car though, I can't walk from there every morning especially if I'm on the 4.42.'

'But the rent's six guineas a week, Ronnie, we can't pay that and car finance too,' I said, horrified that he was considering putting us into more debt again.

Ronnie shrugged his shoulders.

'It's up to you then. If you want to move next door to your Dad, you'll have to come up with the extra money yourself.'

I was moaning to Mother next time I visited, that it was going to be impossible to move in next door, because Ronnie was insistent he had to have a car if he was so far away from the depot.

'There's no way we can afford six guineas, Mum,' I said sadly 'and I don't think I'm up to getting another job at the moment.'

'Well, I was thinking about that, Vivienne, so I wondered if you would like to share my little venture? I managed to get a cosmetic round recently, you know leaving brochures for housewives to look in, then they give me orders for beauty products and the like? It would still be in my name, but I could ask the supervisor if I could have a bigger area and you could help me with it. How would you feel if I gave you a percentage, it would be something to bring extra money in?'

'Oh, that sounds perfect, Mum,' I replied gladly. 'I'm surprised that Dad allowed you to take that on though.'

'He's mellowing in his old age, Vivienne, he thinks its good that I'm getting out and meeting people. So, shall we say that you'll be moving in at the end of next week, because we'll have to arrange a removal van for you?'

The old man who owned their flat, wasn't happy as I joyfully told him that we were leaving at the end of the following week.

'You'll have to pay me for that week, Mrs. Hopkirk, it won't be easy finding someone to replace you and it was a week in arrears when you first moved in. Not in advance like you've just said.'

I thought I'd paid him in advance before we'd taken the tenancy, but Ronnie said that I was to leave that problem to him. The old sod had made a mint out of us, I wasn't to worry now I was in the family way.

We moved on the Sunday morning, as the owner of the flat and his family went to church, then visited a restaurant later for their dinner. Ronnie brought his mates to help and they loaded up our furniture onto a friend of Father's brick wagon, although the furniture got covered in a film of brick dust. But everything looked perfect once I'd arranged it to my liking and I settled down in my new home to await the happy event.

It was a few weeks later when Mum asked me had I been for confirmation to the doctor's?

'Oh, I didn't know you had to, Mum, I thought you just turned up at the hospital when you started getting pains.'

'No, you have to get booked in, Vivienne. You'll probably be sent to Clatterbridge Hospital, but it's wise to see the doctor anyway in case of complications.'

'What kind of complications?', I asked fearfully.

'Nothing to worry about really, but Audrey had to have her blood changed over after her birth, because I was rhesus negative.'

'Oh.'

'Don't worry, you're young and healthy. You'll sail through it like I did with Gina, but try to rest a bit more than you do, because you never seem to be off your feet.'

You're not wrong there, I thought. I was enjoying my work as an Avon lady and because it was a new product to the area, my orders were exceeding one hundred pounds a month. It gave me the extra I needed to help with paying the car repayments, as Ronnie had got his wish and was the owner of a small black car. Though what I was going to do when my bump made me give up work because of decency sake, I wasn't sure.

'Just pop yourself up on to the examining table, Vivienne,' said Doctor Roscoe as I kept my appointment with him the very next day.

'Hmm, you're quite narrow down there, aren't you?', he said after he had examined me internally and taken off his polythene gloves.

'Oh, am I, I didn't know that? Is it going to cause a problem, Doctor, do I have to give up work?'

'You shouldn't be working, Vivienne, you should be resting, giving the baby a good start in life. Anyway, I think we'll book you into Grange Mount initially and then if I think there'll be complications I'll have you down at St. Catherine's.'

'Complications, Doctor?', I asked worriedly, thinking about what my mother had said, though having the baby's blood changed over wouldn't be a big problem, would it?

'Nothing to concern you, Vivienne,' the doctor said calmly, 'but like I said, you must rest.'

One morning around three months later, after Ronnie had gone out to do an early shift, I began to have a down bearing pain in my abdomen. I felt frightened. What the hell was happening? I was only five months pregnant and I was sure you couldn't have a baby until you were seven months.

I looked at my watch on the bedside table, it was only six o'clock but maybe my father was up and about, he was an early riser anyway. I got out of bed and walked slowly into the back bedroom, feeling a trickle of stickiness in between my legs. I whacked on the wall with a broom handle that Ronnie had left behind when he was decorating the baby's 'nursery'; my father shouted 'I'm coming', from the other side of the wall.

'I think I'm losing the baby, Dad,' I said, as he ran up the stairs to where I lay on the bed trembling, having let himself in with the spare key. 'Do you think I should go to hospital or get the doctor instead?'

'I'll go and ring for the doctor, then I'll send your mother in.'

I sat there petrified as my mother found a pad, then I held her hand while we waited together for Doctor Roscoe. The man appeared in his pyjamas underneath his overcoat.

'Good job I only live up the road from you, Vivienne,' he said as he ambled into the bedroom, 'though I was hoping for a lie in this morning, you know? Now let's see what the problem is......... oh, it's the placenta, have you quickened yet?'

'What does that mean?', I asked puzzled.

'Has the baby moved inside your tummy yet?,' Mum asked.

'Oh, yes a couple of weeks ago.'

'Well, I can only advise you to lie in bed, Vivienne,' said Doctor Roscoe. 'There probably won't be anymore bleeding, but I think you should stay here for at least a week.'

'Who's going to look after Ronnie?', I wailed. 'He'll go mad if he has to get his own dinner and there's all the shopping to do.'

'Leave that to me, Vivienne,' said my mother, 'we'll sort it out later when the doctor's gone. It's very kind of you to come so quickly, Doctor Roscoe and we'll look after Vivienne from now on.'

Ronnie didn't like that.

'You mean I've got to find my own meals, while you're waited on hand and foot?'

'You'll have to go to your mother's, Ronnie,' I said firmly. 'I can't expect my parents to feed you as well, or you could eat in the canteen in the depot, that's what you always seem to like to do.'

'Not since we've moved here I haven't. Not with the price of petrol and the paint and wallpaper I bought for the baby's bedroom. If I'm going to do that, you'll have to give me some money out of your housekeeping. You won't be spending the money on food, so I'll deduct that in the future and just give you the rent.'

'But what about the Provident checks and the telly payments?' I wailed. 'What about that bedding bale I got when we moved in here and you've still to pay off the Dansette; then I'll need money for personal things and wool to knit jackets for the baby.'

'You'll have to ask your parents then for some money. Anyway, what happened to all your commission that you earned from that Avon job?'

'I was saving that for a rainy day.'

'Then your rainy day has just arrived, Vivienne.'

I spent the next few days in bed knitting and reading, getting bored with my incarceration, though I knew that it was doing the baby good. Then at the weekend when I couldn't stand it any longer, I put on my winter coat to cover up my burgeoning belly and went out to deliver my beauty books.

Mother was furious with me when I came back home, saying if anything happened to the baby it would be my own silly fault. But I hated that feeling of being beholden to my parents and my selfish husband, Ronnie.

It was the middle of November and I got my first twinges after I had eaten my evening meal.

I was sitting in my parent's house finishing off a bowl of apple pie and custard. Ronnie was out on a late shift and would probably stay at his mother's that night. He'd been doing that more and more since I had got bigger with the baby. I secretly wished that he had another woman and maybe one day he would leave me.

'Mum, I think this is it!,' I gasped, as a wave of pain clutched at the bottom of my back, as if I was fast in a vice.

'I don't think so, Vivienne,' Mum said calmly. 'It's probably the baby having a bit of a wriggle, it'll go in a minute you'll see.'

The next wave of pain had me doubled up in agony, so Father said it was best if he called an ambulance.

'Where are you booked in, my lovely?', asked the ambulance man, as he helped me up the steps into the back of the vehicle a little later.

'Grange Mount I think, but the doctor did mention St. Catherines too.'

'I'll get onto the blower,' said the driver's mate.

I lay on the trolley inside the main door of St. Catherine's hospital, alone and very frightened as I waited for a porter to come. No one suggested that my parents came with me, so I had to do this on my own.

'Vivienne! It's me, Benny!' a familiar voice cut into my misery. 'Do you remember we used to dance together at Sparks Lane?'

I looked up with shock at the grinning face above me. It was indeed Benny and he hadn't changed a bit!

'Oh, Benny, thank heaven's for somebody I know,' I said in wonder. 'What are you doing here, I thought you'd joined the Army?'

'Couldn't hack it, Viv', then I met my wife Gillian, so my parents bought me out. I've just become a proud parent too. Gillian gave birth to twins the other week.'

'How lovely, Benny,' I gasped, as another pain gripped the bottom of my abdomen.

'Hey, let's get you down to the Maternity section,Viv',' he said quickly as he saw me wincing.

'You can hold my hand for comfort if you like.'

I lay on a bed later while I was poked and prodded by various nurses dressed in different coloured uniforms. I was told to get some rest as it was going to be a long night for me. One nurse said I was hardly dilated and perhaps I should be sent home again, then a doctor came and I was moved into a freezing little ante room and given a buzzer to press if the pain got too bad.

I felt as if I had been shoved into a morgue at a funeral parlour and stared up at a high bare window wondering what time it was? In my panic there had been no time to pack and I had left my watch on the table at home. I had a thin hospital nightie on, the blanket that covered me was coarse and rather lightweight and I shivered as I wondered what was to come? I wished I'd been more attentive to Miss Fleming, my Biology teacher. Even if it was the reproduction of rabbits she'd been on about, I might have learnt what was going to happen to me today.

Suddenly a spasm gripped my body so fiercely, that I thought I was going to pass out with the pain. I pressed the buzzer frantically and waited for somebody to come. The minutes passed, another cramp, I pressed the buzzer yet again and still nobody came to help me. Then I began to scream in agony!

A doctor came, bursting through the door with a nurse following closely behind him. He listened to my tummy with his stethoscope and told the nurse to get a trolley ready. The patient should be taken to the operating theatre straight away. I was asked to count up to five while someone injected something into the back of my hand, my baby couldn't come out by itself because my passage was too narrow for it to struggle through.

Had I died and was on my way to the spirit world?, I wondered later, as I looked down onto that motionless body with the green aproned figures surrounding it. Would I hover up here until the baby was born, then float away to a different place? I hoped not. The baby would need a mother and I was damn sure that Ronnie wouldn't be bringing it up instead of me!

'Mrs. Hopkirk, Mrs Hopkirk, wake up now, this poor little boy needs his mother to feed him!'

I opened my eyes to see a grim looking nurse with a bundle in her arms, patting the side of my bed purposefully.

'Oh, go away, I'm not well enough, I think I'm going to be sick anyway' I groaned.

And with that I turned to lean over the bedside and was sick all over the nurse's shoes!

'Fine, Mrs. Hopkirk, I'll bring him back later when you're up to it,' she said with an edge in her voice. 'Nurse Howard, clean this up, then bring me some disinfectant and a cloth for my shoes.'

'What time is it, Nurse?', I asked the poor little probationer nurse, who was cleaning up the vomit on the floor.

'It's quarter past.'

'Quarter past what?'

'Quarter past three.'

Good heavens, I thought, I'd been out for the count since the early hours of the morning! Or was that yesterday morning, I couldn't be sure?

'What did I have, Nurse?'

'I believe it was a little boy. I've only just come on duty, but he was wrapped in blue when she brought him just now.'

'A little boy, that's nice.'

Then I drifted off to sleep again.

'Mrs. Hopkirk, Mrs. Hopkirk!'

I opened my eyes, it was the grim looking nurse again.

'Come on now, this child wants feeding. Look at the poor little thing, he's been crying for his mammy all afternoon.'

'What do I do then?,' I asked resignedly, not sure what was expected of me. Would I be given a bottle to feed the baby with?

'Here,' the nurse said, handing me the baby.

She whipped open the bodice of my new clean hospital nightie, grabbed my right boob and clamped the baby on it!

'Ow, that hurt,' I cried, feeling the baby pulling on my nipple, with my stomach feeling as if somehow it was being hauled up like gangplank.

'Well, you'll have to get used to it, won't you?'

And the grim faced nurse walked away.

I looked down on the round head of my baby as it snuffled and sucked, wondering at the tiny scrap of humanity that had given me so much pain in the last twenty four hours.

'We'll have to think of a name for you,' I whispered softly. 'I can't keep calling you baby for the rest of your life.'

'So where is he?', demanded Ronnie, as he pulled up a chair besides my bed later that day.

'I think he's gone to the nursery, they said he had an infection in his umbilical cord.'

'How did he get that then?,' Ronnie said suspiciously.

'I don't know, do I, they just took him away from me?'

'I got a shock when they told me you'd been taken in. I only found out this afternoon when your mother put a note through the front door. I thought the baby wasn't due for another week or so.'

'I was overdue. You never listen to anything I say.'

'Well, it doesn't matter now, do you think they'll let me see him in the nursery?'

'I don't know, you'll have to ask someone.'

Two weeks later, I came home with little Simon. I had stayed in hospital until his infection had gone, but I was champing at the bit to get out from under the strict regime of Sister Wallace's Nursing

Ward, and had nearly discharged myself twice after falling out with her.

'Never mind, dear,' said Mother, as Ronnie carried our baby up to the nursery and I poured my heart out to my mother, while drinking a cup of tea.

'You can feed little Simon any way you want to now. If you want to give him a bottle, then that's up to you.'

'Well, as soon as I feel better I'm going to go back to selling Avon. You have still been canvassing haven't you, while I've been away?'

'Yes, dear, and everyone sends their love and best wishes, but you shouldn't be rushing about until you've got the baby sorted out.'

'That's easy to say, Mother, you haven't got the debts that me and Ronnie have.'

It was the second week of December, and I came home one evening with my briefcase bulging with orders that I had to give to my supervisor for a Christmas delivery. As I was passing the gate of my parent's home, Father came running down the path to meet me, his face looking indignant and annoyed.

'What's the matter, Dad?,' I asked worriedly. 'Is it Simon, he's not got another infection has he and been taken to hospital?'

'No, it's that bloody Ronnie,' Father said angrily. 'We were having our dinner and all we could hear was Simon screaming. So I took a peek through the living room window and what did I see, that bloody husband of yours fast asleep, without a care for anyone?'

'But he must have heard the baby crying?'

'Well, if he did he never bothered going upstairs to comfort him. Honestly, Vivienne, do you have to keep running out chasing the pound, as it were? You're never home in the evenings and it isn't the first time that Simon's been crying, when that clown has been supposed to be looking after him.'

'Dad, what the hell can I do?' I asked wearily. 'We're in debt up to our necks, you're lucky that I even manage to pay the rent sometimes.'

'It's a pity you didn't keep up with your studies and then you wouldn't be in the mess you're in.'

'Fine, then I'll tell you what I'll do then, Dad. You look after Simon and I'll go to evening class, I'll get my O' levels if it's the last thing I do and then you can't say to me, I told you so.'

The following January, I enrolled myself in two subjects, English Language and English Lit', the two that I knew would be easy to do because I had got good marks in my mock O' levels.

Ronnie was pleased as punch with me.

'I keep telling my mates about you at work, how I'm married to a scholar and how well you're doing. You know, Vivienne, you might get a really good job out of this and perhaps we'll be able to buy a little house.'

'Mmm, we'll see, let me get my qualifications first.'

'Anyway, how about we have an early night? You and me haven't got together since you had Simon. My mates were saying you should be over it all by now and you never know, this time next year you could have had a brother or sister for this one.'

'You've been discussing our sex life with your mates at work?,' I said, feeling outraged with Ronnie.

'You know what it's like, men's talk and all that. I wasn't being rude or anything, it's just I don't know about women's things.'

That night I gave in to my husband's insistence that we resume our marital relations, but what I didn't tell him was I had been to the doctor's earlier that month for the birth pill. There was no way I was ever going to go through that agonizing performance again and if I was to achieve the plan I had got in mind, I knew I never would.

The first attempt of penetration by Ronnie was excruciating and I pushed him away firmly and told him 'No way.'

'Oh, come on, Vivienne,' he said coaxingly. 'Just relax and it'll soon be over. Look at the state you've got me in, what will I do with this?'

'What you were doing when I was in hospital having the baby,' I said crudely. 'Look, I'm in terrible pain here, it's something to do with the scarring from having a Caesarian.'

Next minute I was on my stomach and Ronnie was trying to force himself into my back passage. I screamed. 'Get off me, will you', but he had me in a vice like grip.

I threw myself off the bed when he'd finished and spent the night in a quivering mess on the sofa in the living room.

Ronnie tiptoed around me in the morning as he got himself ready for work. I pretended I was sleeping, then made myself a cup of tea when he'd gone. The baby started crying and I cried along too. I promised myself it would be a very long time before I slept again in that marital bed.

One morning as I pushed Simon along in his pram', on my way to the local shops, I met a woman who had bought some Avon from time to time, so we walked together a little way.

'I noticed you at evening classes the other week,' the woman said. 'I go to French on a Tuesday night. I wondered if you'd like me to take you in the car instead of you travelling by bus?'

'Oh, that would be really nice of you, Mrs. Bennett. It can be chilly sometimes waiting at the bus stop, especially if I've just missed one.'

'Call me Bev' and I know you're Vivienne,' she said. 'Call in on your way back home and we'll have a cup of tea together.'

It would be really good to have a friend locally, I thought to myself. I hadn't seen Julie since our wedding day, though I did get a congratulation card on the birth of the baby. I ought really to be thinking of having Simon christened, but somehow it was one of those things that didn't seem too important at the time.

It was pleasant sitting later in the lounge of my new friend's detached house, with it's bright modern furnishings, fitted kitchen and upstairs bathroom. One day, I promised myself, I'd have a house like this, but somehow Ronnie didn't figure in my future plans.

Ronnie must have picked up on my thoughts regarding Simon's christening.

'It'll be a good excuse for a party, we never had one when we moved in. You go and see the Vicar and I'll do the invites and sort the booze out. My mother was only saying that her grandson should be christened by now.'

'That'll be the grandmother whose only ever seen him once and never bothered to visit me in hospital,' I said churlishly.

'Oh, give her a chance, Vivienne, she's working now and she's too tired to come traipsing up here.'

The Christening was planned on Sunday, three weeks later and I spent my meagre savings on an outfit for Simon and a Christening cake.

That evening after everyone had gone home, burbling messages of goodwill to the baby and how they'd all be back again to see him soon, I surveyed the presents we'd been given. I was glad to receive the baby clothes, as Simon was growing quickly and was nearly out of his birth to six month ones; someone had put a fiver in an envelope which would help to buy some more bedding for his cot, as I had to keep washing the only set he had, and someone else had bought him a changing mat with little ducks and chickens on, which would be a boon to me when I got him out of the bath.

I was feeling tired and rather tipsy when I made the journey up the stairs, as Ronnie had kept topping up my glass with Asti, as toasts were made to 'wet the baby's head'. I snuggled down feeling glad of my comfortable mattress, then Ronnie started caressing me and stupidly I had my back to him. It was all over in a couple of minutes, but I made my mind up there and then. I was going to do something about this miserable marriage, if it was the last thing that I ever did.

CHAPTER 15

One morning in June, as I sat in the back garden catching up on a bit of studying, with Simon fast asleep in the Silver Cross pram' that my parents had bought him, I heard the sound of a vehicle pulling up at the top of the driveway.

I was puzzled for a moment when I saw the recovery truck, as Ronnie had left the car that day because it had run out of petrol. Why would someone be bringing a recovery truck?

Two men ambled along towards me, stocky sturdy persons wearing well worn business suits. They peered into the windows of Ronnie's car as they passed it, then one of them showed me some sort of identity card, which bore his photograph and company name.

'We've come to pick up the Austin, Mrs. Hopkirk. Did your husband tell you we were coming today?'

'But why do you want his car, Mr. Flaherty,' I asked him in bewilderment. 'He's left it here because there isn't any petrol in?'

'We're bailiffs, Mrs. Hopkirk. Your husband has defaulted on his payments and he's been ignoring our letters asking for the debt to be repaid.'

'Are you sure? He's never said anything to me about it.'

'They rarely do, usually it's the wife who finds out last in these cases. I've got the paperwork to prove it, so can you get me the key?'

The bloody swine, I thought as I rushed to the kitchen where Ronnie kept his keys in one of the drawers. For months he'd been deducting money from my housekeeping, saying that he was dealing with the repayments for the car himself.

How had he managed to keep the letters from me? I was usually around to collect the post each morning.

I watched as the Austin was driven onto the truck. I didn't feel sad or even disappointed, it was one more nail in Ronnie's coffin as far as I was concerned.

My mother, who had been watching from the living room window, came over and put her arm around my shoulder.

'He'll never learn about money, Vivienne,' she said. 'It's the way his mother must have brought him up.'

Of course there was ructions that night when Ronnie got home. Did I get a receipt for it, why did I give them the key? It was all my fault, he worked long hard hours and I didn't seem to manage on the money that he gave me. Maybe I should be working for a living, instead of sitting around all day doing nothing?

I took the baby to my parents' house and let Ronnie sit and stew.

'How are you doing with your studying, Vivienne?', Mother asked, when we had fed Simon and lain him on the settee for a little nap.

'I think I'm going to pass the exam's, Mum,' I said hopefully. 'Though I've had a lot of catching up to do with the course starting last September, but because I had already passed the Mocks, the tutors allowed me on the course.'

'Well, that's good,' said Father approvingly. 'Have you got a plan, Vivienne?'

'I have, but I'm not sure how I'm going to go about it yet. It will involve putting Simon into a nursery.'

'Oh, surely not,' cried Mother. 'He's only little, couldn't you find yourself a part time job?'

'No, it has to be a full time one if I'm going to get anywhere in a new career. I've seen an advert' for a clerical assistant in the Civil Service, it was in the Birkenhead News. I need the minimum of two O' levels, I'm going to send off for an application form.'

Next morning Ronnie wouldn't get up for his morning shift. He lay in bed staring at the ceiling when the alarm clock went off. I tried to persuade him to get up and go.

'I've lost my car and I'll not be making a show of myself having to travel by bus again. Besides I've no money for food or ciggies,' he eventually said.

'Oh, great,' I hissed. 'So I'll have to hide myself in the broom cupboard when the tally woman comes on Friday for her money?'

'Looks like it, doesn't it? Unless we get another car again?'

I put Simon in his pram' after I had changed and fed him, then walked around the streets while people were getting out of bed and preparing their breakfasts. How long was I going to be able to put up with this marriage?, I thought despairingly. Ronnie was beginning to do my head in!

Two weeks later, Beverly and I arrived by car one morning to take our examinations. We were both nervous and Beverly was wondering why she was even there, because her French course had only been vocational, although she and her husband hoped to visit France one day. We cheered each other on as we sped up the college steps, as both our exam's were at ten o'- clock; then we stood outside the lift waiting for it to come down to the ground floor.

'Have you seen that notice on the wall,Viv'?,' asked Beverley. 'What's an Invigilater? It says lifts are for Invigilaters only.'

'I don't know, Bev',' I answered, feeling puzzled, 'but whatever it is we'll have to be one, because we've only ten minutes to get to our rooms.'

I soon found out what an Invigilater was. It was the man who looked over my shoulder as I concentrated on the nine column sentence analysis of verbs, adverbs, nouns, pronouns, adjectives etc. Was that a swift intake of breath I heard as he moved on to the candidate at the next table? I had to pass my English Language, it was so important. It was one of the subjects I needed if I was to be accepted by the Civil Service. I glumly wrote my composition on the 'Evils of watching too much television' and ended up contradicting myself as I never watched the thing anyway.

Soon it was all over and the two of us escaped to treat ourselves to lunch. Then I had another worry, it was the English Lit' exam the following day!

The application form landed on my doormat the day after my exam's and I confidently filled in the bit regarding my possible O' levels. I returned the official looking envelope that afternoon and waited patiently to hear from the headquarters at 'Alencon Link!'

Meanwhile Ronnie had returned to his duties a very chastened man, after Father had had a quiet word with him.

One evening, as I was dishing up a plate of stew for Ronnie, then hacking at a loaf of bread in the kitchen, he made a comment on a topic of conversation that he'd had with his mates in the pub', while they'd been for a swift pint.

'One of them was saying you can have an operation.'

'What was that you said?,' I asked.

'I said, you can go and have an operation to have it stretched a bit and then we don't have to be messing about like we do.'

'You mean you've been discussing our sex life again with them bloody mates of yours?'

I suddenly felt the blood rush up into my head with anger, as I stood there holding the bread knife in my hand.

'How dare you, you filthy sod? I'm sick of this washing our dirty linen in public for everyone to know what we're up to!' I screamed.

And through a haze of righteous anger, I saw that Ronnie's arm was pinned to the formica table, where I had whacked the knife into his shirtsleeve.

'Bloody hell, Vivienne,' he shouted, snatching the knife out with his left hand and looking with horror at the rip that had torn his cuff apart.

'What the hell do you're think doing, you could have drawn blood, you know?'

'I'll take that,' said a quiet voice from the kitchen doorway. It was Father, who had heard me screaming from his lean-to, while he was sampling a glass of his parsnip wine.

'It's either the divorce courts or the murder courts for you, Vivienne,' he continued. 'I think you should come back home with me right now and we'll decide what we're going to do.'

I was shaking from head to foot, as Father lead me away to my parents' kitchen. Then Mother went to fetch the baby and Father put the kettle on. There was no sign of Ronnie according to my mother. The house was empty when she'd gone to get Simon, so we presumed he'd gone to the pub' or down to his mother's house.

I was put to bed in Audrey's room with a hot water bottle and a sleeping pill. Simon was in my parents' room in his cot, which father had dragged in from next door.

I awoke next morning when my sister tried to tiptoe around the bedroom as she got ready to go to her school. Audrey looked at me anxiously for a minute or so, then quietly went to get her breakfast downstairs.

The memory of what I had done washed over me as I lay there, had I really gone for Ronnie like someone insane? I supposed I'd better go and find him, apologize for the terrible thing I had done, but hadn't he deserved it for trying to wind me up?

But my father was ready and waiting for me, as I went downstairs in my dressing gown. He'd decided to change the locks on the next door house. That was the finish of my marriage as far as he was concerned.

'You can't go on the way you are, Vivienne,' he said, after I explained that I needed to see Ronnie. 'It isn't fair to Simon the way you two carry on. It isn't the first time I've heard you rowing, now let's have some peace for pity's sake.'

Mother, who was rocking the baby in his pram outside the kitchen door, nodded in agreement at Father's words.

'You may as well finish it for everyone's sake,' she said. 'We'll look after Simon if you want to work full time and you can move back into your old room, I'm sure that Audrey won't mind.'

'O.K.,' I said, feeling weak and rather weary, 'you're right, I can't go on with it, I've taken all that I can.'

A week after my nineteenth birthday, I was asked to attend an interview by the Civil Service Commission. The interviews were being held in a government office in Birkenhead.

I went to a local hairdressers the day before and had my hair cut short in a manageable style, then I caught the bus to town, where I bought two new outfits.

I decided to wear the aqua blue one for the interview. It was a knee length dress with a smart long jacket, though I'd had to buy it from my Social Security benefits, because Ronnie had decided he wasn't giving me any money.

'You were the one who caused the split up, Vivienne,' he said, when he'd tried to get in the house a few days after I had left him. 'You'll not get a penny for yourself or Simon, because I have the feeling he isn't mine anyway.'

That had been said in front of my parents, after he had banged on their door demanding to see me. They were shocked at his suggestion and many angry words were spoken, but Ronnie left the house quite peacefully, when Father threatened to call the Police.

There was a panel of three sitting at a rectangular table, when I was shown into the interviewing room. I smiled at the interviewers tentatively, as my heart was thudding like a drum.

I had to make them like me, my future life would depend on them.

'Why do you want to work for the Civil Service, Mrs. Hopkirk?' asked an attractive woman in her forties, dressed in a rather smart business suit.

'Because I think I could offer qualities needed to enhance the service,' I answered. 'I am hardworking, diligent and I would be sympathetic in any dealings that I would have with the public.'

This was said because I still felt resentment towards the snappy young man, who had gone through my application for benefits with a lordly air the other week.

'I see you have a child who is only nine months old. What arrangements will you be making for his care if you are successful today?'

This was addressed to me by a man who was old enough to be a granddad. He was probably only worrying about me taking a lot of time off work.

'My parents are going to look after him, we live with them anyway.'

'No husband?', said another man, who looked down his nose as he waited for me to reply.

'Separated,' I answered, wondering if I had to qualify what I had just said.

'And I see you're waiting for the results of the two O' levels you have recently taken?'

This was said by the nice lady who made me feel at ease.

'Yes, and I'm planning to study for three more subjects, so that I can be promoted if you give me a job.'

There, it was over. Now I only had to wait until the panel got in touch with me. I hoped it would be soon, because I had to decide what subjects I was taking when the college opened again.

I opened the official looking envelope with shaking hands, as Mother passed it to me one morning. My parents stood with fingers crossed, as I drew out the sheet of paper that was going to decide my fate.

'I've got it!', I screamed with delight. 'I start next Monday at the Social Security.'

'Well, that'll be one in the eye for that young whipper snapper, the one that was giving you the grief.'

'I'll ignore it Dad, he probably won't even recognize me, but I meant what I said to the panel, I'll treat the public with a bit of sympathy.'

'And does it say what the wages are, Vivienne?' Mum asked.

'Yes, Mum, it starts at twelve pounds weekly, then rises to fourteen after I've been trained.'

'See I told you, Vivienne, qualifications open doors. We're proud of you, now that you've got two O' levels under your belt.'

That was said by Father, who had been going around like a dog with two tails, since I got my exam' results.

'Well done,' said Mother. 'Now perhaps we can all get on with our lives. We'll begin by advertising the house next door.'

I found it warm in the office that first day, when I was being introduced to my new colleagues by the Office Manager. He had been one of the panel members at my interview, the granddad who had been concerned with arrangements for my child. He took me to the section where I would be learning how to file the documents, and a pleasant faced woman was instructed to take me under her wing.

'Phew, it's hot in here,' I said, taking my new red jacket off and placing it on the back of the chair, 'though it must be nice in winter when it's freezing cold outside.'

'I wouldn't rely on it,' replied the woman, who said her name was Peggy, 'the heating system here is buggered and they don't seem to want to replace it. We'll be moving premises in a few months time, so I suppose we'll fry one day and freeze the next!'

'Everyone seems very friendly,' I said.

'They mostly are, but give some respect to the HEO's, they can make or break a person's career.

'Oh,' I said, as I helped sort through some claimants' papers, 'you'll have to point them out to me, in case I step on their toes!'

I found out a few days later who I had to be respectful to. The Office Manager called me to his office, saying he wanted a word.

'Mrs. Hopkirk, or can I call you, Vivienne? Come in and take a seat, shut the door behind you.'

I did as he asked me to, wondering what I was doing there?

'Now then, Vivienne, how are you settling in?'

'Fine, thank you, Sir. It's quite an easy job to do.'

'And probably a bit monotonous for a person of your calibre. I believe you will be going again to college to get the rest of your O' levels.'

'Yes, I'm thinking of enrolling next week.'

'Good and then you'll be looking for promotion this time next year?'

'I'd like to be promoted, I'm sure it would be a far interesting job.'

'Then I suggest you sit on my knee for a while and we'll see what we can do.'

Thank heavens he was only after a bit of slap and tickle, I thought, as I waited that evening at the bus stop. I could have lost my job in the same week that I'd started and that would never have done.

A few months later I decided to file divorce papers on my husband, Ronnie. There was no point in me being Mrs. Hopkirk anymore and I was anxious that Simon was acknowledged as his son.

I'd enrolled in college and was taking three new subjects; Geography, History and the British Constitution. All my tutors seemed pleasant enough and seemed to know their subjects inside out.

I had to take the day off work to appear in court and I went along, hopeful of a satisfactory outcome. I was dreading seeing Ronnie though, who hadn't once tried to visit his son, which made me think he might be up to something.

I was to meet my solicitor in an ante – room before the hearing. The woman had been very sympathetic, when I had poured out my story of my mismatched marriage and my desire to end it as soon as possible.

'What if he asks for a reconciliation, sometimes a husband does that to get the judge on his side?' the solicitor asked.

'I wouldn't want him back,' I shuddered, thinking of all that kerfuffle that had gone on in our bed. 'I'm hoping for a clean break, so that I can get on with the plans I've made.'

Ronnie was sitting with his solicitor on the other side of the courtroom. He turned and smiled when I entered and I noticed he was wearing a brand new suit. The judge called the place to order and Ronnie's solicitor outlined the case.

'So you see, Your Honour,' he said in mitigation, 'Mr. Hopkirk would like to try for a reconciliation, he never wanted a separation in the first place.'

'And Mrs. Hopkirk, what does she want to do about the situation?'

'Mrs. Hopkirk wants to end the marriage and is looking for maintenance for their son.'

'Never,' said Ronnie, making his voice heard as he said it.

My spirits plummeted to the ground.

'Mrs. Hopkirk, are you not willing to try to repair your marriage with your husband?', the judge asked me.

'No, Your Honour, I am not. I'm not wanting to put myself through that again.'

'Then, all I can say is that you apply again for your divorce after the marriage has reached a five year period. As far as I am aware there are insufficient grounds for a decree nisi, unless there are circumstances that I am unaware of?'

'No, Your Honour,' my solicitor said, 'but can we apply for maintenance for Mr. Hopkirk's son?'

'Yes, Mr. Hopkirk can pay the weekly sum of two pounds ten shillings. Two pounds to be paid directly to the mother of his child and ten shillings to be paid weekly into a savings account until the child is eighteen.'

'Very well, we accept that,' said Ronnie's solicitor.

I put my head in my hands as I sat once more in the ante – room with my solicitor.

'Oh no,' I said, 'another three years of being Mrs. Hopkirk.'

'Look on the bright side, Vivienne, he's not going to hang around waiting for you if he sees you're not interested. Keep your fingers crossed that he finds another woman. A lot of men do.'

I walked out of the chambers with my head down. I needed cheering up and I planned to go to the market. I nearly collided with Ronnie though, as he waited for me at the bottom of the court steps.

'What do you want, Ronnie?'

'I want you and me to get back again.'

'I thought I made it clear in the courtroom that I don't want us to get back together again.'

'You don't mean it. Come on, Vivienne, let's try again, things will be different, I promise you.'

'Get lost, Ronnie.'

I walked off towards the market. I was going to do some Christmas shopping before the seasonal rush.

I stood outside the market later waiting for the bus. I was laden with bags and my arms were aching, and I hoped that the bus would appear on time. There was a big queue at the bus stop, as other women seemed to have had the same idea as me.

A small blue car drew up beside me and a man shouted through the open window.

'Get in, Vivienne!'

It was Ronnie.

I ignored him, pretending I hadn't heard.

'Get in the car, Vivienne.'

I didn't reply or turn my head.

'There's a man here, wanting you, love,' said the woman next to me. 'Why don't you get in the car with him, this blooming bus might be late?'

Embarrassed, because all eyes were now upon me, I heaved my bags onto the rear seat then climbed into the passenger seat.

Ronnie smiled and took off at speed along the High street.

'I just wanted to be with you one last time,' he said. 'Do you like the car? Davie's standing guarantor for me and Mum's only taking peanuts in housekeeping.'

'Well, don't forget about Simon's money,' I said. 'You can start sending me a postal order through the post. Anyway, where are you taking me Ronnie, this isn't the way to Whaley Lane? What are we doing on the bloody dock road?'

'You'll see, Vivienne. If I can't have you nobody else will, so I'm going to end it here and now.'

'What!?' I squeaked. 'Oh, don't be stupid, Ronnie, there isn't anybody else. Slow the car down and drop me at a bus stop.'

In answer to my plea, Ronnie accelerated and swung the car onto a large piece of waste land, then hurtled towards a perimeter wall at sixty miles an hour!

I started screaming, as my life began to flash in front of my eyes and I saw my little baby Simon crying for his Mum! I threw myself towards the driving seat, trying to wrest the wheel from Ronnie's control! Then suddenly he slammed the brakes on and the car slewed unsteadily to a halt. My breath came from me in a mighty whoosh, as I collapsed in my seat and began to cry.

Ronnie sat and looked at me with tears in his eyes.

'I only wanted us to be together until the end of time.'

'You're a maniac,' I shouted. 'Take me to the nearest bus stop now! No, I'll get out and walk instead. I don't know where I am, but I'll get myself home.'

'No, stay where you are,' he replied shakily. 'I'll take you home, then I can see little Simon when we get there.'

It took weeks of nightmares before I could sleep well at night and I looked over my shoulder each time I went out.

It was coming up to Easter and everywhere was spring like. Daffodils nodded their heads in my parents' garden, birds began to build their nests in the hedges and Mother sprinkled seeds in the planters, hoping for a good summer show.

I had settled in well at the office and had a lot of exercise being chased by the Office Manager around his room.

One Saturday afternoon, I was sitting on a chair in the back garden, watching mother stringing up the beginnings of her runner beans shoots, looking out for Simon who was tottering about.

'Did I tell you I got an Easter card off that nice boy who lives in Wigan, Vivienne?', Mother asked. 'He sends me a Christmas card and an Easter card every year, you know?'

'You've never said.'

'There hasn't been much point, has there? You've been tied up with other things and anyway he'll still be at university, so you wouldn't be happy just seeing him on a Sunday.'

'I might. Does he ever mention me?'

'Oh yes, he always says to give you his love.'

'Oh.'

I spent a restless night as I thought about Andy. Why hadn't I been patient with him, I never would have got myself in such a terrible mess? He'd been a good man, a caring man. Look how he'd talked me into returning home and taking up my studies again. Just because I couldn't wait for him to finish university. I'd been selfish, put myself first, only wanting a bit of fun and look where that had got me at the end of the day?

The next morning I got up early, dressed myself up in my favourite blue outfit and hurried down to the kitchen, where my mother was spoon feeding Simon some porridge.

'You look nice, dear, are you going out?' she said. 'I'd take an umbrella if I were you?'

'I'm off to Wigan, Mum,' I said, with a determined look on my face. 'And though I might be wrong, something tells me you'll be getting cards signed from me and Andy in the future!'